Building Intelligent Systems

Utilizing Computer Vision, Data
Mining, and Machine Learning

Sanjay Addicam
Shahzad Malik
Phil Tian

No part of this publication may be reproduced, stored in a retrieval system or transmitted in any form or by any means, electronic, mechanical, photocopying, recording, scanning or otherwise, except as permitted under Sections 107 or 108 of the 1976 United States Copyright Act, without either the prior written permission of the Publisher, or authorization through payment of the appropriate per-copy fee to the Copyright Clearance Center, 222 Rosewood Drive, Danvers, MA 01923, (978) 750-8400, fax (978) 750-4744. Requests to the Publisher for permission should be addressed to the Publisher, Intel Press, Intel Corporation, 2111 NE 25th Avenue, JF3-330, Hillsboro, OR 97124-5961. E-Mail: intelpress@intel.com.

This publication is designed to provide accurate and authoritative information in regard to the subject matter covered. It is sold with the understanding that the publisher is not engaged in professional services. If professional advice or other expert assistance is required, the services of a competent professional person should be sought.

Intel Corporation may have patents or pending patent applications, trademarks, copyrights, or other intellectual property rights that relate to the presented subject matter. The furnishing of documents and other materials and information does not provide any license, express or implied, by estoppel or otherwise, to any such patents, trademarks, copyrights, or other intellectual property rights.

Intel may make changes to specifications, product descriptions, and plans at any time, without notice. Fictitious names of companies, products, people, characters, and/or data mentioned herein are not intended to represent any real individual, company, product, or event.

Intel products are not intended for use in medical, life saving, life sustaining, critical control or safety systems, or in nuclear facility applications.

Intel, the Intel logo, Intel Atom, Intel AVX, Intel Battery Life Analyzer, Intel Compiler, Intel Core i3, Intel Core i5, Intel Core i7, Intel DPST, Intel Energy Checker, Intel Mobile Platform SDK, Intel Intelligent Power Node Manager, Intel QuickPath Interconnect, Intel Rapid Memory Power Management (Intel RMPM), Intel VTune Amplifier, and Intel Xeon are trademarks or registered trademarks of Intel Corporation or its subsidiaries in the United States and other countries.

Software and workloads used in performance tests may have been optimized for performance only on Intel microprocessors. Performance tests, such as SYSmark and MobileMark, are measured using specific computer systems, components, software, operations and functions. Any change to any of those factors may cause the results to vary. You should consult other information and performance tests to assist you in fully evaluating your contemplated purchases, including the performance of that product when combined with other products.

For more complete information about performance and benchmark results, visit www.intel.com/benchmarks

†Other names and brands may be claimed as the property of others.

This book is printed on acid-free paper.

Publisher: Richard Bowles
Editor: David J. Clark
Program Manager: Stuart Douglas
Text Design & Composition: MPS Limited, a Macmillan Company
Graphic Art: MPS Limited, a Macmillan Company (illustrations), Dan Mandish (cover)

Library of Congress Cataloging in Publication Data:

Printed in China

10 9 8 7 6 5 4 3 2 1

First printing,

IMPORTANT

You can access the companion Web site for this book on the Internet at:

noggin.intel.com/registermybook

Use the serial number located on the last page of the book to register your book and access additional material, including the digital edition and pointers to development resources.

Contents

Foreword　　xv

Acknowledgements　　xvii

Chapter 1　　**An Introduction to Intelligent Systems 1**

Technologies for Enabling Intelligence 2

Industries that Benefit from Intelligent Devices 2

    Smart Digital Signage 3

    Retail Intelligence 5

    Intelligent Medical Devices 6

    Home Energy Management 6

Building Real-World Intelligent Systems 7

    Processing Speed 7

    Accuracy and Robustness 10

    Privacy 10

Summary 11

Chapter 2　　**Fundamental Visual Metrics for Computer Vision 13**

What Is Covered, What Is Not Covered 15

History of Key Ideas in Visual Metrics 15

Overview of Visual Computing Topics in the Vision Pipeline 17

    Sensor Technology and Sensor Processing 17

    Image Preparation 18

    Segmentation 18

Local Features and Interest Points 19

Object Shape and Local Feature descriptors 20

Global Textural and Statistical Features 20

Algorithms, Classifiers, Training and Supervised Matching, Mapping, Tracking 20

Sensor Processing for Visual Metrics—A Rich Area 22

Sensor Characteristics, Configuration and Resolution 23

Sensor Color Patterns, Eye Light Sensitivity, Color De-Mosaicing 27

Sensor and Optics for 3D Depth Sensing and Computational Imaging 29

Image Processing Prior to Visual Metrics and Analysis 38

Intel® Integrated Performance Primitives (Intel® IPP) 38

OpenCV† Library (Open Computer Vision) 39

What Is a Good Visual Metric for a Given Application? 41

Region Segmentation, Shape Descriptors, and Object Descriptors 42

MSER Interest Region Detection 44

Mathematical Morphology 44

Binary Morphological Overview 44

Binary Morphological Operations 45

Grayscale and Color Morphology 46

Adaptive Auto-Threshold for Binary Morphology 46

Intensity Thresholding Refinements for Improved Morphology 48

Global Thresholding Methods 48

Local Thresholding Methods 50

Superpixel Segmentation via Graph-based and Gradient-Ascent 50

Graph-based Superpixel Methods Survey 52

Gradient-Ascent-based Superpixel Method Survey 52

Color as a Method of Region Segmentation 53

Region Shape Metrics 54

Texture Segmentation and Texture Metrics 55

History of Key Ideas in Texture Analysis 57

Augmented Reality (AR) and Scene Mapping Metrics 59

Dynamic Textures (DT) 60

Co-Occurrence Matrix as a Texture Metric 60

Histograms and Multiresolution Histograms 63

Local Interest Points for Feature Extraction 64

Interest Points or Key Points 65

  Sobel 66

  Canny Detector 67

  Laplacian and Laplacian of Gaussian (LoG) 67

  Harris and Shi-Tomasi Type Detectors 67

  FAST interest point corner detector 68

  Hessian Matrix Interest Point Detector (DoH) 68

  DoG (Difference of Gaussians) 68

  Salient Regions 69

  Moravac Corner Detector 69

Feature Descriptors or Feature Signatures or Region Signatures 69

Digital Correlation and Template Feature Matching 72

Survey of Feature Descriptors, Common and Uncommon 73

  Common Features 73

  Haar-like Features 74

  Local Binary Patterns (LBP) 76

  Rotation Invariant LBP (RILBP) 79

  Dynamic Texture Metric Using 3D LBPs: VLBP and LBP-TOP 81

  Scale-Invariant Feature Transform (SIFT) 82

  ORB – Oriented Brief Descriptor 85

Variations on Feature Descriptor Methods 86

Chapter 3   **Face Detection: Overview and Accuracy Measurement 95**

Frontal Face Detection using Viola Jones 96

  Training a Face Classifier 96

  Detecting Faces 102

  Algorithm Optimizations 106

  Training More Advanced Classifiers 109

Measuring the Accuracy of Face Detection 110

  Ground Truth Data 110

  Generating Ground Truth Data 111

Accuracy Metrics 112

Summary 116

Chapter 4 **Object Detection Algorithms and Optimization 117**

Histogram of Gradients 117

Step A: Normalization of Gamma and Color 119

Step B: Compute Gradients 119

Step C: Accumulate Weighted Votes for Gradients Orientation Over Spatial Cells 122

Step D: Normalize Contrast within Overlapping Block of Cells 124

Training a HoG Model Using Latent SVM 125

Step A: Star-Structured Deformable Part Model 126

Step B: Mixture Model and Intra-Class Variation 128

Step C: HoG Feature 128

Step D: Multiscale Pyramid Approach 128

Step E: Combining All Things Together 131

Step F: The Training Procedure 131

Step G: Data Mining Hard Negative Examples 135

Optimization 136

Optimizations Using Intel® IPP 136

Optimizations Using Intel® IPP/Intel® SSE/Intel® AVX 137

Evaluating Code for SIMD Possibility 137

Coding Techniques 137

Coding Methodology 138

Base Code of Filter Convolution 140

Chapter 5 **Optical Flow and Patch Recognition 145**

Optical Flow Algorithms 145

Lucas Kanade Implementation 146

I. Selecting Good Features for Tracking 147

II. Fine-Tuning with Subpixel Accuracy 148

III. Feature Tracking Using Lucas Kanade Optical Flow 148

Algorithm Accuracy Checker 150

Patch Recognition 151

Ferns Algorithm 151

  Creating the Training Model 152

  Object Recognition 153

  Frame Preprocessing 154

  Key Point Generation 155

  Formation of Classes under Training 159

  Recognition Phase 161

  Checking Algorithm Accuracy 163

Chapter 6   An Overview of Data Mining 167

Data Mining Overview 167

Data Mining Algorithms 171

  Classification and Prediction 172

  Algorithm 6.1: Back Propagation (BP) 177

  Algorithm 6.2: Algorithm Quasi-optimal 180

  Algorithm 6.3: Ripper 181

  Algorithm 6.4: Tree Augmented Naïve Bayes (TAN) 187

  Algorithm 6.5: k Nearest Neighbors (KNN) 194

  Algorithm 6.6: AdaBoost   197

  Algorithm 6.7: Random Forest 198

  Regression 199

  Clustering 203

  Algorithm 6.8: k-Means 205

  Algorithm 6.9: k-Medoids 206

  Algorithm 6.10: Agglomerative Hierarchical Clustering 207

  Algorithm 6.11: Density-Based Spatial Clustering of Applications with Noise (DBSCAN) 209

  Association Rules 210

  Algorithm 6.12: Apriori 215

Privacy-Preserving Data Mining Approaches 217

  Anonymization 217

  Randomization 218

  Condensation 219

  Downgrading Application Effectiveness 219

  Cryptographic Techniques 219

Data Mining Process 220
  Business Understanding 221
  Data Understanding and Preparation 223
  Modeling and Evaluation 225
  Deployment and Integration 229
  Model Update and Maintenance 229
Cloud-Based Data Mining Services Infrastructure 230
  Introduction to Cloud-Based Service 230
  Cloud-Based Data Mining Services 232

Chapter 7   The Intelligent Advertising Framework (IAF) 233

IAF Architecture 234
  Data Ownership 235
  Targeted Advertising 238
  Real Time Triggering 238
Main Components in IAF 240
  Data Mining Module 240
  Content Management System 249
  Digital Player 257
  Functionality 257
Targeted Advertising 266
  Targeted Advertising Process 266
  IAF Working Modes 268
Data Mining for Targeted Advertising 269
  Multiple Advertising Model Training 269
  Audience Targeting Methods 270
  Prediction-Based Targeting 270
  Weighted Audience Counting 271
  Passer Prediction Models 272
  Advertising Rule Example 272
  Ad Selection Based on Advertising Models 274
Training data collection and preparation 275
  Viewer event collection 276
  Player Event Collection 277

Weather Data Collection 279

Training Data Correlation 279

Advertising Models Creation 282

Algorithm Selection and Orchestration 282

Training and Retraining process 284

Sample Advertising Models 289

Advertising Rule Deployment and Selection 292

Chapter 8   Privacy in Intelligent Systems 297

Information Privacy 298

Personally Identifiable Information 298

Privacy Concerns 299

Data Capture Module 301

Data Analysis Module 303

Output Module Privacy 304

Development of Privacy Safe Systems 304

Design Stage 304

Implementation Stage 305

Deployment Stage 307

Summary 308

Chapter 9   Healthcare Applications and Analytics 309

Growing Healthcare Demands 309

Standards: An Absolute Necessity for Analytics 311

Real-Time Analytics: Ultrasound Object ID 312

Ultrasound Basics 312

Ultrasound Software Prototype 314

Receive Beamformer 315

Envelop Detector 316

Display Processing 317

Distribution of Performance 318

Analytics in Healthcare: Consumerization of Data 320

Analytics in Healthcare: From Data to Information 321

Conclusion 327

Chapter 10   Optimizing Machine Learning Algorithms on GPUs 329

Overview 330

GPU Architecture 330

Intel Ivy Bridge Architecture 331

   CPU Features 331

   GPU Features 332

Nvidia GPU Architecture 334

   GeForce† GTX 400/500 Fermi Architecture 334

   Cache Architecture 336

Comparison of Ivy Bridge and Nvidia GPU Architectures 337

Optimizing VA Algorithms for Ivy Bridge 338

Understanding Intel® AIM Suite 338

Right Candidates for GPU 338

GPU Optimization 340

   Optimization Using HMPP 340

   OpenCL 341

   OpenCL Threading Model 341

   OpenCL Memory Model 344

   Global Memory 345

   Work Items and Workgroups 346

   Profiling of OpenCL Functions 348

   Optimization Techniques 350

   Porting Video Analytics Algorithms to a GPU 356

   Haar Classifier Optimization Using OpenCL as an Example 357

   Other Hotspot Functions (GPU Candidates) from the Intel® AIM Suite Application 368

   Code Difference between Nvidia and Ivy Bridge 372

CPU Optimization with Intel® Threading Building Blocks (Intel® TBB) 372

   Task-Based Programming (Intel® TBB Threading Model) 373

   Explanation of the Intel® TBB Intel® AIM Suite Application 374

   Intel® Streaming SIMD Extensions (Intel® SSE) 376

CPU-GPU Combined Optimization 381

   Data Transfer between CPU-GPU 381

Thread Interaction between CPU and GPU 382

Optimization Using Intel® TBB (Haar Classifier) and OpenCL (Haar Classifier) 383

Optimization Using Intel TBB (Haar Classifier) + OpenCL (Non-Haar Classifier Hotspot Functions) 384

Accuracy Model 384

Method of Calculating Accuracy 385

Accuracy of OpenCL (Haar Classifier) 386

Accuracy of Intel® TBB (Haar Classifier) + SSE 387

Accuracy of Intel® TBB + OpenCL (Haar Classifier) 388

Accuracy of Intel® TBB (Haar Classifier) + OpenCL (Non-Haar Classifier) 388

Performance Measurement 388

GPU Performance 388

CPU Performance 388

CPU + GPU Performance 389

Appendix 397

References 421

Index 435

Foreword

I've always been a science fiction fan, rushing home every day after high school to watch the latest interstellar adventure of Captain Kirk, Spock, and Scotty. As I write this, I am thinking about Ray Bradbury who died this year (June 5, 2012) and who throughout his long and distinguished writing career plumbed the possibilities, the practicalities and yes, the perils, of a world in which technology plays a more pervasive role in every aspect of our lives.

It's this sheer pervasiveness that struck me most in reading the vast amount of information that my colleagues Sanjay Addicam, Shahzad Malik, and Phil Tian have assembled on designing and implementing intelligent systems.

Just twenty years ago, a computer connected to a network was a novelty. Today, it's the accepted reality. But in fact, we haven't even scratched the surface. The coming era of intelligent systems—billions of smart, connected devices— will weave new levels of intelligence into every aspect of our lives.

I have been with Intel for over two decades, holding a wide range of management, director, and general management-level positions in business, marketing and engineering. Early in 2009, I became part of the Intelligent Systems Group, focused on providing the processors for these billions of intelligent devices. Over the years, I've seen a familiar process repeat itself over and over again, like a constant state of evolution for devices: as a device goes from being analog and standalone to digital and interconnected, it becomes more intelligent and multifunctional. That's the scenario we are seeing played out today in cars that keep drivers and passengers more informed and safer, retail systems that make shopping more convenient and personal, and medical devices that are more context aware and adaptive to our needs.

It's not just the vast increase in computing devices that will make this new era so different. In the computer era we associated machine "intelligence" with the ability to follow a set of predefined steps operating on structured data. But today's intelligent systems are regularly called upon to solve complicated problems across unstructured data sets—telling whether the shopper at a kiosk is male or female, or whether the dark spot on the x-ray is a tumor or something else—for which there are no specific, preprogrammed steps.

Creating systems for this new era involves a wide range of subdisciplines (such as machine learning, data mining, and computer vision) involving the ability to recognize complex patterns, make intelligent decisions, and take action, while continuously improving and learning in the process. Cars get better at avoiding accidents. Energy systems get better at responding to shifts in consumption. Retail systems become more attuned to shopper needs.

This book was written for software engineers, architects, and product planners who are venturing into this brave new world and want to know how to actually build things. It lays out an architecture and methodology, breaking down the problem into small, manageable, practical chunks: in effect providing a template upon which a wide range of intelligent system devices can be built. It allows the reader to move quickly from the conceptual to the practical plane and start sorting out all the actual nitty gritty details of architecting, implementing, and testing.

You might find bits and pieces of the intelligent systems era in Ray Bradbury's many stories. But there's nothing fictional about it. It's happening right now, right before our eyes. If you want to be part of creating this new world, this book is the place to start.

Jose A. Avalos

Visual Retail & Digital Signage Director

Intelligent Systems Group, Intel Corporation

Acknowledgements

The case studies, concepts, code, architecture, and guidelines compiled in this book are the result of years of research, development, and implementation from many talented engineers at Intel who have a strong passion for computer vision, machine learning, and data mining. We are hugely indebted to these individuals for the contributions they have made and the time they have spent, much of it outside of their normal duties, in order to make this book a reality.

First, we'd like to thank the following talented engineers for the significant contributions they made to specific chapters, analyses, and case studies in the book:

- Scott Krig: Chapter 2 ("Fundamental Visual Metrics for Computer Vision"). Scott has extensive experience in image processing and is an expert in applying and measuring the various concepts on a practical basis.

- Shweta Phadnis: Chapter 3 ("Face Detection: Overview and Accuracy Measurement"), Chapter 4 ("Object Detection Algorithm and Optimization"), and Chapter 5 ("Optical Flow and Patch Recognition"). Shweta was instrumental in taking the vast amounts of code, data, and literature that we had compiled from various projects over the past few years and distilling everything down to the material in these three chapters. Shweta is an exceptional software engineer who is very good at architecting practical software solutions around complex concepts such as computer vision and data mining.

- Chiranjeevi Kunapareddy: Chapter 7 ("The Intelligent Advertising Framework"). Chiranjeevi is an expert in the field of data mining and was responsible for the implementation of the data mining module for the Intelligent Advertising Framework as well as the development of the IAF demo, which was shown at Research at Intel Day and Intel Developer Forum. His hard work and great contribution is much appreciated.

■ Dr. Abhishek Ranjan: Chapter 8 ("Privacy in Intelligent Systems"). Abhishek brings an incredible amount of experience in machine learning, computer vision, and human-computer interaction concepts to Intel, and he is credited with implementing many of those concepts in a commercially available video analytics system. His overview of privacy considerations when building practical vision solutions is much appreciated.

■ Michael Taborn and Celeste Fralick: Chapter 9 ("Healthcare Applications and Analytics"). Michael is the platform architect in the Medical Segment at Intel, and Celeste is a principal engineer. Both of them are experts in the healthcare field and their take on healthcare analytics adds a very valuable perspective to machine learning and data mining in the intelligent systems space. We are very grateful for their contribution and insights.

We also extend our thanks and gratitude to David Clark for his excellent copyediting, which has made the book more readable and consistent throughout. Stuart Douglas, our program manager at Intel Press, also deserves a huge thanks for guiding us through the entire phase of writing a book for the first time; we are very grateful for his patience with us.

Reviewer comments and suggestions were also extremely valuable. We deeply appreciate those who took the time to provide indispensable feedback on the manuscript including Dr. Mark Fiala, Dr. Gerhard Roth, Lokesh Narasimha, Uma Gadamsetty, Milind Ghande, Kapil Jaisinghani, Huimei Lu, Qingjie Zhao, Victor Eruhimov, Vadim Pisarevsky, Mariano Phielipp, and Dean Pomerleau.

We are also grateful to our managers Raj Maini, Bill Colson, and Vishwa Hassan at Intel for providing their reviews, the time, resources, and encouragement to compile the book's contents. A huge thank you also goes to Jose Avalos for writing the wonderful foreword.

Sanjay Addicam is very grateful to his wonderful parents Dr. A. J. Rao and Mrs. Rukmini Rao in providing an environment where dreaming big was the norm and everything was possible and achievable. Sanjay is very thankful for the love and support of his wife Sona who showed great patience and gave him lots of courage, encouragement, and was his ever-reliable sounding board in this endeavor. He also is grateful to his wonderful daughter Shreya who continues to amaze him and provides him with the inspiration to move forward in building intelligent systems.

Shahzad Malik would like to thank his wonderful wife Jawairia and his daughter Sophia for their love, support and for putting up with the many extra hours he spent in front of the computer for the past few months.

Phil Tian is very grateful to his family, his wonderful wife Lijun Li and lovely daughter Mengyuan Tian for their love and great support, as well as their tolerance and patience in his working at home, even in the early morning and late at night. Phil also wants to express his special gratitude to his mother-in-law Shumian Lv for her helping taking care of Mengyuan in the past few years.

Chapter 1

An Introduction to Intelligent Systems

The significant problems we face cannot be solved at the same level of thinking we were at when we created them.

—Albert Einstein

The human brain is a remarkable system. Almost instantly, the brain allows us to perform a variety of complex tasks, such as recognizing people we know, performing sophisticated mathematical computations, and making critical decisions based on years of knowledge and training. While today's computers are now capable of crunching numbers significantly faster than the average human, they still lack the ability to perceive, reason, and learn as well as we do.

The field of Artificial Intelligence (AI) has been focused on closing the gap between humans and computers by attempting to equip machines with the ability to behave intelligently. Although the dream of an artificial human brain is far from being realized, we are now at a stage where a number of tasks that have traditionally been considered hard for computers to perform can now be accomplished fairly well. This allows us to create *intelligent systems,* which are devices and components that solve some practical problems that would traditionally require a human to perform. Examples of such intelligent systems in operation today include mobile devices that can translate and interpret foreign languages, software that can play chess like a grand master, and machines that can automatically analyze medical images such as CAT scans to discover tumors or bone fractures.

Technologies for Enabling Intelligence

In the simplest display of intelligence, a device could follow a set of predefined steps that have been programmed by a developer in order to resolve a problem. While this works well for simple tasks, more complicated problems such as finding a face in a photograph or translating text from one language to another are extremely difficult to define. For this reason, the field of AI has evolved over the past few years into specialized areas of research that effectively focus on mimicking specific human senses or behaviors, as shown in Table 1.1. The resulting technologies and algorithms are what can be used to create smart devices and applications.

Table 1.1 Active AI Research Fields and the Corresponding Intelligence They Enable

Research Field	Intelligence Enabled
Machine Learning	Gaining knowledge from empirical data.
Data Mining	Discovering unknown patterns, properties, and knowledge from large data sets.
Computer Vision	Ability to analyze and interpret visual data.
Natural Language Processing	Ability to read and understand human languages.
Speech Recognition/Synthesis	Converting spoken language into text, and converting text into audible speech.
Knowledge Representation	Representing facts or knowledge as symbols, and using that representation to infer new knowledge.

Industries that Benefit from Intelligent Devices

There are a myriad of industries today that already benefit immensely from AI. For example, computer vision is now employed on assembly lines in the manufacturing and baked goods industries in order to automatically inspect finished products for visual defects. Machine learning is actively used in most e-mail servers in order to differentiate useful messages from spam/junk messages. Data mining is regularly used by large enterprises to extract trends from and make sense of voluminous amounts of data. While these applications benefit by leveraging a single field of AI to perform a critical operation, a fruitful area to investigate is whether the combination of multiple AI fields can be combined together for even greater benefits. A few potential industries that could benefit from this combination are described below.

Smart Digital Signage

Digital signage refers to the use of electronic displays, such as LCD and LED screens, for presenting advertising or information in public and private spaces. This includes screens inside of retail stores or airports, on menu boards in fast food restaurants, and large outdoor billboards such as those in Times Square. While the digital signage industry has been growing rapidly, the lack of data to assess reach, accountability, and awareness has been considered one of the industry's pain points since advertisers are now demanding quantified viewership data similar to what is possible with online advertising. Figure 1.1 shows how computer vision can be used to enable such viewership measurement. By embedding a camera into the bezel of the display, real-time face detection algorithms can be used to find frontal human faces. The assumption is that faces that are looking towards the digital sign will also be frontal with respect to the camera. Once a face has been detected, it can be processed further to extract information such as the gender or age of the individual, along with other metrics such as a viewer's distance from the screen, how long a viewer observed the on-screen content, and possibly even the emotional response of the viewer based on facial expressions. Going further, using demographic data, content can be dynamically chosen based on the audience currently in front of the display. For example, if the digital sign detects more females than males, it can choose an ad that is targeted towards women. If the audience subsequently switches to contain more males than females, the system can choose to show a male focused advertisement. This sort of intelligence helps optimize the presentation of advertising and media content by delivering the right message to the right audience at the right time. From a business standpoint, it also allows signage operators to charge a premium for quantified viewers, or enabling alternative revenue models such as pay-per-view billing.

While collecting viewership data alone provides advertisers with compelling information, what becomes even more interesting is when the sign can *predict* viewership a few hours, days, or even weeks ahead of time. By combining data mining techniques with long-term viewership data as well as other data sources such as weather or location, such prediction may be possible in order to extract rich viewership trends that may not be immediately obvious. For example, it is possible that in some particular retail store, there are a large number of seniors that enter between 10 a.m. and 11 a.m. whenever it was raining the previous night, but only in the month of April. This information could allow a digital sign to extract upcoming forecast data during the rainy days every April in order to choose targeted product advertisements that seniors would find more appealing. More importantly, the advertising spots could be sold by the retailer or signage operator weeks ahead of time. This sort of deep decision making would not be possible without combining data mining with computer vision and machine learning.

Figure 1.1   A Camera Embedded into a Digital Sign Can Use Computer Vision to Measure Audience Viewership and Demographics.

Retail Intelligence

Over the past few years, the retail industry has been looking at ways to improve operational efficiencies and provide a better customer experience by measuring how customer traffic flows inside of stores. The traditional approach is to hire human counters that manually measure footfall at the front entrance of a single retail store using a pen and clipboard, and then extrapolating those counts to estimate overall traffic at all other locations. While this works, the approach is costly, hard to scale, and prone to error. Recent advances in Computer Vision can now enable automated video-based tracking of people using cameras mounted on the ceiling. For example, Figure 1.2 shows an overhead camera view of individuals standing in a checkout line. Object segmentation and tracking algorithms (Szeliski 2010) can be used to detect the number of people standing in the line and how long each person has been waiting. This information could be used to automatically notify a store manager to open an additional checkout, which improves the customer experience and ultimately leads to more sales.

Figure 1.2   An Overhead Camera Combined with Computer Vision Algorithms Can Be Used to Monitor Wait Times in a Checkout Line.

Other uses for this technology could be to count overall customer traffic that enters a retail store at different times of the day to optimize staffing levels, or to estimate traffic flows throughout a store to determine prime locations or aisles for placing high-margin promotional items.

Similar to digital signage, the retail industry could benefit immensely by combining traffic counting data with point-of-sale (POS) data to extract rich insights into how people shop. For example, a retailer could determine that two separate stores with roughly similar traffic counts perform differently in terms of sales on certain days. This could suggest that sales associates at the poorly performing location need additional training to help close sales. Such information would be extremely difficult to extract using manual counting techniques with a pen and clipboard.

Intelligent Medical Devices

With the mounting costs of healthcare around the world, there is an opportunity to build intelligence into medical devices that can help reduce these costs. Computer vision can help significantly in this regard. It is now possible to use a simple webcam to non-intrusively monitor vital signs such as heart rate (Poh 2011), which can help reduce the need for physical visits to a doctor's office for regular checkups. Similarly, the combination of machine learning and computer vision algorithms can be used to monitor elderly or ill patients in their homes to detect falls or other anomalous events in order to alert emergency personnel if required. This allows individuals to avoid long-term hospital stays, which significantly reduces costs, while also allowing patients to recover in the comfort of their own home.

Home Energy Management

With the rising cost of energy, home energy management is a prime area that can benefit immensely from intelligence due to the potential cost savings. Current home energy systems are quite simple, often consisting of a single temperature sensor that can be used to automatically toggle heating and cooling systems on or off to maintain a target temperature. More advanced systems allow programmable target temperatures based on the time of day or day of week. However, these systems are not optimal since they don't take actual needs or usage into account. Computer vision algorithms combined with heat sensing cameras and motion detection can be used to detect the presence of people or pets in a room, and use that to dynamically control heating/cooling systems, adjust lighting, and toggle electronics such as TVs or computers on or off. Illumination sensors could also be used for more advanced light level adjustments. For example, rather than simply toggling lights on or off, bulbs could instead be brightened or dimmed based on the amount of detected ambient light coming through windows in order to achieve a target illumination. Finally, machine learning algorithms could be used to allow future energy usage to be predicted based on past usage behaviors and trends.

Building Real-World Intelligent Systems

Until recently, AI was primarily a research field that proposed solutions that weren't mature enough for real-world deployments. With the advent of the Internet, high-performance commodity processors, and low-cost sensors such as cameras and microphones built into mobile devices, we are now at a stage where decade's worth of AI research can now be applied to solve real problems and to enrich our everyday lives. However, while the research community has made significant progress in the various subfields of AI, there are many practical considerations that are often overlooked during theoretical discussions but which are important when building real-world systems. For example, while many algorithms have been proposed in the computer vision literature for finding faces in an image, there is very little information on how to efficiently implement these algorithms on commodity hardware or an analysis of how well they perform under real-world lighting conditions. In this section we outline a few of the practical issues that need to be considered in order to build compelling intelligent devices and experiences.

Processing Speed

While today's mobile devices and commodity PCs now pack enough processing power to accomplish most everyday tasks, intelligent tasks such as computer vision and data mining can easily exhaust all available CPU resources. Therefore, when building intelligent systems that have target processing rates or real-time requirements, we still need to choose the most efficient algorithm for the job while also making sure that we optimize the algorithm as best as possible given the capabilities of the underlying hardware. A few available technologies that are readily available but are often overlooked in the academic AI literature are listed below.

Single Instruction Multiple Data (SIMD) Instructions

Most commodity processors now contain SIMD instructions that provide significant speed boosts for applications that exhibit data parallelism. For example, a common computer vision task is to subtract two images together when performing background subtraction, in order to extract moving foreground objects from stationary parts of a scene. The traditional serial approach for background subtraction is to operate on each pixel independently as shown in the pseudo code in Figure 1.3.

```
void backgroundSubtraction(unsigned char *raw, unsigned char
*foreground, unsigned char *background, int totalPixels)
{
   for(int i = 0;i < totalPixels;i++)
   {
      foreground[i] = raw[i] - background[i];
   }
}
```

Figure 1.3   Serial Background Subtraction Algorithm

The algorithm performs a subtraction operation between each incoming image pixel and each pixel in the static background image, storing the result in a new foreground image. For example, using an HD resolution image of 1920x1080 pixels, the serial approach would require 2,073,600 subtraction operations. Using a recent Intel or AMD processor that supports the Streaming SIMD Extensions (SSE) instructions, a single SIMD command would allow us to subtract 16 pixels at a time as shown in the pseudo code in Figure 1.4.

```
void subtractSSE(unsigned char *dest, unsigned char
*minuend, unsigned char *subtrahend)
{
   __mm128 *destSSE = (__m128 *)&dest[0];
   __mm128 *minuendSSE = (__m128 *)&minuend[0];
   __mm128 *subtrahendSSE = (__m128 *)&subtrahend[0];

   *destSSE = __mm128_sub_epi8(*minuendSSE, *subtrahendSSE);
}

void backgroundSubtraction(unsigned char *raw, unsigned char
*foreground, unsigned char *background, int totalPixels)
{
   for(int i = 0;i < totalPixels;i += 16)
   {
      subtractSSE(&foreground[i], &raw[i], &background[i]);
   }
}
```

Figure 1.4   SIMD Background Subtraction Algorithm Using SSE Instructions

In other words, the background subtraction operation can be performed up to 16 times faster than the serial version, since it requires only 129,600 subtraction calls. A large number of other computer vision and machine learning tasks exhibit similar types of repetitive operations on images, vectors, and matrices, so there is an opportunity to see tremendous speed improvements using SIMD instructions when building intelligent systems.

Multiple Processing Cores

A common trend in the microprocessor industry is to develop CPUs that feature two or more cores, where each core can independently read and execute a set of instructions. Therefore, if an application is properly designed so that time-consuming tasks are equally parallelized across multiple threads, then it is theoretically possible to achieve speedup factors near the number of cores (Akhter 2006). Unfortunately, parallelizing complex serial algorithms is not an easy task. Multithreaded code often requires complicated coordination between threads, which can easily lead to subtle but hard-to-detect bugs. For this reason, there has been very little investigation into how common machine learning, computer vision, and data mining applications can be parallelized. Nevertheless, much like SIMD instructions, there are opportunities to see huge improvements in the speed of many intelligent algorithms if we focus some efforts on re-engineering existing serial techniques to take advantage of task parallelism. This has been made easier through the use of APIs and frameworks such as Open Multi-Processing (OpenMP) or Intel® Threading Building Blocks (Intel TBB).

General Purpose Graphics Processing Units (GPUs)

A GPU is a massively parallel processor that is traditionally dedicated to performing graphics operations in parallel to the primary CPU. Recently, designers have equipped these GPUs with programmable stages and higher precision arithmetic, allowing programmers to take advantage of the GPU to perform general purpose tasks that go beyond only graphics operations (Kirk 2010). Due to their ability to perform the same operation on a large data set, GPUs provide functionality similar to SIMD instructions. This makes GPUs ideal for performing image processing and matrix algebra, both of which are used extensively in computer vision and machine learning. The challenge is trying to rethink existing algorithms into a form that can be mapped into the limited instruction sets that are available on modern GPUs. OpenCL is a parallel computing framework that can help ease the development of GPU optimized code on a variety of platforms.

Accuracy and Robustness

One of the biggest challenges when building intelligent systems is achieving sufficient accuracy due to uncertainty that is inherent with many AI algorithms. For example, a face recognition system that is used to automatically tag faces on a social networking site might be perfectly fine with an accuracy of 95 percent, but that same accuracy rate might be insufficient for a security system where face recognition is used to control access to sensitive material. A real-world application must therefore consider the following:

1. Determining the minimum accuracy level for the desired application

2. Choosing an algorithm and possibly a training set that can provide the target accuracy level

3. Benchmarking and profiling the algorithm to see if it achieves the desired accuracy

Benchmarking is extremely important since it helps to determine the robustness of an algorithm in the target environments and under the anticipated conditions. For example, computer vision algorithms frequently have to deal with variations in lighting, shadows, occlusion, and image noise. Machine learning algorithms also need to deal with noise, handling outliers, and overtraining. Finally, data mining algorithms need to consider scalability, noise, and missing data.

Profiling an implementation helps pinpoint bottlenecks and hotspots in an algorithm, which can be used to determine candidate areas for optimizations via SIMD, multithreading, or GPU acceleration.

Privacy

As intelligence becomes more pervasive in the devices and technologies we use each day, the protection of privacy becomes a critical concern. This includes either avoiding the collection of personally identifiable information, or putting in appropriate safeguards to protect sensitive data such as data encryption. The AI research community often overlooks these privacy issues, but real-world systems cannot ignore this topic due to strong government legislation. A recent concept known as Privacy by Design (Cavoukian 2010), where privacy is built right into a system by following a set of guiding principles, can and should be applied to many existing AI algorithms. Privacy issues will be discussed in more detail in Chapter 8.

Summary

Consumers are now demanding and expecting more from technology. Building intelligence into our devices is a promising way to satisfy this demand by providing more personalized experiences. In this book we investigate how computer vision, machine learning, and data mining can be used together to build smarter devices and systems. Additionally, we explore some of the practical considerations of using artificial intelligence in the real world, tackling issues that are often overlooked in academic circles, such as performance optimization, benchmarking, robustness, and privacy.

Chapter 2

Fundamental Visual Metrics for Computer Vision

Of making many books there is no end; and much study is a weariness of the flesh
—Solomon, Ecclesiastes

Perception is the process of using sensory information to gain knowledge and understanding of the surrounding environment. The field of computer vision aims to address the issue of visual perception by providing machines with the ability to extract meaningful data from images and video. This chapter examines visual metrics taken from images that comprise the basis for computer vision and data mining across a variety of intelligent applications. The material includes a survey of the fundamental metrics used to describe features of images, a survey of the sensors and optical systems used to capture images, and a survey of the image processing methods and practical architecture considerations from the engineering perspective to create real solutions.

For a given application domain, there will be a group of image metrics that are most useful for understanding the visual features in the image, so metrics must be carefully chosen or uniquely developed to provide an advantage. Consideration must be given to the processing methods used to prepare images for analysis and the image sensors used. Visual metrics can be used to identify characteristics of complete images and subregions, leading to description and understanding of the image content. Visual metrics are constantly being derived as improvements from existing metrics, and new and novel metrics are being devised all the time. A *feature descriptor* or *feature signature* is an example of a visual metric, image or region *texture* is another. While this chapter is general in nature, other chapters in this book describe specific applications such as face and logo recognition methods, which use a small set of visual metrics discussed in this chapter.

To understand where visual metrics fit into the big picture, Figure 2.1 illustrates the visual computing pipeline and highlights where this chapter focuses.

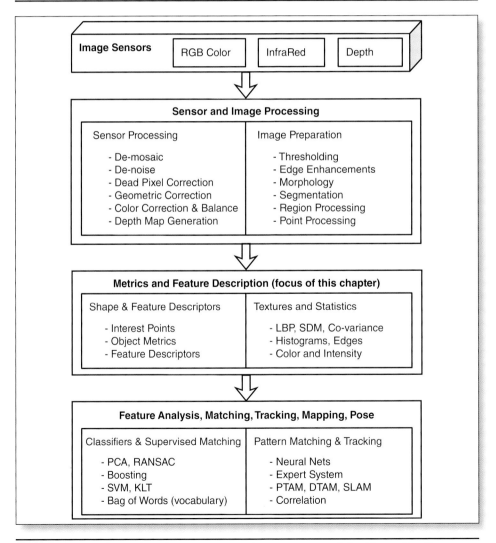

Figure 2.1   Where This Chapter Fits into the Big Picture of the Vision Pipeline

What Is Covered, What Is Not Covered

The focus of this chapter is to survey the state of the art and history of visual metrics and visual features that have been proven useful across a wide range of applications, and as a result of this focus some topics are treated lightly.

This chapter provides engineering-level information for building real applications rather than academic treatises, but references to useful academic research are provided throughout. In particular, applications such as home energy management, medical, security, and industrial automation are kept in mind and relevant insights are highlighted throughout.

Also included throughout this chapter is some direction on where the future of visual metrics and visual feature research and development is heading, as well as practical guidance on areas for optimization in the vision pipeline. This is fundamentally an engineering-oriented approach to visual metrics rather than an academic approach filled with theoretical foundations and proofs.

The literature on visual metrics is vast. Useful references are given throughout this chapter and in the "References" section at the end of the book for those who wish to dig deeper.

History of Key Ideas in Visual Metrics

To understand visual metrics it is useful to survey the modern history of machine vision and the key ideas, approaches and metrics which have been used. Often the choice of metrics was limited to those metrics which were possible at the time given limitations rising from sensor technology, memory capabilities and compute performance. As time passes and technology develops, images are becoming *multi-modal* combining intensity, color, multiple spectrums, depth, and 3D sensor information, multiple-exposure sets, faster frame rates, with more precision and accuracy in x, y, and depth. Increases in memory bandwidth and compute performance give rise to new approaches to creating visual metrics and visual analysis.

What follows is a brief history showing major trends and milestones in visual metrics research, and while this is not a precise timeline of events, it provides a general overview of mainstream industry and academic activity.

1960s through 1980s: Whole-Object Approaches. Patterns and metrics describe mostly whole objects or images, pattern matching via correlation, recognition includes object, shape and texture metrics, simple geometric primitives used for object composition. Low resolution images primarily grayscale with some color when adequate memory was available.

Early 1990s: Partial-Object Approaches. Patterns and metrics describe smaller pieces of objects and parts of images; large sets of subpatterns and metrics are developed, increasing use of color information, but little tolerance for scale, rotational or affine variations, recognition based on finding parts of object with appropriate metrics. Higher image resolution, increased pixel depths (medical applications especially), and color information used.

Mid-1990s: Local Feature Approaches. Patterns and metrics identify small features (interest points) in images, feature descriptors add more details from a window or patch surrounding each feature, recognition is based on searching for sets of features via matching descriptors.

Late 1990s: Classified Invariant Local Feature Approaches. New feature descriptors are developed and refined to be *invariant* to changes in scale, lightness, rotation and affine transformations. Features act as an alphabet for spelling out complex feature descriptors or vectors where the vectors are used for matching. The feature matching and classification stages are refined to increase effectiveness.

Early 2000s: Scene and Object Modeling Approaches. Scenes and objects are modeled as sets of feature components or patterns with well-formed descriptors, spatial relationships between features are measured and used for matching, while new complex classification and matching methods use boosting to combine strong and weak features together for more effective recognition. Intel Performance Primitives (IPP) are released, Intel releases the Open CV package for computer vision as open source.

Mid-2000s to Present: Finer Grain Feature and Metric Composition Approaches. Various combinations of features and metrics (Bags of Features) are used to describe scenes and objects, new local feature descriptors are created and old ones refined, increased interest in real-time feature extraction and matching methods, local metrics and feature descriptors are used together for increased pattern match recognition.

Future: Multi-Modal Visual Metrics Fusion. Increasing use of depth sensor information and depth maps to segment images, VOXEL metrics and 2D texture metrics in 3-space based on 3D and light field camera images, increasing use of high resolution images and high dynamic range (HDR) images to increase feature accuracy, increased accuracy of color images yielding valuable color-based metrics, increasing processing power to handle the increased amount of image data and memory bandwidth. Another future trend is that feature descriptors are becoming larger such as the Pyramidal Histogram of Gradients (PHoG) where instead of using an image pyramid for matching the *monoscale* descriptor, larger *multiscale, multiresolution and multivariate descriptors* are developed that contain a pyramid of descriptors, or in cases such as the Volume Linear Binary pattern (VLBP) the descriptor contains 3D volumetric information.

In the end, future computing research may even come full circle when sufficient compute and memory capacity exist to perform the older methods like correlation across multiple scales and perspectives in real-time using generic compute platforms and parallel and fixed-function hardware methods, obviating the current focus on small invariant sets of local features. Therefore, history is worth knowing in the field of visual computing since it might repeat itself in a different technology embodiment.

Since there is no single solution to obtaining the right set of visual metrics, all of the methods developed over time have applications today and are still in use. It is therefore worthwhile to understand the history of visual metrics and look for ways to use or improve older and often overlooked metrics and methods.

Overview of Visual Computing Topics in the Vision Pipeline

Topics to be covered in this chapter are outlined in Figure 2.1 above, and will follow the processing flow through the system from image capture, processing, feature extraction, description, analysis, and tracking.

Sensor Technology and Sensor Processing

This is the first step to prepare an image for image analysis and the most critical step. Without a well-prepared image that takes the sensor capabilities into consideration, the rest of the visual computing process becomes more difficult.

Here are the major topics to be considered.

■   Sensor technology

■   Computational imaging and cameras, optics, depth sensing

- De-mosaicing

- De-noise

- Dead pixel correction

- Geometric correction

- Color correction and balance

- 3D depth map generation

Image Preparation

This is the classic area of image processing, and there is a large body of knowledge in place for guidance (Szeliski 2011; Pratt 2007; Russ 2011; Gonzalez and Woods 2007), so this topic is covered lightly here. However, key topics and best practices are covered.

Methods include:

- Thresholding

- Edge enhancements

- Intensity and contrast enhancements

- Color enhancements

- Region filtering and processing

- Point processing

Segmentation

Once the image is prepared for subsequent processing, one of the main challenges can be to segment the image into regions or areas of interest for further processing. For example, certain types of regions are more interesting depending on the application, such as surfaces in the background for augmented reality, and foreground features for face recognition.

Methods discussed include:

- Morphological shapes

- Texture regions

- MSER (Maximally Stable External Regions)

- Edge and boundary delineation

- Color region segmentation

- Gray scale or luminance region segmentation

- Depth map region segmentation

Local Features and Interest Points

Most of the modern algorithms for visual understanding rely on locating *interest points* and calculating a description of the region or patch surrounding the interest point, as opposed to the older methods such as correlation where a larger rectangular pattern is stepped over the image at pixel intervals and the correlation is measured at each location.

In general a good interest point must be easy to find and ideally fast to compute, so there are many methods currently in use and this is an active area of research.

Methods discussed include:

- Canny detector

- Harris and Stephens corner detection

- Shi and Tomasi corner detector (improvement on Harris method)

- LoG Laplacian of Gaussian

- DoG Difference of Gaussians (DoG is an approximation of LoG)

- DoH Determinant of the Hessian

- Harris-/Hessian-Laplace

- Harris-/Hessian-Affine

- Hessian and Harris

- EBR and IBR

- Salient Regions

- Moravac corner detector

Object Shape and Local Feature descriptors

This is another main focus of this chapter and probably the largest area of research in visual computing. This chapter will cover both object (blob) analysis methods and local feature descriptor methods.

Topics include:

■ Object shape metrics such as area, perimeter, centroid, Fourier metrics

■ Local Feature descriptors such as GLOH, SIFT, DAISY, LBP

■ Wavelets, Haar, Gabor Features

■ Bag of Features and visual vocabularies

Global Textural and Statistical Features

Texture is a powerful metric all by itself. Textures can be measured globally for use in segmentation into like-textured regions, or locally as feature descriptors. Also, common statistics like scatter plots, spatial dependency matrices (SDMs) and their visual plots, and histograms are valuable as well.

Topics covered here include:

■ LBP, CS-LVP, VLBP, PLBP

■ SDM, co-variance matrices, scatter diagrams

■ Histograms, edges

■ Region segmentation

■ Color and intensity

■ Autocorrelation

Algorithms, Classifiers, Training and Supervised Matching, Mapping, Tracking

In many cases, it is not simple to cleanly separate the discussion of descriptors, algorithms, compound primitives, and atomic primitives since some well-known methods like SIFT and SURF combine interest points, feature descriptors, matching, classification and training into a complete algorithm.

However, this chapter does not cover high level vision algorithms, classifiers, training, supervised matching, tracking, mapping, and pose estimation in any detail, so just a few noteworthy classification methods are mentioned here for completeness.

For applications involving scene analysis and object recognition, which might rely on shape factors and region descriptors, the classification and training stage may be of less importance. For applications where small features must be recognized such as face recognition, this section is more relevant.

As we will explain in Chapter 3, the popular Viola-Jones object detection framework (Viola and Jones 2001) uses the AdaBoost training method to create a cascaded pattern matching and classification network by generating strong classifiers from many weak learners through dynamic weighting during training.

Binary Histogram Intersection Minimization, or BHIM (Raja and Shaogang 2006) uses pairs of Multi-Scale Local Binary Patterns (MSLBP) to form pairwise-coupled classifiers based on strong divergence between pairs of MSLBP features. Histogram intersection on pairs of MSLBP features using a distance function such as SAD (sum of absolute differences) is used to find the largest divergence of histogram distance. The BHIM classifier is then composed of a list of "pairs" of MSLBP histograms with large divergence, and MSLBPs are matched into the classifier. BHIM uses features created across a scale of training data. BHIM has proven to be more accurate than AdaBoost, and the MSLBP features have proven to be more discriminant than LBPs.

Conditional Mutual Information Maximization, or CMIM (Fleuret 2004) is another training method that efficiently chooses unique features in pairs that together have high synergy for improved correspondence reducing redundancy in the training set and reducing the size of the training set. This method is also very high performing.

Here are the some of the methods in use today.

High-level algorithms

■ LK (Lucas Kanade)

■ Viola Jones

■ SURF

■ SIFT, PCA-SIFT

- SVM

- BHIM

- CMIM

Pattern Matching and tracking, tracking, mapping (for AR), pose estimation

- Neural nets

- Expert systems

- Tracking methods, PTAM, DTAM, SLAM

To dig deeper into general image processing and visual computing topics not covered in this chapter the following resources are recommended: Szeliski (2011), Pratt (2007), Russ (2011), and Gonzalez and Woods (2007).

Sensor Processing for Visual Metrics — A Rich Area

Novel image sensors and cameras using computational photography methods have created a rich area for innovation in the field of visual metrics. For example, 3D metrics will emerge and displace many current 2D methods for image analysis, which were limited due to lack of 3D depth-perception sensor information. Computational photographic methods create opportunities to leverage high resolution images and faster frame rates to devise new visual metrics. We will review some of the novel camera architectures and sensors in this section and point the way towards some of the new types of visual metrics that can be expected.

The first step in creating visual metrics is dealing with the raw image itself. This includes understanding the sensor that produced the image and then creating a realistic model of the entire imaging system characteristics including the image sensor, lighting conditions, and optics, and finally performing appropriate image processing to correct and optimize the image for subsequent metrics extraction.

The characteristics of the sensor are key when preparing an image for visual metrics extraction, feature processing, and analysis. For optimal results, it is necessary to understand and evaluate the entire camera system, sensor, optics, and lighting conditions to optimize the images for a specific visual computing task. When the source of the images is unknown, it is still useful and recommended that a model of the image device be built into your system to guide the image processing.

> Model and understand the imaging systems used in your application, including the sensors, optics, lighting, and camera. This model will guide the processing of images prior to visual metrics and feature extraction for optimal results.
>
> For example, a *home energy application* may incorporate low light imaging conditions, and specific processing is needed to enhance the images close to the IR range. An *outdoor surveillance system* may require special processing to deal with natural light settings, which saturate cells in the image sensor. In either case, the image must be prepared to compensate for these characteristics.

Sensor Characteristics, Configuration and Resolution

Typical image sensors are created from either charge-coupled device (CCD) cells or standard CMOS cells. Both types of sensors have similar characteristics and are widely used today in commercial cameras. The vast majority of sensors today use CMOS cells mostly due to manufacturing considerations.

Here we will review some of the image sensor configurations and camera designs in common use, as well as some emerging sensor types.

Sensors and optics are often integrated together on-chip as shown in Figure 2.2. In some cases, wafer-scale cameras are constructed with optics built on chip specifically for applications like biology or microscopy.

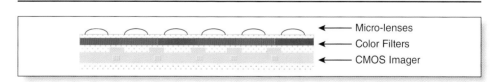

Micro-lenses
Color Filters
CMOS Imager

Figure 2.2   Common Integrated Image Sensor Arrangement with Optics and Color Filters

Image sensors are designed to reach specific design goals, so specific sensors may be better suited for your application. For example, the size and material composition of each photo-diode sensor element is optimized for a given semiconductor manufacturing process to achieve the best tradeoff between silicon die area and dynamic response for light intensity and color detection. One key consideration is photo-diode size or cell size.

A sensor cell which is comprised of a small photo-diode will not be able to capture as many photons as a large photo-diode, thus smaller geometries have less sensitivity and in the extreme case small sensors may be more sensitive to noise. If the photo-diode sensor cells are too large, there is no benefit either and the die size and cost for silicon increases to no advantage. Common commercial devices today use sensor cell sizes ranging between 1.4 square microns and 8 square microns.

The sensor cell size also affects the bit resolution of each cell. For example, a smaller cell would likely have less effective bit resolution than a larger cell, all things being equal. However, pixel size alone does not entirely define bit resolution since readout noise also affects resolution, where each pixel cell is read out of the sensor one at a time and sent to an electrical interface with A/D converters where the pixels are formed into digital format as lines and columns. Even the A/D converters can introduce noise as well. There is a lot of effort spent on noise reduction in the pixel cell readout circuits and A/D converters to reduce readout noise to ensure accurate resolution.

Calibrate your camera system to determine sensor noise and dynamic range for pixel bit depth under different lighting and distance situations and develop appropriate sensor processing methods and realistic expectations for your system.

A simple calibration method can be devised using a simple test pattern with fine and coarse gradations of gray scale, color, and size of features by imaging the test pattern and looking at the results. Try different methods of image processing to deal with noise, nonlinear response, dead pixels, geometric distortion, and so on.

Also, the effects of sampling theory must be considered, that is, the Nyquist Frequency as applied to pixel coverage of the target scene, where the sensor resolution and optics together must provide adequate resolution to image the features of interest, so it follows that a feature of interest should be imaged or sampled at 2x minimum the size of the smallest pixels of importance, and of course 2x oversampling is just a minimum target, so the more samples the better for accuracy. In practice, single pixel wide features are not easily resolved.

As shown in Figure 2.3 silicon image sensors have a known spectral response curve where the near infrared part of the spectrum is sensed well or amplified, while blue, violet, and near UV are sensed poorly and compressed. Note that the silicon spectral response must be accounted for when reading the raw sensor data and quantizing the data into a digital pixel, and sensor manufacturers make design compensations in this area. However, sensor color response should also be considered when calibrating your camera system and devising sensor processing methods for your application—do not rely on the sensor manufacturer.

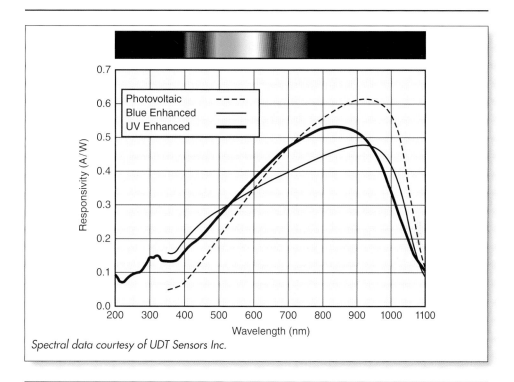

Spectral data courtesy of UDT Sensors Inc.

Figure 2.3   Typical Response of a Few Types of Silicon Photo-Diodes with Highest Sensitivity in the Near Infrared Range, and Nonlinear Sensitivity in the Visible Spectrum Where Violet and Blue Suffer the Most

Colorimetry or color science will not be covered in this chapter since this is a large topic; however the reader is encouraged to dig deeper into the area of color spaces, color gamut mapping between color spaces, and mathematical color device modeling of sensor and display device characteristics. To dig deeper, look at the resources available at the Munsell Color Science Laboratory, the Microsoft† Color Management System, as well as Berns, Billmeyer, and Salzman (2000), Fairchild (2005), and Fairchild and Johnson (2004).

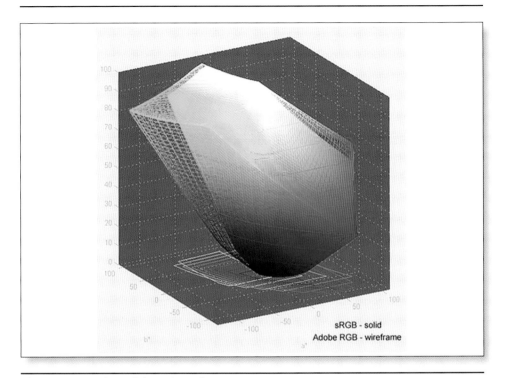

Figure 2.4   The Adobe RGB color space

Figure 2.4 shows the Adobe RGB color space enclosing the standard sRGB color space. Note that the standard sRGB color space does not cover all the colors represented in the Adobe RGB color space. When capturing and processing color images, a larger color space is preferred, otherwise color information is thrown away. This image was generated using the Gamutvision† software package.

For example, many common methods to improve contrast or color rely on using simple and generic methods such as a *gamma curve* applied to image intensity, or histogram-based intensity modification methods such as histogram equalization and histogram specification, and while these methods can be visually appealing, the results are distorted away from the true characteristics of the sensor. Better to calibrate the sensor with a known calibration pattern test image containing known gradations of gray intensity and accurate colors using a known colorimetrically accurate light source type (natural, fluorescent, halogen) to empirically determine the sensor characteristics and then design proper image processing compensation methods to increase the accuracy of the intensity and color values based on the calibration results. *Create a mathematical device model of your sensor's independent RGB color response, and let the model determine the sensor processing methods.*

An accurate baseline calibration model and image processing pipeline based on true sensor characteristics is a good place to start from to get the best visual metrics and results. Simple gamma curves are not recommended.

Sensor Color Patterns, Eye Light Sensitivity, Color De-Mosaicing

There are various on-chip configurations for multispectral sensor design, including mosaics and stacked methods as shown in Figure 2.5. For color sensors, color filters placed above mosaiced cells are commonly used, however there are other spectral imaging techniques such as the Foveon† sensor in Figure 2.5 that rely on the depth penetration of color wavelengths into the semiconductor material, where depth penetration is used to image the separate colors. Where mosaiced color cell patterns are used, sensor processing includes reading out the color patterns on the cells and *de-mosaicing* the spatially-separate color cells together into a single pixel.

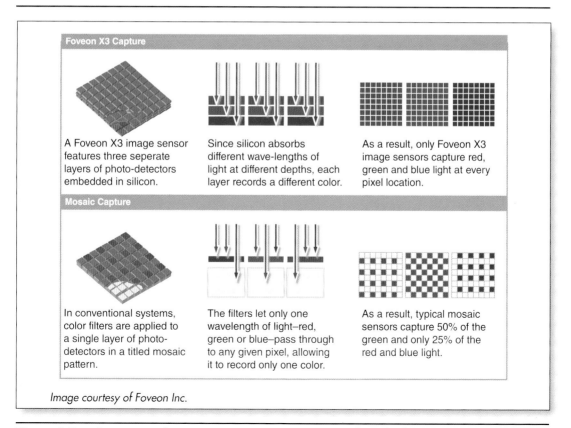

Image courtesy of Foveon Inc.

Figure 2.5   Comparison between Mosaic Sensor Design and Stacked Sensor Design

Image sensor mosaic configurations are still coming to market in novel arrangements. As shown in Figure 2.6, various color sensor patterns are designed to allow for color information to be optimized for various colorimetric requirements.

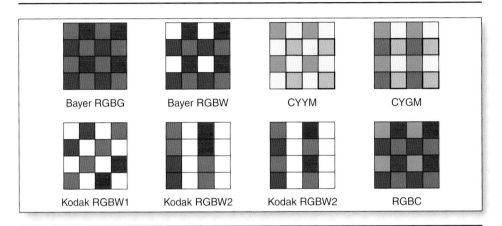

Figure 2.6　Various Color Image Sensor Patterns

While today's image sensors commonly produce 8 bits for each RGB color, higher bit depths such as 10, 12, 14, and 16 are expected to become mainstream, offering opportunities for high dynamic range (HDR) imagery, more accurate color, and additional color processing opportunities. HDR imagery combines multiple images of the same scene taken at different illumination levels into a composite image with increased dynamic range.

See Figure 2.7 showing the visible light spectrum. Since the human eye can only resolve about 10 bits of color for each RGB (roughly 1024 colors), the advantages of using additional bits for color appear during the computation stages of various image enhancements and color space conversions, and also at display time where intelligent display systems may take advantage of additional bit depth. For example, during image processing higher bit resolutions can be used as containers to combine lower dynamic range images together into HDR images, and then a portion of the dynamic range can be processed as needed to reach various image display goals. For example, image details hidden due to glare or darkness may be restored through careful processing methods if enough bit depth per pixel is available.

When considering human eye response to color as shown in Figure 2.7, note that the green response overlaps into the blue and red spectral regions and therefore green can act as a perceived *intensity proxy*. This is the case with the YIQ color space where green is heavily weighted as perceived intensity, and in the old days of black and white monitors, the green color channel of an RGB signal was often used as a proxy for intensity to drive the black and white monitor.

The human eye can only resolve about 10 million colors at about 600 dpi on a sheet of film or paper, which indicates that 8 bits per RGB color, which is about 16 million colors, provides adequate resolution for viewing in most cases. However, higher bit depths for increased color intensity resolution such as 10, 12, 14 and 16 bits are still required and useful when processing color accurately. A 16-bit floating point number might be a good tradeoff for color accuracy all around when processing is considered.

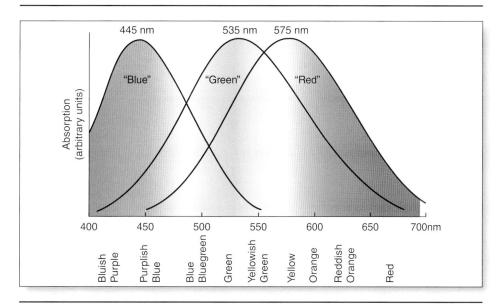

Figure 2.7　The Visible Light Spectrum: the Color Overlap in the Light Spectrum Creates Challenges for Processing Color Accurately.

Sensor and Optics for 3D Depth Sensing and Computational Imaging

Methods of *depth sensing* are being developed to create a 3D field of *voxels* (volume pixels) from inexpensive cameras and die-level image sensors, so this is a critical emerging area to consider with tremendous potential. Over time, depth-based metrics will be developed and become more common. Nearly all of the common visual metrics in use today are trying to locate 3D objects within a 2D image field (no 3D information a priori), so the current 2D methods are quite challenging and the source of a lot of the uncertainties and lack or precision. Using 3D depth sensors can provide obvious advantages.

With the emerging depth sensing capabilities based on novel sensor and optical arrangements, the field of *computational photography* has emerged to take advantage of the rich visual 3D field to compute various types of renderings from the same data after the image is taken, such as changing the focal plane, depth of field, or apparent viewing angle. Computational imaging capabilities provide the opportunity for novel 3D visual metrics to be devised, which are better than standard methods of extracting 3D information from 2D images.

At this time there is no comprehensive set of 3D depth metrics that can be used in any standard image feature detector or classifier, so 3D field information derived from computational imaging is largely ignored in visual metrics and data mining applications (some notable exceptions such as PTAM and DTAM will be considered later in this chapter). Instead, only 2D information is used in feature detectors to solve a variety of problems including rotation, scale, and perspective problems. Many difficulties surrounding feature detection result from the 2D data field, which is used as the starting point. For example, feature detection with scale invariance, affine projective invariance, and rotational invariance can be improved in many applications if 3D depth information is used in the descriptors.

Consider using 3D sensors and depth maps for your application to create richer visual metrics and feature descriptors using depth information combined with texture, shape, and color. For scene and object recognition, applications like surveillance, automotive, and gesture recognition may find great value in using depth maps to simplify the vision task.

Note that depth information can be extracted from a single camera image using various methods as discussed below.

An overview of common depth sensor technologies is shown in Table 2.1 courtesy of Kenneth Salsman (2010) of Aptina Inc.

Table 2.1 Various Methods for Capturing Depth Information (Courtesy of Ken Salsmann [2010] of Aptina).

Technique	No. of Cameras	Lighting Requirement	Characteristics
Parallax and hybrid parallax	2/1	Passive – normal lighting	Positional shift measurement in field of vision (FOV) between two camera positions
Size mapping	1	Passive – normal lighting	Utilizes color tags of specific size to determine range and position
Depth of focus	1	Passive – normal lighting	Multiframe with scanned focus

Differential magnification	1	Passive – normal lighting	Two-frame image capture at different magnifications creating a distance based offset
Structured light	1	Active – projected lighting	Multiframe pattern projection
Time of flight	1	Active – pulsed lighting	High speed light pulse with special pixels measuring return time of reflected light
Shading shift	1	Active – alternating lighting	Two-frame shadow differential measurement between two light sources as different positions
Pattern spreading	1	Active – multibeam lighting	Projected 2D spot pattern expanding at different rate than camera lens field spread
Beam tracking	1	Active – lighting on object(s)	Two point light sources mounted on objects in FOV to be tracked

3D metrics based on depth maps and 3D volume data will be increasingly used for image segmentation and also incorporated into 3D texture descriptors for object recognition. Depth information can be used to both segment the image into near and far regions, as well as create surface maps of objects which can be analyzed into 3D surface shape descriptors and new classes of volume metrics. Nearly all vision tasks can benefit from depth information.

Following is a brief survey of selected novel depth camera architectures including stereo, 3D depth field imaging, as well as high resolution and high dynamic range cameras. These powerful types of camera are critical areas of emerging technology that can enable novel visual computing algorithms and image metrics.

1. *Stereo, binocular, trinocular imaging using two or more cameras* is a well-known method to acquire depth information. Stereo methods are becoming more prevalent as image sensor prices decrease. State-of-the-art research and development of stereo imaging algorithms is very active given the range of computer architectures and processing power available, and systems using more than two cameras are beginning to become common.

2. *Diffraction gratings* (Wang, Gill, and Molnar 2009; Willett et al. 2008) above the photo-diode cells or arrays of cells can be used to provide angle-sensitive pixel sensing, where the light is refracted into surrounding cells at various angles as determined by the placement

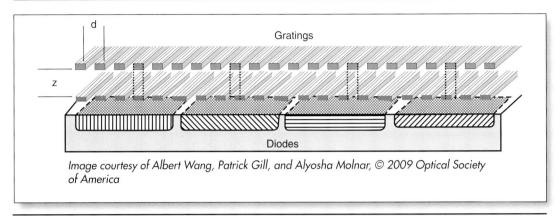

Image courtesy of Albert Wang, Patrick Gill, and Alyosha Molnar, © 2009 Optical Society of America

Figure 2.8   Diffraction Gratings above Silicon Used to Create the Talbot Effect to Create Depth Images

of the diffraction gratings, allowing the same sensor data to be processed in different ways with respect to a given angle of view to yield different images, as shown in Figure 2.8. This method allows camera system size to be reduced while providing higher resolution images using a series of low-resolution images captured in parallel from narrow aperture diffraction gratings. As a result, diffraction gratings make it possible to produce a wide range of information from the same sensor data including depth information, increased pixel resolution, perspective displacements, and focusing at multiple focal planes after the image is taken.

3. *Multiview radial cameras* (Nayar 2006) capture 3D scene geometry and depth maps by imaging through a conical mirror onto a 2D image sensor, creating a composite standard 2d image combined with a conical ring image, which contains depth information. By processing the conical ring together with the 2D image, depth information is extracted, surface texture maps are obtained, and 3D surfaces are produced.

4. *Plenoptic cameras* (Fife, El Gamal, and Wong 2006; Georgeiv et al. 2006) use an array of optics with a set of micro-lenses positioned between the main lens and the image sensor, providing full 3D light field imaging within the lens aperture, where the 3D field contains information from a range of depths and viewpoints. Plenoptic cameras are also referred to as *light field cameras* or 4D cameras, where the light field is a volume and the fourth dimension is volumetric.

An array of micro-lenses capture light from different angles and perspectives onto a 2D sensor array. There are a few variations of plenoptic methods which vary the position of the focal plane to be either at or above the sensor. The image is then processed to yield depth information, perspective displacements, and focusing at multiple focal planes after the image is taken. This camera supports shorter exposure times.

Figure 2.9 shows a plenoptic array of lenses, where multiple views of the image with varying depth of field can be produced by processing the sensor data to account for the desired viewing angle and depth of field. The focal plane can be adjusted to be either above the sensor or at the sensor.

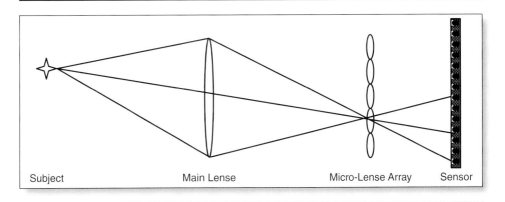

| Subject | Main Lense | Micro-Lense Array | Sensor |

Figure 2.9   A Plenoptic Array of Lenses

Figure 2.10 shows how plenoptic camera volumetric data can be processed into various 2D views.

In order to obtain a 2D slice from the 3D field or volume, the data is processed in the frequency domain by way of the *Fourier Projection Slice theorem*, which is the basis for a variety of medical imaging methods for processing MRI and CAT scan data. Applications of the method are described by Krig (1993, 1995), Levoy (1992), Baker and Matthews (2003), and Lowe (2004) and the key algorithm is described as follows:

■   The volume data is forward transformed using a 3D fast Fourier transform (FFT) into magnitude and phase data. (The Fast Hartley transform may be used also.)

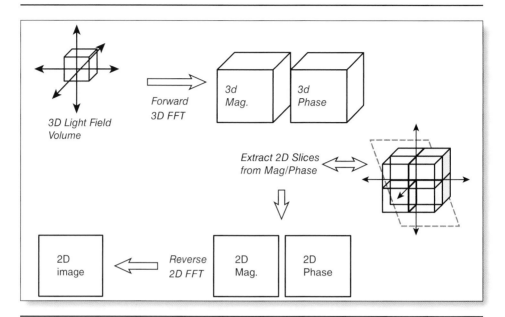

Figure 2.10 Fourier Volume Processing and Fourier Slice Method of Obtaining 2D Images from 3D Volumes from Plenoptic or Light Field Cameras

■ To visualize, the resulting 3D FFT results in the frequency volume are rearranged by *octant shifting* each cube in 3-space to align the frequency 0 origin data around the center of a 3D Cartesian coordinate system in the center of the volume, similar to the way 2D frequency spectrums are *quadrant shifted* for frequency spectrum display about the center of a 2D Cartesian coordinate system.

■ An arbitrary planar 2D slice is extracted from the volume parallel to the FOV plane where the slice passes through the origin (center) of the volume. The angle of the slice taken from the frequency domain volume data determines the angle of the desired 2D view and depth of field.

■ The 2D slice from the frequency domain is run through an inverse 2D FFT to yield a 2D spatial image rendering corresponding to the chosen angle and depth of field.

5. *Structured and coded light* illumination patterns are projected into a scene, and then an image sensor reads the scene data to locate the

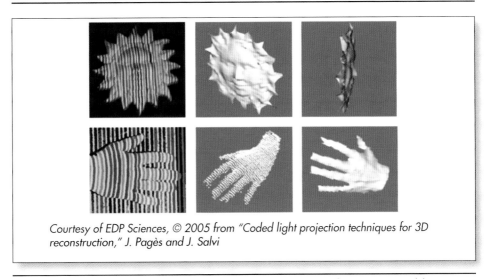

Courtesy of EDP Sciences, © 2005 from "Coded light projection techniques for 3D reconstruction," J. Pagès and J. Salvi

Figure 2.11 Structured Light Patterns Projected onto a Surface Using Visible or Infrared Light, Where Depth Information Is Detected by Analyzing the Pattern Geometry as Imaged on the Surface.

patterns and measures pattern size and shape to determine depth. Often infrared light is used to project structured light patterns and infrared sensors are used to detect the patterns. There are many different types of patterns used for structured and coded light. The pattern dictates the processing method required to extract the depth information. See Pagès and Salvi (2005). Figure 2.11 shows the results of projecting structured light and some corresponding derived depth maps, and Figure 2.12 shows various methods of creating structured light patterns.

6. *Time of flight (TOF) sensors* are like infrared radar on a chip, creating depth maps directly from a scene by sensing infrared light that has been projected directly into the scene, reflected back, and imaged in the TOF sensor. Current TOF sensor silicon implementation methods require a large sensor area for each pixel in order to capture enough infrared light to generate quantitative depth information, rendering the TOF sensors fairly high priced. Currently TOF sensor bit resolution is not very good: some commercial sensors claim 8-bit resolution but in reality the accuracy is closer to 5–6 bits. Currently, TOF sensors are used for close range applications where the subject

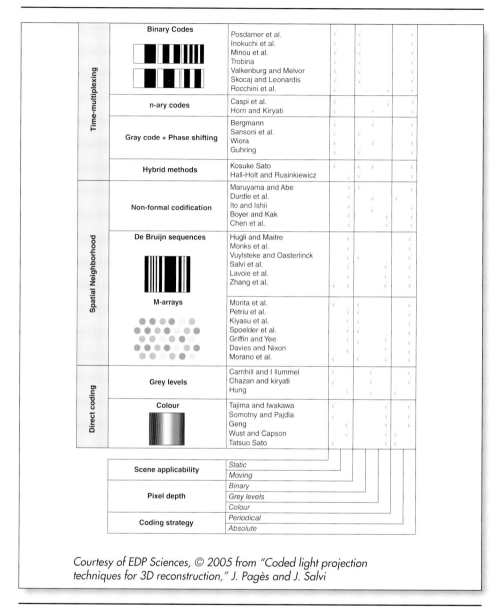

Figure 2.12 Structured and Coded Light Methods Summary. SOURCE J3EA Vol4, Hors Serie 3 (2005)

is close enough to illuminate with IR light. Of course, the IR light projection requires power, so power is an issue and limits applications of TOF sensors. Future TOF sensor improvements are expected since the technology is a very promising. See Figure 2.13.

Figure 2.13 TOF Sensor Image

7. *Multiple illumination pattern synthesis* using a programmable flash lighting unit can be used to create a variety of illumination patterns that are projected onto a scene, and subsequent image processing of the illumination patterns combined with the scene can yield depth maps derived from projected light pattern defocus measurements, and also provide separation of global and local illumination using high frequency illumination patterns (Nayar 2011).

8. Very high resolution cameras and camera arrays will be increasingly used to capture fine details from scenes, which can improve video metrics accuracy. Such cameras are composed of arrays of cameras and lenses arranged to create image tiles which must be computationally assembled into a larger image. See Cossairt, Miau, and Nayar, (2011).

9. *Microsoft Kinect†* serves as a commercial example of where depth sensing can make an impact in gaming and augmented reality. Microsoft has been marketing the Kinect system, which incorporates depth sensing primarily for gaming applications and immersive AR using structured light methods at 640 × 480 resolution and 30 frames per second. The Kinect™ approach to depth mapping uses an IR pattern projected via laser through a diffraction grating, then the scene is IR imaged and

compared to a reference pattern at a calibrated image plane, and since points will shift in the image plane based on distance, a disparity map can be computed from correlation of points in the reference & live images.

Image Processing Prior to Visual Metrics and Analysis

After sensor processing, the next stage in the vision pipeline is image processing, which is a very well developed field and will not be covered in great detail here. The goal of image preprocessing is to get the images ready for visual metrics extraction and analysis. This section provides a light overview and references to dig deeper.

Common tasks performed at this stage include:

■ *Point operations* (math, lookup-table transforms, global histogram equalization, color corrections, geometric corrections)

■ *Kernel operations* (convolutions, contrast enhancement, sharpening, blurring, morphology)

■ *Area operations* (median filtering, local histogram equalization)

■ *Basis function transforms* (FFT, DCT, KLT, Slant transform)

It is recommended that one becomes familiar with some of the image processing literature and available software packages that will be of value. Here are some starting points:

1. Intel® Integrated Performance Primitives (Intel® IPP) for Image and Signal Processing, which are optimized for Intel processors and discussed below.

2. OpenCV† open source library for computer vision (Bradski and Kaeler 2008) used by many industry applications and academic research organizations, discussed below.

Intel® Integrated Performance Primitives (Intel® IPP)

The Intel IPP library contains a wide range of visual computing primitives covering imaging, mathematics, as well as interest point and feature descriptor functions. The primitives are optimized for Intel architecture. The IPP library is available for download at http://software.intel.com. Figure 2.14 provides a summary of the approximately 1000 IPP functions.

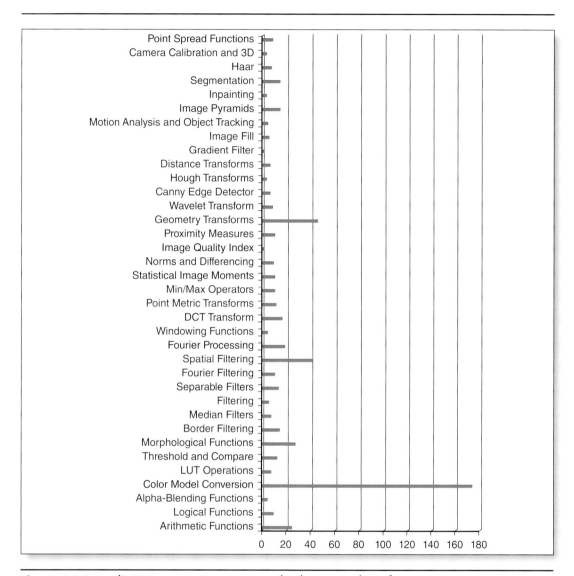

Figure 2.14 Intel® IPP Function Categories and Relative Number of Functions per Category

OpenCV† Library (Open Computer Vision)

The OpenCV library is an open source project that is a spinoff from Intel and is the de-facto standard computer vision library. It is available for download at http://opencv.willowgarage.com. OpenCV can be linked with the Intel Integrated Performance Primitives for increase performance on Intel platforms. An overview of OpenCV functions is shown in Figure 2.15.

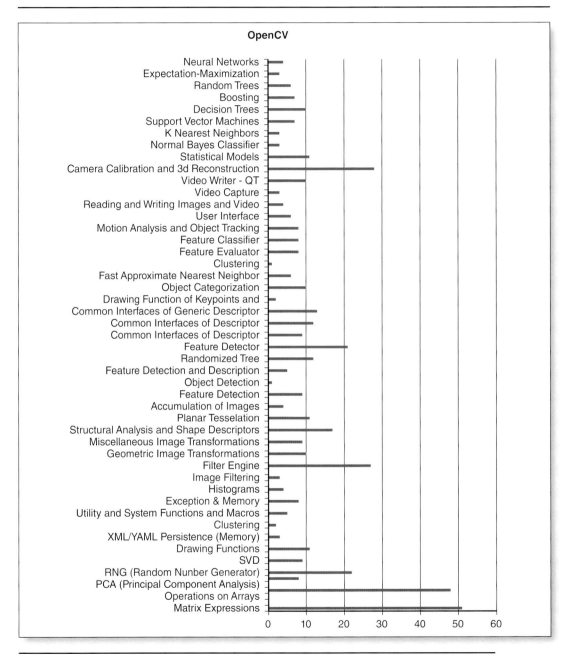

Figure 2.15 Function Categories and Relative Function Counts for the OpenCV Library

What Is a Good Visual Metric for a Given Application?

There are many visual metrics that can be considered *good* and many *better* metrics can be found in the literature, and metrics are constantly being developed and refined. To quantify *good*, two basic questions can be asked:

1. *What features are useful for a given application?* For example, the shape of a region may be useless in a face recognition algorithm, which looks for a specific set of key interest points, feature descriptors and the directional vector relationships between feature descriptors. In other applications such as biology or chemistry, the shape descriptors such as area, perimeter, and centroid of regions are often more useful.

2. *What is a good metric or feature?* This is the hard part, and there is no good answer. A good feature should share some of the following characteristics as shown in Table 2.2.

Table 2.2   Attributes of Good Feature Descriptors and Metrics

Good feature metric attributes	Details
Scale invariance	Should be able to find the feature at different scales
Perspective invariance	Should be able to find the feature from different perspectives in the field of view
Rotational invariance	The feature should be recognized in various rotations
Translation invariance	The feature should be recognized in various positions in the FOV
Reflection invariance	The feature should be recognized as a mirror image of itself
Affine invariance	The feature should be recognized from various viewing directions or perspectives in 3-space
Noise invariance	The feature should be detectable in the presence of noise
Illumination invariance	The feature should be recognizable in various lighting conditions including changes in brightness and contrast
Ease of computation	The feature should not be computationally difficult to define or describe, find in an image, or match against known feature databases
Distinctiveness	The feature should be distinct and detectable, with a low probability of mismatch, amenable to matching from a database of features

Compact to describe	The feature should not require large amounts of memory to hold details
Occlusion robustness	The feature or set of features can be described and detected when parts of the feature or feature set are occluded
Focus or blur robustness	The feature or set of features can be detected at varying degrees of focus (image pyramids can provide some of this capability)
Clutter and outlier robustness	The feature or set of features can be detected in the presence of outlier features and clutter

Visual computing and visual metrics is a fast moving area of research so there is no way to cover all the methods in this brief text. However, a sampling of typical features and metrics are covered to provide some guidelines for the type of features that are useful, with references given to other materials for the interested reader to dig deeper.

> It is a good idea to analyze your application domain and create or use as many visual metrics as required for proper visual understanding, and not be strictly limited by common methods—understand your application and make use of all the visual metrics that are important within your compute budget. Larger *multivariate* and *multiscale* feature descriptors aggregated together are becoming more common.

Often, many features or visual metrics are combined together as a *metrics set* or *feature descriptor* to collectively describe the objects of interest. For example, a set of metrics including region shape, region texture, and region color of an object may be helpful in an application to locate automobiles, while other applications do not need color or shape and rely instead on sets of interest points, invariant features, and their spatial relationships. Various methods of feature description and interest point detection are surveyed and analyzed in this chapter.

Region Segmentation, Shape Descriptors, and Object Descriptors

After an image has been processed to account for the sensor and further processed to make it ready for analysis, many applications require that the image should be *segmented into regions* to allow independent processing and analysis of each region according to some policy or processing goal.

Images are composed of various polygon *regions*, where the regions are defined as having a specific boundary, shape, or cohesive internal texture or content. Regions are *segmented* out of the larger image and then each region can be described using various *descriptors* as discussed below.

Regions cover an area smaller than the global image but larger than local interest point features; so an application might make us of global, regional, and small interest point metrics for different purposes.

Recent advances in visual computing metrics have focused on small local *interest points* and descriptors such as SIFT features, Haar features, LBPs, Harris Corners, MSER, Histogram Pyramids, and several other methods, some of which are discussed in this section. However the earlier work on global statistical feature metrics and regional texture descriptors is equally valuable for data mining.

Region descriptors and *shape descriptors* are used together to define *object descriptors*, where the object descriptor is a composite set of various metrics. Basically, a set of descriptors are combined together to form a signature of an object.

An overview of region segmentation methods is shown in Table 2.3.

Table 2.3 Region Segmentation Methods.

Morphological segmentation	The region is defined based on a threshold using morphological operators in grayscale, color, or binary spaces.
Texture-based segmentation	The texture of a region is used to group like textures into connected regions.
Edge boundary segmentation	Gradients or edges alone are used to define the boundaries of the region with edge linking in some cases to form boundaries.
Color segmentation	Color information is used to define regions.
Superpixel segmentation	Kernels and distance transforms are used to group pixels and change their values to a common value.
Grayscale/luminance segmentation	Grayscale thresholds or bands are used to define the regions.
Depth segmentation	Depth maps and distance from viewer is used to segment the image into foreground, background, or other gradations of inter-scene features.

Note that once a region has been defined or segmented according to any of the methods shown in Table 2.3, the region has a *shape* and can therefore be described using *shape feature descriptors* such as area, perimeter, and so on, which are discussed later in this chapter. Shape all by itself is a powerful metric that can be composed of the vector distance and angle relationships between smaller features to form a wire-frame sort of shape descriptor.

MSER Interest Region Detection

The maximally stable extrema regions (MSER) detector was designed to effectively resolve differences over a small range of scale and affine variations, so MSER features are valuable for frame-to-frame tracking and stereo frame co-registration. MSER regions are similar to blobs or arbitrarily shaped objects, are considered fairly robust to skewing and lighting, and are useful in stereo matching applications and mapping methods similar to PTAM and DTAM.

The method is compute-intensive and involves sorting pixels into regions based on intensity; regions with pixels whose intensity does not vary much (stable regions) are consider *maximally stable*. To compute an MSER, the intensity threshold is set to a low value such as zero on a single image channel (luminance for example) and the threshold is increased by increments and regions that do not grow or shrink or change as the intensity varies are considered maximally stable. Of course, this method requires a lot of bookkeeping and iterations over the image. See Matas et al. (2002).

Mathematical Morphology

Morphology is used to *morph* a feature shape into a new shape for analysis by removing shape noise or outliers and strengthening predominant feature characteristics. For example, isolated pixels may be removed using morphology, thin features can be fattened, and the predominant shape is still preserved.

Morphology can be accomplished on binary images, grayscale images, and color images. Binary morphology is helpful to prepare the binary region when a shape is to be used as a *binary region mask* or stencil cutout that is used to isolate a nonrectangular region of the image. Grayscale morphology is useful to synthesize and combine pixels together into homogeneous regions that have similar local texture or intensity values. Grayscale morphology can be used on individual color components to provided color morphology affecting hue, saturation, and color intensity in various color spaces.

Binary Morphological Overview

Binary morphology is a neighborhood operation and uses a forming kernel to guide the processing. The process starts with binary images, so typically thresholding is first done to create images with *binary-valued* pixels composed of 8-bit black-and-white values, 0 value = black and 255 value = white.

Next, a forming kernel is used to guide the morphology process by defining which surrounding pixels contribute to the morphology. Figure 2.16 shows two forming kernels: kernel a, where all pixels touching the current pixel are considered and kernel b, where only orthogonally adjacent pixels are considered. The notation used for the fundamental morphological operations is ∪ for *dilation* and ∩ for *erosion*. In binary morphology, dilation is a Boolean OR operator, while erosion is a Boolean AND operator. Only kernel elements with a "1" are used in the morphology calculation allowing for neighborhood contribution variations.

Binary Morphological Operations

The fundamental operations of binary morphology use Boolean AND operations for *erode*, and Boolean OR for *dilate*. As shown in Figure 2.16 for erosion, if the pixels *and* all kernel elements are 1, the result is 1. Erosion attempts to reduce sparse features until only strong features are left. Dilation attempts to inflate sparse features to make them fatter. As shown in Figure 2.16, the forming kernel can be used to directionally guide the morphology as well as define the region over which the morphology operates.

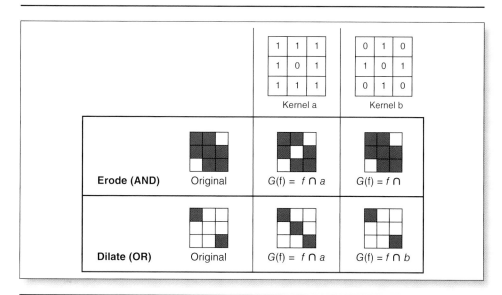

Figure 2.16 3×3 Forming Kernels and Binary Erosion and Dilation Using the Kernels; Other Kernel Sizes and Data Values May Be Useful in a Given Application.

Note that morphology all by itself is quite a large field of study with applications to general object recognition, cell biology, medicine, particle analysis, and automated microscopy. Since the basic idea of morphological region processing applies to any image scene, the basics are covered here as a starting point. For more information on morphology see the public domain software package "ImageJ" from the US National Institutes of Health (NIH); it provides an extensive set of morphological operations and shape metrics.

Based on simple erosion and dilation, a whole range of morphological operations are derived as shown below, where $\oplus$ = dilation and $\ominus$ = erosion.

```
Erode                            G(f)  =   f ⊖ b

Dilate                           G(f)  =   f ⊕ b

Opening                          G(f)  =  (f ⊕ b) ⊖ b

Closing                          G(f)  =  (f ⊖ b) ⊕ b

Morphological Gradient           G(f)  =  f ⊖ b    or
                                 G(f)  =  f ⊕ b − f ⊖ b

Morphological Internal gradient  Gᵢ(f) =  f − f ⊖ b

Morphological External gradient  Gₑ(f) =  f ⊕ b − f
```

Grayscale and Color Morphology

For grayscale morphology or color morphology the basic operations are MIN, MAX, and MINMAX, where pixels above the MIN are changed to the same value, and pixels below the MAX are changed to the same value, and pixels within the MIN MAX range are changed to the same value. MIN and MAX are a form of thresholding, while MINMAX allows bands of pixel values to be coalesced into two equal values forming a region.

Adaptive Auto-Threshold for Binary Morphology

Besides simple morphology, there are other methods of morphologically segmenting image regions based on *adaptive methods*. The simple morphology methods rely on using a fixed kernel across the entire image at each pixel, while the adaptive methods use variable kernels based on the local pixel intensity, allowing the morphology to adapt to the local region intensity and in some cases, produce better results. See Figures 2.17 and 2.18 for various examples of adaptive morphology.

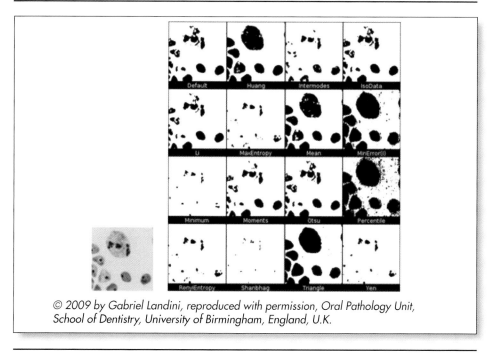

Figure 2.17 Various Adaptive Morphology Methods (Original Image at Left)

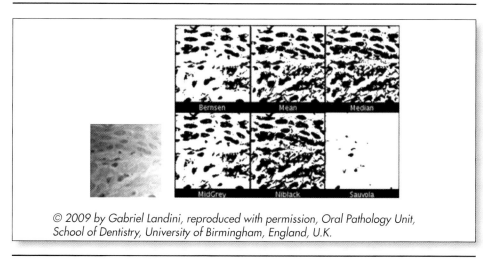

Figure 2.18 Various Adaptive Morphology Methods (Original Image at Left)

Intensity Thresholding Refinements for Improved Morphology

Prior to morphology, *intensity thresholding* functions may be required to improve delineation of specific regions of interest to optimize metrics collection. Morphology is a powerful tool for what it does to delineate regions, but morphology alone is only a part of the pipeline of operations needed for image region segmentation.

> No thresholding method is good for all applications. In fact, some applications do not use thresholding at all. Experiment with a variety of methods to optimize for your image data and chosen metrics.

Global Thresholding Methods

Global thresholding adjusts the entire image using a global function. The global thresholding function may be designed to produce binary results, band-limited grayscale results, or color results in an RGB image, depending on the image component to be morphologically processed. Global thresholding methods include:

1. *Simple binary thresholding*, where pixels below a threshold are black, and above the threshold are white.

   ```
   G(t) where pixel > t = WHITE, pixel < t = BLACK
   ```

2. *Pixel remapping* using a lookup table (LUT), where all pixels are run through a lookup table and each pixel is changed to a new value via table lookup. LUT patterns can include ramps and other filter shapes designed to compress or expand various ranges of the intensities.

3. *Histogram processing,* where the entire image is histogrammed into a lookup table, then the lookup table is adjusted to achieve using various functions such as equalization, compaction, bin aggregation, or any other useful method, and the generated lookup table is used to remap all pixels as explained above. A variation of global histogram equalization is localized histogram equalization, where the image is divided into tiles and each tile is equalized separately.

4. *Auto-Thresholding*, which uses a variety of other algorithms to determine a threshold value as shown in Figure 2.19 and Table 2.4.

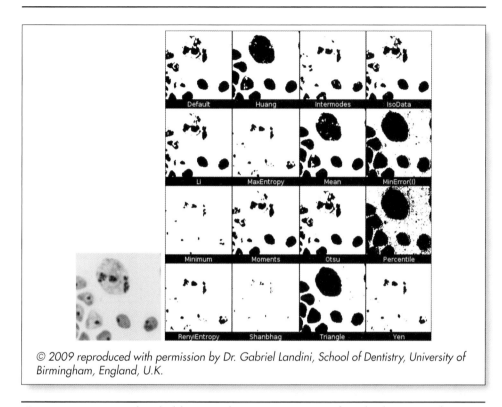

Figure 2.19 Auto-Thresholding Results Using a Variety of Methods (Original Image on Left, Auto-Thresholded Version on the Right)

Table 2.4   Various Auto-Thresholding Methods

Default	A variation of the IsoData method also known as Iterative Intermeans
Huang	The method of Huang's using fuzzy thresholding
Intermodes	Iterative histogram smoothing
IsoData	Iterative pixel averaging over a local region
Li	Iterative cross-entropy thresholding
MaxEntropy	Kapur-Sahoo-Wong (Maximum Entropy) algorithm
Mean	Local region gray-level mean value as the thresholding fence
MinError	Iterative method from Kittler and Illingworth to converge on a minimum error threshold
Minimum	Iterative histogram smoothing assuming a bimodal histogram
Moments	Tsai's thresholding algorithm intending to threshold using the original image moments
Otsu	Otsu clustering algorithms to set local thresholds

Percentile	Adapts the local threshold based on preset allocations for foreground and background pixels
RenyiEntropy	Another entropy-based local method
Shanbhag	Uses various informational metrics as local thresholding criteria
Triangle	Uses image histogram features and local intensity distribution
Yen	Another local intensity based thresholding method

Local Thresholding Methods

Local thresholding adapts the threshold based on the immediate area surrounding each target pixel in the image, so local thresholding is more like a standard area operation or filter. Local thresholding methods are thus locally *adaptive*, and operate differently on different images and image regions. This may be an advantage.

Figure 2.20 shows the results of a wide range of *adaptive local thresholding* methods, which are briefly described in Table 2.5.

> Simple morphology alone may not be an effective segmentation method. Other methods such as adaptive local thresholding may be required, as well as compositing multiple types of morphology-processed images together to produce a suitable region shape.

Table 2.5 Various Adaptive Local Thresholding Methods

Bernsen	Bernsen's algorithm using circular windows instead of rectangles and local mid-gray values
Mean	Uses the local gray level mean as the threshold
Median	Uses the local gray level mean as the threshold
Mid Grey	Uses the local area gray level mean − C (where C is a constant)
Niblack	Niblack' s algorithm is: p = (p > mean + k × standard_deviation − c) ? object : background
Sauvola	Sauvola's variation of Niblack: p = (p > mean × (1 + k × (standard_deviation / r − 1))) ? object: background

Superpixel Segmentation via Graph-based and Gradient-Ascent

A *Superpixel* segmentation method attempts to collapse similar pixels in a local region into a larger superpixel region of equal pixel value so similar values are subsumed into the larger superpixel. Superpixel methods are implemented for

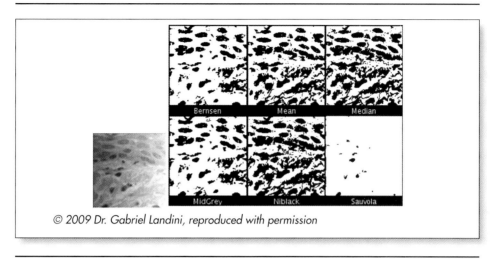

Figure 2.20 Local Auto-Thresholding Results Using a Variety of Methods, All Different

digital photography applications to create scaled or watercolor special effects. (Note: if the region boundaries are black as in Figure 2.21, scales appear; if the region boundaries are the same color as the region, the look is more like watercolors.) Feature descriptors may be devised based on and including the shape of each superpixel, the value of the superpixel, and the neighborhood relationships between the superpixels.

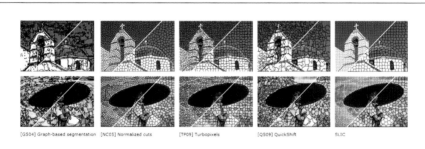

SOURCE: Ecole Polytechnique Fédérale de Lausanne (EPFL) R. Achanta, A. Shaji, K. Smith, A. Lucchi, P. Fua, and S. Süsstrunk, "SLIC Superpixels Compared to State-of-the-art Superpixel Methods," IEEE Transactions on Pattern Recognition and Machine Intelligence (TPAMI), Vol. 34, Nr. 11, pp. 2274–2282, 2012.

Figure 2.21 A Comparison of Various Superpixel Segmentation Methods

SuperPixel methods treat each pixel as a node in a graph, and edges between regions are determined based on the similarity of neighboring pixels and graph distance.

Graph-based Superpixel Methods Survey

Graph-based methods structure pixels into trees based on the distance of the pixel from a centroid feature or edge feature for a region of like-valued pixels. The compute complexity varies.

1. *SLIC* (Achanta et al. 2010) - Simple linear iterative clustering (SLIC) creates superpixels based on a 5D space including the CIE *Lab* color primaries and the XY pixel coordinates. The SLIC algorithm takes as input the desired number of superpixels to generate and adapt well to both grayscale and RGB color images. The clustering distance function is related to the size of the desired number of superpixels and uses a Euclidean distance function for grouping pixels into superpixels.

2. *Normalized cuts* (Shi and Malik 2000; Vedaldi and Soatto 2008) - use a recursive region partitioning method based on local texture and region contours to create superpixel regions.

3. *GS-FH method* - The graph-based Felzenszwalb and Huttenlocher (2004) method attempts to segment image regions using edges based on perceptual or psychological cues. This method uses the minimum length between pixels in the graph tree structure to create the superpixel regions. The computational complexity is O((N log N), which is relatively fast.

4. *SL method* - The superpixel lattice (SL) method finds region boundaries within tiled image regions or strips of pixels using the graph cut method.

Gradient-Ascent-based Superpixel Method Survey

Gradient ascent methods iteratively refine the super pixel clusters to optimize the segmentation until a convergence criteria is reached. These methods use a tree graph structure to associate pixels together according to a function which in this case may be the RGB or XY values of the pixels, and then a distance function or other function is applied to create regions. Since these are iterative methods the performance can be slow.

1. *Mean shift* (Comaniciu and Meer 2002) - Mean shift works by registering off of the region centroid using a kernel-based mean smoothing approach to create regions of like pixels.

2. *Quick shift* (Vedaldi and Soatto 2008) - The quick shift method is similar to the mean shift method but does not use a mean blur kernel and instead uses a distance function calculated from the graph structure based on RGB values and XY pixel coordinates.

3. *Watershed* (Vincent and Soille 1991) - The watershed method starts from local region pixel value minima points to find pixel value-based contour lines defining *watersheds* or basin contours inside which similar pixel values can be substituted to create a homogeneous pixel value region.

4. *Turbopixels* (Levinshtein et al. 2009) - The turbopixel method uses small circular seed points placed in a uniform grid across the image around which superpixels are collected into *assigned regions*, and then the superpixel boundaries are gradually expanded into the *unassigned region* using a geometric flow method to expand the boundaries using controlled boundary value expansion criteria to gather more pixels together into regions with fairly smooth and uniform geometric shape and size.

Color as a Method of Region Segmentation

To use color hue and saturation as a part of the image segmentation process, an image may be prepared for segmentation according to the goals, such as gamut corrections or boosting the hue or saturation of each color to accentuate differences, and then performing region segmentation on hue or saturation regions. The color segmentation results may be combined with other types of segmentation methods such as morphology and depth maps to yield a hybrid segmentation method using a variety of methods together.

> Color all by itself is a powerful image metric, especially when we can analyze the color within a region that has been segmented out of an image and use color as a basis for region and object pattern matching.

Region Shape Metrics

Once a region has been identified, various metrics can be calculated. This section will focus primarily on 2D metrics, although most of the metrics discussed can also be calculated in three dimensions and higher dimensions. In general, region metrics are rotational and shape invariant.

> Region shape metrics can be used for virtually any scene analysis application to find common objects. Example application areas include surveillance, home energy, crowd flow monitoring, and traffic control.

Table 2.6 provides a sampling of some of the common metrics that can be derived from region shapes, both binary shapes and grayscale shapes.

Table 2.6   Common Shape and Blob Object Metrics

Binary Object Shape Metrics	Description
Perimeter	Length of all points around the edge of the object
Area	Total area excluding the particles.
Convex Hull	Polygon shape (set of line segments) enclosing all perimeter points
Centroid	Center of object mass
Fourier Descriptor	Length of a set of radial line segments passing from centroid to perimeter at regular angle is used to model a signal function, the signal function is fed into a 1D FFT and the set of FFT magnitude data is used as a metric
Major/minor axis	Longest and shortest line passing through centroid to perimeter
Feret	Largest caliper diameter of object
Breadth	Shortest caliper diameter
Aspect Ratio	Feret/Breadth
Circularity	$4 \times \pi \times$ Area/Perimeter2
Roundness	$4 \times$ Area/($\pi \times$ Feret2) *Can also be calculated from the Fourier Descriptors
Area Equivalent Diameter	$\sqrt{\frac{4}{\pi} \times Area}$
Perimeter Equivalent Diameter	Area/π
Equivalent Ellipse	($\pi \times$ Feret $\times$ Breadth)/4

Compactness	$\dfrac{\sqrt{\frac{4}{\pi} \times Area}}{Feret}$
Solidity	Area/Convex_Area
Concavity	Convex_Area-Area
Convexity	Convex_Hull/Perimeter
Shape	Perimeter2/Area
Modification Ratio	(2 × MinR)/Feret
Grayscale Object Shape Metrics	*Note: Binary object metrics also apply to grayscale objects*
SDM Plots	See Figure 2.22
Scatter Plots	See Figure 2.22
Statistical moments of Greyscale pixel values	Minimum Maximum Median Average Average deviation Standard deviation Variance Skewness Kurtosis Entropy

As shown in Table 2.6 on shape metrics, the Fourier descriptor provides a rotationally invariant and size invariant shape metric. The method for determining the Fourier descriptor set is to take a set of equally spaced radius measurements from the centroid out to points on the perimeter and then assemble the radius measurements into a 1D array, which is run through a 1D FFT to yield a Fourier spectrum of the harmonic series showing the Fourier moments of the object. Thus, the 1D FFT is used to obtain a 2D region Fourier descriptor that is rotational and scale invariant.

Other examples of useful shape metrics include the major and minor axis (longest and shortest diameter), which can also be used to determine rotational orientation of an object, area, perimeter, and their ratios, which in turn can yield spatial and rotational invariant descriptors.

Texture Segmentation and Texture Metrics

Within an image, each image region has a *texture signature* where texture is defined as a common structure and pattern within the region. Texture signatures may be a function of position and intensity relationships as in the spatial domain, or be based on functional transformations to the frequency domain, or be based on comparisons in some other function basis and feature domain. For example, textures have a signature in the frequency domain. There are many possible textural relationships and signatures that can be devised in a range of domains, with new ones being developed all the time. Here we will survey some of the most common methods of calculating texture metrics.

Texture metrics can be used to segment, describe, and differentiate regions based on texture homogeneousness, and as a result texture works well as a method for region segmentation. Texture is also a good metric for feature comparison, and as a result is useful for feature detection, matching, and tracking.

Major areas for future development in texture metrics include using 3D depth map and volumetric information to create 3D textural metrics, and taking advantage of additional compute power to create and use more detailed texture methods in other domains such as the frequency domain.

Texture all by itself is a key visual metric for classification and identification of objects, and textures metrics can be used for region segmentation, region description, and region identification.

Consider which texture metrics are valuable for your application domain and develop code to detect and record metrics you need, rather than using only standard algorithms with minimal metrics.

Here we will briefly survey some the major developments in texture description and analysis and then dig deeper into some of the more useful texture metrics.

Historically, many approaches to texture analysis have been tried and fall into the following generally recognized taxonomy:

- *Structural*, describing texture via a set of microtexture patterns and associated numerical descriptors

- *Statistical*, based on gray level statistical moments describing pixel area properties

- *Model-based*, including fractal models, stochastic models, and various semi-random fields.

■ *Transform-based*, methods include Fourier, Wavelets, Gabor Filters, and so on.

History of Key Ideas in Texture Analysis

The limitations of imaging sensors and compute capabilities in the past have limited the development of texture metrics to mainly 2D grayscale metrics that have been extended to color. Past technology limitations pertaining to sensor resolution, pixel depth resolution, color resolution, and lack of depth information have dampened the accuracy and therefore limited potential applications of texture in visual metrics. However, with the advances towards pervasive computational photography in every camera providing higher resolution images, higher frame rates, deeper pixels, depth imaging, more memory, and faster compute, we can expect that corresponding new advances in texture metrics will be made.

1950s through 1970s: Global uniform texture metrics. Autocorrelation or cross-correlation is developed by Kaizer (1955) as a method of looking for randomness and repeating pattern features in aerial photography, where autocorrelation is statistical method of correlating a signal or image with a time-shifted version of itself, which yielded computationally simple methods to analyze ground cover and structures.

Bajcsy (1973) developed Fourier spectrum methods using various types of filters in the frequency domain to isolate various types of repeating features as texture.

Gray level SDM or Co-occurence matrices (Haralick, Shanmugam, and Dinstein 1973) were developed by Haralick in 1973 along with a set of summary statistical metrics from the SDMs to assist in numerical classification of texture. Some but not all of the summary of the metrics have proven useful, however analysis of SDMs and development of new summary metrics has continued (Krig 1994) involving methods using 2D visualization and filtering of the SDM data within spatial regions.

Statistical methods can be considered micro-textures as opposed to macro-textures or regions containing a homogenous texture.

1980s: Structural and model-based approaches for texture classification. While early work focused on micro-textures describing statistical measures, macro-textures are concerned more with the structure of textures within a region. Laws developed texture energy detection methods in 1979 and 1980 (Laws 1979, 1980a, 1980b) and texture classifiers, which may be considered the forerunners of some of the modern classifier concepts. The Laws method could be implemented as a texture classifier in a parallel pipeline with stages for taking gradients via of a set of convolution masks over Gaussian filtered images to isolate texture *micro features*, followed by a Gaussian *smoothing* stage to deal with noise, followed by the *energy* calculation from the combined gradients, followed by a *classifier* that matched texture descriptors.

Eigenfilters were developed by Ade in 1983 as an alternative to the Law's gradient or energy methods, where Eigenfilters are implemented using a covariance matrix representation of local 3x3 pixel region intensities, which allows texture analysis and aggregation into structure based on the variance within eigenvectors within the covariance matrix.

Structural approaches were developed by Davis (1979) to focus on gross structure of texture rather than primitives or micro-texture features.

Hough transforms (a method of finding lines and curves) were used by Eichmann and Kasparis (1988) to provide invariant texture description.

Fractal methods and *Markov random field* methods were developed during this time as texture descriptors, and while these methods may be good for *texture synthesis*, the underlying problem for texture classification is that both fractal and Markov random field methods use random fields, thus there are limitations when applied to real-world textures that are not random.

1990s: Optimizations and refinements to texture metrics. Lam and Ip (1993, 1994) used pyramid segmentation methods to achieve spatial invariance, where an image is segmented into homogenous regions using Voronoi polygon tessellation and irregular pyramid segmentation techniques around Q points taken from a binary thresholded image, and five shape descriptors are calculated for each polygon: area, perimeter, roundness, orientation, and major/minor axis ratio combined into texture descriptors.

Local binary patterns (LBPs) were developed in 1994 by Ojala et al. as a novel method of encoding both pattern and contrast to define texture (Ojala et al. 1994, 1996; Pietikäinen and Heikkilä 2011; Shu and Chung 2008) and since that time (Pietikäinen et al. 2011) hundreds of researchers have added to the LBP literature in the areas of theoretical foundations, generalization into 2D and 3D, domain-specific interest point descriptors used in face detection, and spatiotemporal applications to motion analysis. LBP research remains quite active at this time.

This chapter will cover some level of detail on LBPs since there are so many applications for this powerful texture metric as a feature descriptor as well. In addition, the LBP is used as an image processing operator and has been used as a feature descriptor in the SIFT method of object detection with excellent results.

2000 – Today: 3D features and robust invariant texture metrics. The goal now in visual metrics research is to define texture metrics that are invariant to scale, rotation, lighting, perspective, and so on to approach the capabilities of human texture discrimination. In fact, texture is used interchangeably as a feature descriptor in some circles. The work by Pun and Lee (2003) is an example of the development of rotational invariant texture metrics as well as scale invariance; many more invariant metrics are discussed in this chapter.

The next wave of metrics being developed take advantage of 3D depth information. One example is the surface shape metrics developed by Spence (Spence et al. 2003), which provides a bump-map type metric that allows affine invariant texture recognition, or texture description that is closer to viewpoint and distance invariant.

Augmented Reality (AR) and Scene Mapping Metrics

Two other notable recent algorithms with special metrics for AR (Augmented Reality scene mapping) include PTAM and DTAM. While PTAM and DTAM are designed to track camera pose or viewpoint motion from frame to frame, the feature tracking methods used may find their way into more generic feature recognition problems such as face, gestures, etc. so a brief overview of each method is provided below.

The Parallel Tracking And Mapping method PTAM performs tracking and mapping in two separate threads. The method uses a set of coarse interest points detected in each image of a gray scale depth map image pyramid with 4 octave levels using FAST (Features from Accelerated Segment Test) corner detection as a first-pass to identify interest points followed by a fast Shi-Tomasi corner detection method (an improved Harris detector) to reduce the set of interest points, and then 8×8 patches of depth map info are created around each interest point in the key frame images, where each patch has a calculated surface normal to allow for each patch to be perspective transformed around the normal in order to be searched for in subsequent frames based on the predicted position of the motion in 3-space. The depth mapping is maintained as the system tracks frames in a pyramid history buffer which may contain up to 150 frames of pyramids.

The Dense Tracking And Mapping method DTAM uses a dense method to calculate descriptors at every pixel as opposed to sparse feature detection methods around interest points (like PTAM) where every pixel in the image is part of a 3D inverse depth map or texture, and the entire image (or texture) is tracked from frame to frame using whole texture alignment and registration in 3D which provides for occlusion and scale invariance, and the inverse depth map (texture) model is continually refined as more frames are tracked.

Dynamic Textures (DT)

Dynamic textures (Zhao and Pietikäinen 2007) are a method to describe and track textured regions as they change and morph dynamically from frame to frame. In other words, dynamic textures are textures in motion like sea waves, smoke, foliage blowing in the wind, fire, facial expression changes, and gesture and pose changes.

Dynamic textures using LBP methods are discussed in greater detail in the LBP section of this chapter.

Co-Occurrence Matrix as a Texture Metric

Haralick (1979) proposed a set of 2D texture metrics calculated from directional differences between adjacent pixels referred to as *co-occurrence* matrices or *spatial dependency matrices* (*SDMs*). A complete set of four matrices are calculated by evaluating the difference between adjacent pixels in the X, Y, Diagonal X and Diagonal Y directions as shown in Figure 2.22. For example, if a camera has digital circuit readout noise, it will show up in the SDM for the X direction, since the lines are read out of the sensor one at a time in the X direction. Using the SDM information will enable intelligent sensor processing to remove the readout noise.

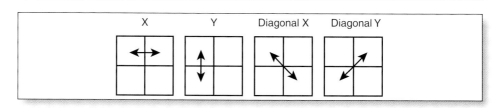

Figure 2.22 The Four Directionality Difference Calculation Vectors Used for the Haralick Texture Feature Know as Co-Occurrence Matrix or SDM, Where the Adjacent Pixel Difference of Each Pixel in the Image Is Plotted to Reveal the Texture of the Image.

One benefit of the SDM as a texture metric is that it is easy to calculate in a single pass over the image. The SDM is also fairly invariant to rotation. Within a segmented region or around an interest point, the SDM plot can be a valuable texture metric all by itself.

Angular Second Moment	$\Sigma_i \Sigma_j p(i,j)^2$
Contrast	$\sum_{n=0}^{N_g-1} n^2 \left\{ \Sigma_{i=1}^{N_g} \Sigma_{j=1}^{N_g} p(i,j) \right\}, \|i-j\| = n$
Correlation	$\dfrac{\Sigma_i \Sigma_j (ij)^2 \; p(i,j) - \mu_x \mu_y}{\sigma_x \sigma_y}$ Where μ_x, μ_y, σ_x, and σ_y are the means and std. deviations of p_x and p_y, the partial probability density functions
Sum of Squares: Variance	$\Sigma_i \Sigma_j (i-\mu)^2 \; p(i,j)$
Inverse Difference Moment	$\Sigma_i \Sigma_j \dfrac{1}{1+(i-j)^2} p(i,j)$
Sum Avvrage	$\Sigma_{i=2}^{2N_g} i p_{x+y}(i)$ Where x and y are the coordinates (row and column) of an entry in the co-occurrence matrix, and $p_{x+y}(i)$ is the probability of co-occurrence matrix coodinates summing to x+y
Sum Variance	$\Sigma_{i=2}^{2N_g} (i-f_s)^2 p_{x+y}(i)$
Sum Entropy	$-\Sigma_{i=2}^{2N_g} i p_{x+y}(i) \log\{p_{x+y}(i)\} = f_s$
Entropy	$-\Sigma_i \Sigma_j p(i,j) \log(p(i,j))$
Difference Variance	$\Sigma_{i=0}^{N_g-1} i^2 p_{x-y}(i)$
Difference Entropy	$-\Sigma_{i=0}^{N_g-1} p_{x-y}(i) \log\{p_{x-y}(i)\}$
Info. Measure of Correlation 1	$\dfrac{HX \;-\; XY}{\max\{HX, HY\}}$
Info. Measure of Correlation 2	$\left(1 - \exp\left[-2\left(HXY2 - HXY\right)\right]\right)^{\frac{1}{2}}$ Where $HXY = -\Sigma_i \Sigma_j p(i,j) \log(p(i,j))$, HX, HY are the entropies of p_x and p_y, $HXY1 = -\Sigma_i \Sigma_j p(i,j) \log\{p_x(i) p_y(j)\}$ $HXY2 = -\Sigma_i \Sigma_j p_x(i) p_y(j) \log\{p_x(i) p_y(j)\}$
Max. Correlation coeff.	*Square* root of the second largest eigenvalue of Q Where $Q(i,j) = \Sigma_k \dfrac{p(i,k) p(j,k)}{p_x(i) p_y(k)}$

Figure 2.23 The Haralick Texture Metrics

Haralick also defined one of the earliest and most basic texture descriptors, where he devised a set of texture metrics based on the co-occurrence matrix statistical features in order to compare and interpret the SDM results in a more uniform manner. However, it should be noted that these metrics are not always useful alone, and should be qualified with additional feature information.

Here are the Haralick metrics shown in Figure 2.23 (see Haralick 1979 for details).

The statistical characteristics of the SDM have been extended by several researchers to add more useful metrics (Krig 1994) and SDMs have been applied to volumetric data by a number of researchers (Aioanei, Arati, and Dong-Hui 2002) with good results.

A complete set of SDMs would contain four different plots, one for each orientation. In other words, the adjacent pixels in each direction (*x, y, diagonal-x,* and *diagonal-y*) are used independently to create SDM plots and the separate results can be revealing. As shown in Figure 2.24, interpreting the SDM plots visually reveals useful information. Note that the right image does not have a lot of outliner points or noise—most of the energy is centered along the diagonal showing a rather smooth set of image pixel transitions and texture, while the left hand image shows a wider range of intensity values or noise spread across the spectrum revealing a wider band of energy and contrast between adjacent pixels. SDM plots or co-occurrence plots are valuable as both

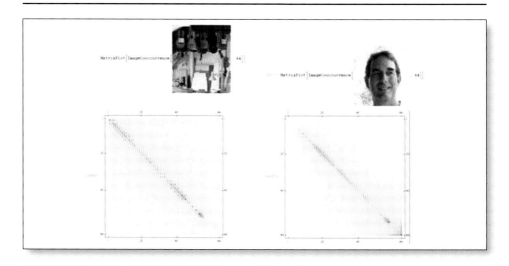

Figure 2.24 A Pair of Image Co-Occurrence Matrix Plots (x-Axis Plots) in the Bottom Row Corresponding to the Images in the Top Row.

global and local texture metrics and can be reduced into a set of summary metrics (Krig 1994) useful for feature and texture description.

An image with a smooth texture will yield a narrow diagonal band of co-occurrence values. An image with wide texture variation will yield a larger spread of values. A noisy image will yield a co-occurrence matrix with outlier values at the extrema. In some cases, noise may only be distributed along one axis of the image, say across rows or the x-axis for example, which could indicated sensor readout noise as each line is read out of the sensor, suggesting a row- or line-oriented image preparation stage in the vision pipeline to compensate for the camera.

Histograms and Multiresolution Histograms

Image histograms alone are commonly used as the key descriptor to find images within image databases. Histograms are useful as measures of both texture and spatial grayscale distribution information.

To use a histogram as a feature descriptor, first a region may be selected as a polygon area and a histogram calculated over it, or a region may be segmented using morphology to create a mask shape around a region of interest, then the region is used as a mask to define a region over which a histogram can be calculated. The histogram may be taken at various bit depths, most commonly 8 bits.

The *multiresolution* histograms (Hadjidemetriou, Grossberg, and Nayar 2004) are a concatenated set of histograms of the same image at multiple levels of Gaussian blur or resolution. This multiresolution histogram representation is useful for recognizing the feature at various levels of resolution or blur.

Steps involved in creating and using multiresolution histograms are as follows:

1.   Apply Gaussian filter to image

2.   Create an image pyramid

3.   Create histograms at each level

4.   Normalize the histograms using N

5.   Create cumulative histograms

6.   Create difference histograms (differences between pyramid levels)

7.   Sub-sample and renormalize the difference histograms

8. Concatenate the multiresolution difference histograms into a feature vector

9. Compare normalized histograms using N against normalized multiresolution histograms

To add scale invariance to the histogram metric, a *multiscale* histogram metric is created from an image pyramid, which can be constructed with different resolutions of the image created using a Gaussian blur function. Then a histogram is created for each pyramid level and concatenated together. This multiscale histogram metric is used in the SIFT algorithm (Lowe 1999) and has the desirable properties of algorithm simplicity, fast computation, low memory requirements, noise tolerance, and high reliability across spatial and rotational variations.

Histograms of textural features have been found useful as affine-invariant metrics as a part of a wider feature descriptor. Histograms can be composed of a wide range of region metrics, such as texture, shape, distance, and color, as well as for further describing interest point descriptors. For example, histograms of the linear binary patterns, or LBPs (Pietikäinen et al. 2011), discussed later on under the texture section) are used for a variety of applications including face detection, and LBP histograms are invariant to rotation and scale.

> A histogram can be made from a wide range of scalar and other metrics. Consider devising and using novel histograms of feature metrics that are useful in your application.

Local Interest Points for Feature Extraction

In contrast to region and shape metrics, which may encompass larger portions of an image, most recent visual computing metrics development has focused on smaller local feature descriptors surrounding *interest points*, where the interest point is a pixel or small group or adjacent pixels such as a corner, line segment, arc, maximum or minimum gradient pixel, or pixels with specific luminance or color.

First the *interest points* are detected, and the *local feature descriptors* are created surrounding the interest points. We will discuss interest points first, and then feature descriptors next.

Interest Points or Key Points

The idea behind finding an *interest point* is to identify a feature in an image that is easy, quick, and reliable to locate (that is, *it is interesting and demands further analysis),* and hopefully the interest point is the key to finding a more complex descriptor of which the interest point is a part. The interest point is thus the qualifier and key point around which a feature will be extracted for further analysis and classification.

Commonly, interest points are deemed to be preferably *maxima and minima points,* such as edges and corners. Corners are usually preferred over edges or isolated maxima points, since the corner is a structure. Interest points can be taken over color components as well as grayscale luminance. A wide range of methods are used to find interest points and the key criteria for a given application will guide the selection of the right interest point, so it is good to get familiar with the common methods for locating interest points since both the computational complexity and final results vary widely.

To get an idea of how each interest point method behaves, try using images relevant to your application and run them through each interest point method and see which results work best.

Note that many of the interest point methods as shown in Figure 2.25 will first apply some sort of Gaussian filter across the image prior to performing a gradient operator, and the idea of using the Gaussian filtering first is to reduce noise in the image that is otherwise amplified by gradient operators.

Images © Wolfram Research

Figure 2.25 Candidate Interest Point Filters Including Left to Right: Color Laplacian, Derivative Filter, and Gradient Filter.

There is no superior method for interest point detection for all applications. Some are edge-based region methods (EBR), some use maxima or intensity-based region methods (IBR), and some may even use corner or intersection patterns. For a comparison of various methods see Haja, Jahne, and Abraham (2008).

Sobel

The *Sobel* operator is one of the earliest methods to detect gradient magnitude and direction for edge detection. Variations exist in the area of the kernels used.

1. Perform two directional Sobel filters (x- and y-axis) using basic derivative kernel approximations such as 3×3 kernels using values and note that in addition to those below, other kernel sets are used well so long as the values cancel and add up to zero such as Scharr, Prewitt, and Roberts.

$$Sy = \begin{pmatrix} -1 & -2 & -1 \\ 0 & 0 & 0 \\ +1 & +2 & +1 \end{pmatrix}$$

$$Sx = \begin{pmatrix} -1 & 0 & +1 \\ -2 & 0 & +2 \\ -1 & 0 & +1 \end{pmatrix}$$

2. Calculate the total gradient as $|Gv| = |Sx| + |Sy|$

3. Calculate the gradient direction as $\theta = \arctan(Sy/Sx)$

4. Calculate gradient Magnitude $Gm = \sqrt{Sy^2 + Sx^2}$

Canny Detector

The *Canny* method is similar to the Sobel-style gradient magnitude and direction methods but adds post-processing to clean up the edges. See Canny (1986).

1. Perform a Gaussian blur over image using a selected convolution kernel (7x7, 5,5, and so on) depending on the level of hi-pas filtering desired.

2. Perform two directional Sobel filters (x- and y-axis).

3. Perform nonmaximal value suppression in the direction of the gradient to set to zero (0) pixels not on an edge (minima values).

4. Finally perform hysteresis thresholding within a band (hi, low) of values along the gradient direction to eliminate edge aliasing and outlier artifacts.

Laplacian and Laplacian of Gaussian (LoG)

The *Laplacian* operator is a method of finding the derivative or maximum rate of change in a pixel area. Commonly the Laplacian is approximated using standard convolution kernels that add up to zero such as:

$$L1 = \begin{pmatrix} -1 & -1 & -1 \\ -1 & 8 & -1 \\ -1 & -1 & -1 \end{pmatrix}$$

$$L2 = \begin{pmatrix} -1 & 0 & -1 \\ 0 & 4 & 0 \\ -1 & 0 & -1 \end{pmatrix}$$

The LoG (*Laplacian of Gaussian*) is simply the Laplacian performed over a region that has been processed using a Gaussian smoothing kernel to focus edge energy. See Lowe (1999). LoG is approximated using the Difference of Gaussians (DoG) in SIFT.

Harris and Shi-Tomasi Type Detectors

The Harris corner detector uses eigenvalues to determine which regions or windows of pixels, when shifted or moved in any x,y or diagonal direction, yield a large variation or derivative when moved in any direction. The derivative value is compared with a scoring factor to identify which features are corners and which features are likely noise (Harris and Stephens 1988).

Variations on the Harris method include:

■ The Shi and Tomasi (2004) corner detector, an optimization on the Harris method that only uses the eigenvalues for discrimination, thus streamlining the computation considerably.

■ The Hessian corner detector is designed to be affine invariant, and uses the basic Harris corner detection method but combines interest points from several scales in a pyramid with some iterative selection criteria and a Hessian matrix. See Haja, Jahne, and Abraham (2008).

■ Many other variations from the basic Harris operator exist, such as Harris- /Hessian- Laplace (Mikolajczyk and Schmid 2001), Harris- / Hessian -Affine (Mikolajczyk and Schmid 2004), Hessian and Harris (Beaudet 1978), and Harris (1988).

FAST interest point corner detector

The FAST (Features from Accelerated Segment Test) interest point detector is actually one of the most accurate and easy to compute methods. FAST is based on the same ideas as the LBP where a threshold is used to determine if neighborhood pixels are above/below the threshold to determine connectedness of a corner edge similar to the uniform patterns of the LBP as discussed later in this chapter.

Hessian Matrix Interest Point Detector (DoH)

The Hessian matrix method (DoH or determinant of Hessian method) is used in the popular SURF method (Bay et al. 2008) and detects interest objects from a multiscale image set where the determinant of the Hessian matrix is at a maximum, and the Hessian matrix operator is calculated using the convolution of the second order partial derivative of the Gaussian to yield a gradient maximum. The DoH method uses an image representation called *integral images* to calculate the Gaussian partial derivatives very quickly. Integral images are described in more detail in Chapter 3. Performance for calculating the Hessian matrix is therefore very good, and the accuracy is better than most methods.

DoG (Difference of Gaussians)

The difference of Gaussians is an approximation of the Laplacian of Gaussians, but computed in a simpler and faster manner using the difference of two smoothed or Gaussian filtered images. The idea with Gaussian smoothing is to remove noise artifacts from the filter, which would otherwise be amplified and result in false features. As used in the SIFT method, a series of images are created across a scale of light to heavy smoothing using various Gaussian kernels to provide various degrees of discrimination, and then the simple image difference is taken across pairs of images to identify maxima regions. See Lowe (1999).

Salient Regions

Salient regions are quite complex to calculate (Chun-Rong, Chu-Song, and Pau-Choo 2008) and will not be described here in detail, yet this method can detect points that show strong invariance to affine rotation, 2D translation, nonuniform warping, contrast and intensity changes, and perspective viewpoint variations. This is another compute-intensive method for finding interest points and worth checking into.

Moravac Corner Detector

The Moravic corner detection algorithm is an early method of corner detection where each pixel in the image is tested by correlating a patch surrounding each pixel with overlapping patches surrounding each neighboring pixel. The correlation difference is calculated using the SSD method (summed square of differences) between the two overlapping patches. Similarity is measured by the near-zero difference in the SSD. This method is quite compute intensive. See Mikolajczyk and Schmid (2004).

Feature Descriptors or Feature Signatures or Region Signatures

Now that the interest points are determined, the next step is to calculate *feature descriptors*, which are typically composed from patches surrounding the interest points. Feature descriptors may be calculated over one or more dimensions such as an image pyramid, various rotations, and various illumination conditions. In fact, combining multiple feature dimensions together provides more discrimination capability. See Figure 2.26.

In some cases, there is no need to find interest points if the feature descriptors themselves include some interest point information. Some methods for feature matching such as template matching via correlation or Haar wavelet detectors could be implemented without interest point detection prior to feature analysis if the feature search is across a regular grid in the image; it all depends on the application. However, finding interest points is far simpler than finding features, unless the feature descriptor itself includes an interest point type description within it as a coarse-grain element of the feature. For example, a feature descriptor could include Haar wavelets combined with gradient information and color. This would allow the feature to be used under various runtime optimization scenarios where one or more methods for feature detection may be employed depending upon available compute resources and performance targets.

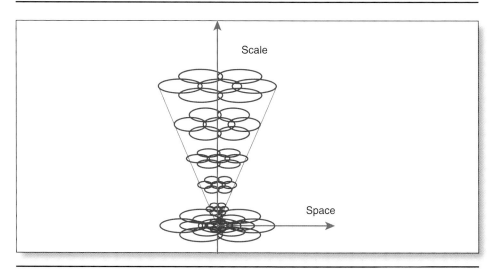

Figure 2.26 A Feature Descriptor May Be Composed of Multiple Overlapping Areas Containing Both Multiscale Information from Different Image Scales and Multispace or Resolution Information.

Feature description is a tradeoff. On one extreme, small simple to calculate features like Haar wavelets offer simplicity of calculation and relatively small size since they represent a simple difference function over the adjacent wavelet sets. However, more recent feature description methods use a wide variety of scales and aggregation of metrics together such as multidimensional histograms, Fourier spectrums of the histograms to provide invariance, and color information.

Simpler indiscriminant features make more work in the classification stage to determine what the small features make up, while larger multivariate descriptors provide more discrimination and less classification burden later in the pipeline.

There is no perfect feature descriptor; choosing the best feature descriptor is a tradeoff between the preprocessing compute budget, desired frame rate, and desired accuracy. All this is based on the available compute resources, which must be partitioned correctly to achieve the desired results for the given applications.

When selecting feature descriptors, it is important to consider attributes such as invariance and computational complexity. See Table 2.2 earlier in this chapter showing attributes of good feature descriptors and metrics. Figure 2.27 and Table 2.7 provide a small example of the type of analysis that might be performed to select descriptors for a given application and compute environment. Note that various other considerations may apply to a given application for optimization and achievement of overall vision pipeline performance goals.

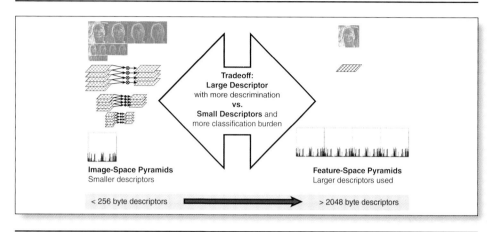

Figure 2.27 Two Extremes in Descriptor Size and Composition: On the Left Descriptors are Designed at a Fixed Scale and an Image Pyramid Is Constructed so the Feature Can Be Matched against the Intended Scale; On the Right the Feature Descriptor Itself Is Composed of a Pyramid of Scales and Other Attributes that Can Track Features in a Fixed Image Frame of Variable Scale. Feature Descriptors Also Vary by Bit Depth.

Table 2.7   Considerations for Choosing Descriptors for a Given Application

Feature Descriptor Type	Invariance under Gaussian noise	Invariance to illumination	Computational complexity
Fourier Power Spectrum Annuli	robust	robust	complex
Gabor Features	robust	Fairly robust	complex
Haar Features	robust	Fairly robust	simple
LBP	Fairly robust	robust	simple
Co-Occurence Matrix	Sensitive	sensitive	simple
Multiresolution Histogram	Robust	robust	medium
Daubechies Wavelets	Sensitive	Robust	Medium
Correlation Templates	Sensitive	Not very robust	Heavy
Histogram of Gradients (HoG)	Fairly robust	Fairly robust	Heavy
LoG POLAR HoG	Fairly robust	Fairly robust	Heavy

Digital Correlation and Template Feature Matching

One of the oldest and most obvious methods for feature description and detection is to simply take an image of the feature and search for it by direct comparison—this is known as *correlation*. This method involves stepping the feature pattern or template across the image and performing a simple pixel by pixel region comparison such as SAD (sum of differences) across the image. Hardly any researchers today are extending correlation methods since correlation is obviously compute intensive. However, correlation will become popular once again as compute power becomes cheap and fixed function hardware such as texture samplers in the graphics processor can be used to accelerate creation of scale, affine and perspective invariant correlation templates that can then be rapidly compared using SIMD instruction sets and other fixed function hardware.

Variations on correlation include cross-correlation (FFT method), normalized cross-correlation (NCC), zero-mean normalized cross-correlation (ZNCC), and texture autocorrelation (TAC). Correlation is illustrated in Figure 2.28.

In summary, take some time to analyze your application and be open to creating your own customer feature descriptors and corresponding classification methods in order to find the right balance between over-computing feature descriptors and over-computing feature extraction and complicating the feature analysis and object classification part of the pipeline.

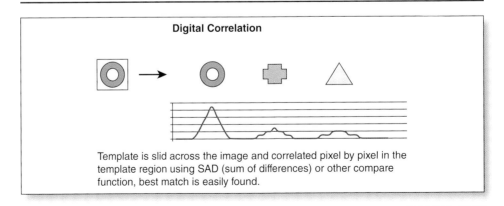

Digital Correlation

Template is slid across the image and correlated pixel by pixel in the template region using SAD (sum of differences) or other compare function, best match is easily found.

Figure 2.28 Simplified Model of Digital Correlation Using Rectangular Regions. Note that Correlation Is Fairly Primitive in its Basic Form, but Can Be Accelerated and Made Invariant to Perspective and Scale Changes.

Survey of Feature Descriptors, Common and Uncommon

This section is divided into two parts:

1. *Common* feature detectors based on published widely used vision algorithms like SIFT, LBP, Viola-Jones, and SURF.

2. *Uncommon* variations from common methods (there are many) as described in current industry and academic research papers.

This section does not deal with feature matching, classification, or training—only the feature description stage.

Current research explores various combinations of interest point detectors, feature descriptors, and variations on the classification and matching stage of the vision pipeline within the context of the common algorithms like SIFT and SURF to look or optimizations, so the research is often a small variation from a common method. Papers are referenced here that provide details on the performance and accuracy of various permutations and combinations of variations. By studying the common feature descriptor methods first, the stage is set to understand the variations and tradeoffs that can be made in the vision pipeline for a given application to achieve desired goals.

Common Features

Local feature description and detection, as opposed to global feature description and metrics, is a very active area of research that cannot be covered in depth here, so only some of the more popular local feature metrics can be covered in detail. In 2011 alone, over 1000 papers were published in major journals on these topics and several thousand more great papers were not published!

Next we will survey some the most common and familiar features used today to set the stage for a discussion on the variations of feature description methods.

Methods covered here in some detail are as follows:

■ Haar-like features, which are a type of simple basis wavelet used in SURF and Viola-Jones methods.

■ LBP or linear binary patterns, which are simple to compute are versatile, and have been extended into many subtypes and used for a wide variety of vision metrics such as texture, interest points, and feature descriptors.

■ SIFT inspired features, which are a type of gradient maxima and gradient orientation feature descriptor method.

■ ORB, which is faster than both SIFT and SURF and is one of the newest feature descriptors in common use since ORB is now available in OpenCV version 2.4.

Haar-like Features

Haar-like features were popularized in the field of vision by the Viola-Jones algorithm (Viola and Jones 2001), and Haar features are based on specific sets of rectangle patterns as shown in Figure 2.29, which approximate the basic Haar wavelets, where each Haar feature is composed of the *average pixel value* of pixels within the rectangle. Note that Haar features can be rotated. Depending on the type of feature to be detected such as eyes (see middle images), a specific set of Haar feature is chosen to revel eye/cheek details and eye/nose details. For example (bottom), Haar patterns with two rectangles are useful for detecting edges, while patterns with three rectangles can be used for lines, and patterns with an inset rectangle or four rectangles can be used for single-object features.

By using the average pixel value in the rectangular feature, the intent is to find a set of small patterns in adjacent areas where brighter or darker region adjacency may reveal a feature, for example, a bright cheek next to a darker eye socket.

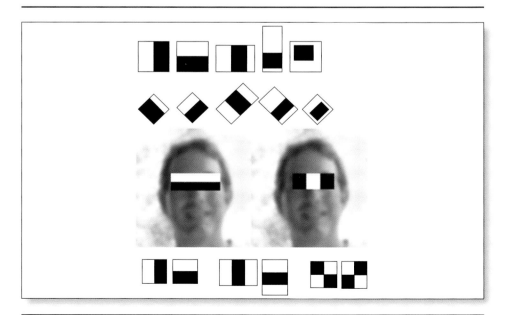

Figure 2.29 Haar-like Features Supported in the Intel® IPP Library (Top) and Other Commonly Used Features (Bottom).

Each region of an image can be searched for known Haar features using a sliding window method stepped at some chosen interval such as every *n pixels* and the detected features can be fed into a classification funnel known as a *Haar cascade classifier*. The top of the funnel consists of feature sets that are fast to calculate and yield low false positive and false negative rates, so the first order results of the cascade contain high probability regions of the image for further analysis. The Haar features become more complex progressing deeper into the funnel of the cascade. With this arrangement, images and regions are rejected as soon as possible if the desired Haar features are not found, minimizing processing overhead.

A complete Haar feature detector may combine hundreds or thousands of Haar features together into a final classifier, where not only the feature is important but the spatial arrangements of features is also important, for example the distance and angular relationships between features. More details of how Haar features can be used for the specific objective of face detection are provided in Chapter 3.

Haar features are closely related to *wavelets*, and wavelets can be considered as an extension of the earlier concept of *Gabor functions* (Szelinski 2011). Wavelets (see Figure 2.30) are designed to meet various goals: there is no single wavelet function. When designing wavelets, a *mother wavelet* is designed as the basis of the wavelet family, and then *daughter wavelets* are derived using translation and compression of the mother wavelet. Wavelets are used in transforms as a set of nonlinear basis functions, where each basis function can be designed as needed to optimally match a desired feature in the input

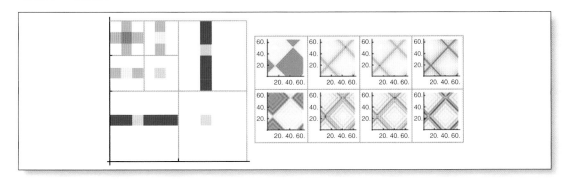

Figure 2.30 Wavelet Matrix Functions Plotted, Some Resembling Haar Features (Left), and Others Resembling Texture Features (Right). Wavelets Can Be Designed for Use as Feature Descriptors. Images Plotted from Mathematica.

function. So unlike transforms, which use a uniform set of basis functions (like the Fourier transform, which uses SIN and COS functions), wavelets use a *dynamic* set of basis functions that are complex and nonuniform in nature.

Wavelets are computationally expensive since they represent complex functions in a complex domain. Haar 2D basis functions are commonly used due to the simple rectangular shape and computational simplicity.

Local Binary Patterns (LBP)

The local binary pattern or LBP (Pietikäinen et al. 2011; Pietikäinen and Heikkilä 2011) creates a descriptor or texture model using a set of histograms of the local texture neighborhood surrounding each pixel. In this case, local texture is the feature descriptor.

The LBP metric is simple yet powerful and the area of LPB research is among the most active and promising for devising new feature description and detection methods, so LBP is treated in some depth here. LBPs and hundreds of variants are used in many ways, including face recognition and as alternative SIFT-style descriptors.

In the simplest embodiment, the goal of the LBP is to create a binary coded neighborhood descriptor by comparing each pixel against the center pixel in the kernel using the > operator and then creating histograms from the comparison as descriptors. The LBP histogram is thus a set of descriptors that becomes the final LBP texture descriptor and provides the feature comparison space for texture analysis and feature analysis. LPB histograms can even be used as signals and passed into a 1D FFT, and the Fourier spectrum of the LBP histogram is rotationally invariant. The FFT spectrum can then be concatenated onto the LBP histogram to form a *multivariate descriptor.*

> Wavelets can be used to describe very complex features, and this may be an advantage in some feature detection applications, since using wavelets can reduce the complexity of the classifier stage, with the tradeoff of making the feature matching stage more computationally expensive to find the wavelets.

As shown in Figure 2.31, the LBP is used as an image processing operator, a region segmentation method, and as a histogram feature descriptor. The LBP has many applications.

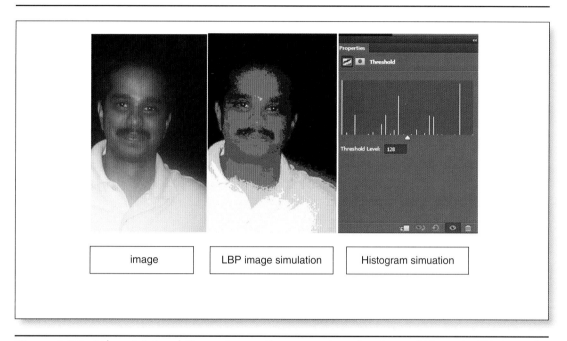

image   LBP image simulation   Histogram simuation

Figure 2.31 (Above) A Local Binary Pattern Representation of an Image Where the LBP Is Used as an Image Processing Operator, and the Corresponding Histogram of Cumulative LBP Features and (Bottom) Segmentation Results Using LBP Texture Metrics.

An LBP may be calculated over various sizes and shapes using various sizes of forming kernels. A simple 3×3 neighborhood provides good coverage for local features, while wider areas and kernel shapes are used as well. Assuming a 3×3 LBP kernel pattern is chosen, this means that there will be 8 pixel comparisons and up to 2^8 combinations of results for a 256-bin histogram. However, it has been shown that reducing the 8-bit histogram to use only 56 LBP bins based on *uniform patterns* is the optimal number, where the 56 bins or *uniform patterns* are chosen to represent only two contiguous LBP patterns around the circle, which consist of two connected contiguous segments rather than all 256 possible pattern combinations (Pietikäinen and Heikkilä 2011), and the same uniform pattern logic applies to LBPs of dimension larger than 8 bits as well. So, uniform patterns provide both histogram space savings and feature compare-space optimization since fewer features need be matched (56 instead of all 256).

LPB feature recognition may follow these steps as shown in Figure 2.32.

The LBP is calculated by assigning a binary weighting value to each pixel in the local neighborhood and summing up the binary values to create a composite LBP value. The LBP thus contains region information encoded in a compact binary pattern as shown in Figure 2.33. The LBP is thus a *binary coded* neighborhood texture descriptor.

Assuming a 3×3 neighborhood is used to describe the LBP patterns, one may compare the 3×3 rectangular region to a circular region suggesting 360 directionality at 45 degree angle increments. See Figure 2.34.

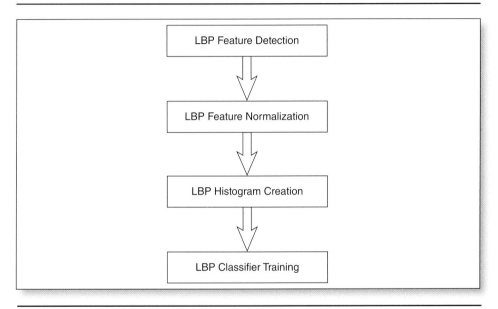

Figure 2.32 LBP Feature Flow for Feature Detection

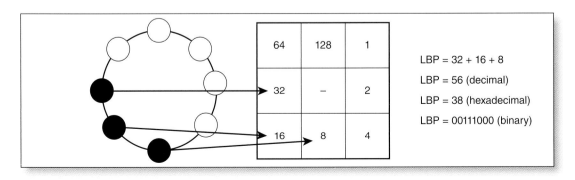

Figure 2.33 Assigned LBP Weighting Values

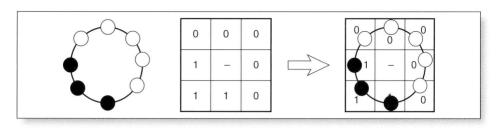

Figure 2.34 LBP Circular Assignments

The steps involved in calculating the LBP over a 3x3 region and using the LBP method in a classification scheme include:

1. *Neighborhood comparison*: each pixel is compared to its neighbors according to a forming kernel, which allows selection of neighbors for the comparison. In this example (see Figure 2.35) all pixels are used in the forming kernel (all 1s). If the neighbor is > than the center pixel, the binary pattern is 1, otherwise 0.

2. *Histogram Composition*: Each LBP descriptor is added to a histogram bin count describing the cumulative texture feature. For example, in the histogram example in Figure 2.36 there are 5 bins populated, thus this texture feature vector is of dimension 5. Uniform LBP histograms would have 56 bins.

3. *Optionally normalize* the final histogram to reduce it to a smaller number of bins using binary decimation or some similar algorithm. In addition it is possible to normalize the histograms to some dominant set of features by thresholding to ignore small bin values.

4. Multiple LBPs taken over overlapping regions may be concatenated together into a larger histogram vector or feature descriptor to sharpen up the contrast and provide better discrimination.

The cumulative LBP histogram feature vectors can then be used for feature comparison and matching in higher level algorithms and classifiers.

Rotation Invariant LBP (RILBP)

To achieve rotational invariance, the rotation invariant LBP (Pietikäinen et al. 2011) is calculated by circular bitwise rotation of the local LBP to find the

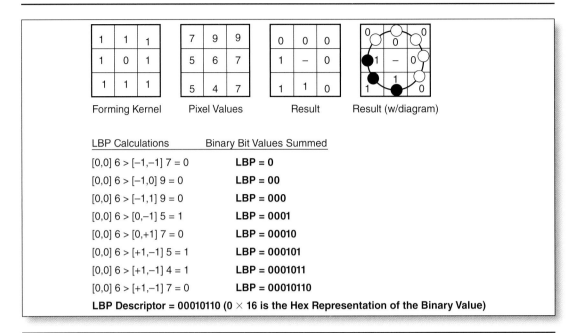

Figure 2.35 Showing LBP value assignment details

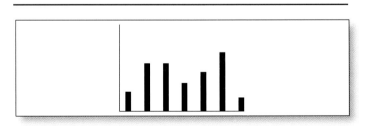

Figure 2.36 LBP Histogram of local texture descriptors over a region

minimum binary value. The minimum value LBP is used as a rotation invariant signature and recorded in the histogram bins. The RILBP is computationally very efficient.

To illustrate the method, Figure 2.37 shows a pattern of three consecutive LBP bits, and in order to make this descriptor rotation invariant the value is *left-shifted* until a minimum value is reached.

Note that many researchers (Shu and Chung 2008; Pietikäinen and Heikkilä 2011) are extending the methods used for LBP calculation to use refinements such as local derivatives, local median or mean values, *trinary* or

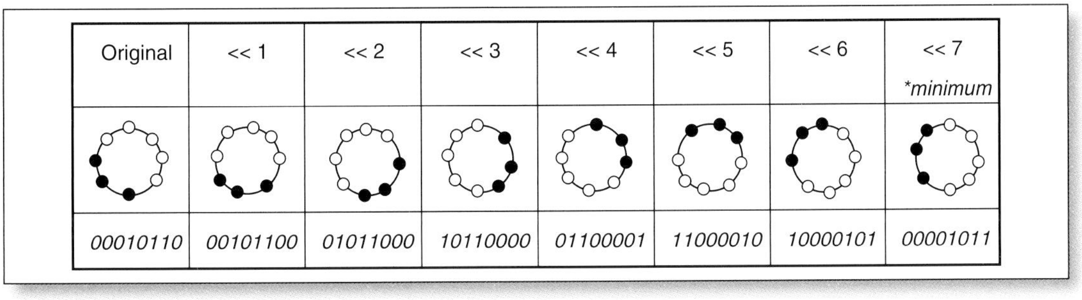

Original	<< 1	<< 2	<< 3	<< 4	<< 5	<< 6	<< 7 *minimum*
00010110	00101100	01011000	10110000	01100001	11000010	10000101	00001011

Figure 2.37 Method of Calculating the Minimum LBP by Using Circular Bit Shifting of the Binary Value to Find the Minimum Value. The LBP Descriptor Is then *Rotation Invariant*.

quinary compare functions and many other methods rather than the simple binary greater than function as originally proposed, and of course, there are many more variations of this method being devised.

Dynamic Texture Metric Using 3D LBPs: VLBP and LBP-TOP

Dynamic textures are visual features that morph and change dynamically as they move and morph from frame to frame; examples include waves, clouds, wind, smoke, foliage, and ripples. Two extensions of the basic LBP used for tracking such dynamic textures will be discussed here: VLBP and LBP-TOP.

Volume LBP (VLBP)

To create the VLBP (Zhao and Pietikäinen 2007) descriptor, first an image volume is created by stacking together three consecutive video frames into a volume of *three parallel planes,* which contain the dynamic textures as they move from frame to frame. Of course, more than three consecutive frames can be considered together into arbitrary depth volumes but three is the minimum. Next, three LBPs are taken, one from each plane, centered on the selected interest point, from each parallel plane in the volume, into a summary LBP large enough to contain a set of binary weights for each LBP component of all three LBPs, and the corresponding histograms of each orthogonal LBP are concatenated together into a single dynamic descriptor vector, the VLBP. The VLPB can then be tracked from frame to frame and recalculated to account for dynamic changes in the texture as over time the VLBP is gradually morphed into a new VLPB as it moves from frame to frame. See Figure 2.38. The VLBP is therefore over three times as large as a normal LBP.

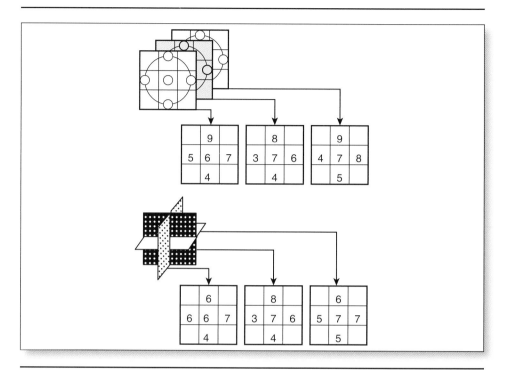

Figure 2.38 (Top) VLBP Method of Calculating LBPs from *Parallel Planes*, and (Bottom) LBP-TOP Method of Calculating LBPs from *Orthogonal Planes*

LPB-TOP

The LBP-TOP (Kellokumpu, Guoying, and Pietikänien 2008) is created like the VLBP, except that instead of calculating the three individual LBPs from *parallel planes*, the three LBPs are calculated from *orthogonal planes* in the volume *(x,y,z)* intersecting the interest point as shown in Figure 2.38. The 3D composite descriptor is the same size as the VLBP and contains three planes worth of data. The histograms for each LBP plane are also concatenated together for the LBP-TOP like the VLBP.

Scale-Invariant Feature Transform (SIFT)

The scale-invariant feature transform (Lowe 1999) is a popular method for finding reasonably invariant interest points and feature descriptors that are reasonably invariant with respect to scale, rotation, and contrast.

SIFT is a complete algorithm and processing pipeline and will be described step by step below. SIFT includes stages for extracting and detecting center-surrounding circular weighted difference of Gaussian (DoG) maxima interest points and creating corresponding feature descriptors for each chosen interest point. The feature extraction step involves calculating a HoG (histogram of gradients) into Cartesian rectangular bins or into log polar bins using the GLOH variation at several scales centered around the maximal response interest point, and the HoG or GLOH descriptors are fed into a matching pipeline to find the nearest distance ratio metric between closest match and second closest match. The SIFT matching stage idea is to test the nearest neighbor distance ratio between the first best and second best match, and if the ratio between first and second match is low, the first is much better than the second—so take the best match. Otherwise, the first and second matches are about equal, so the match is rejected as noise or a false match.

A variation of SIFT for color is known as CSIFT (Abdel-Hakim and Farag 2006).

Here is the basic SIFT descriptor processing flow (note: the matching stage is omitted since this chapter is only concerned with feature descriptors and related metrics):

1. *Define interest points.* A set of candidate interest points are created using local extrema points that are maximum or minimum values found using the Difference of Gradients (DoG) method, which approximates a Laplacian of Gaussian filter. The first step is to create a set of Gaussian blurred images at differing blur levels and then subtract the adjacent images from each other to yield the DoG. See Figure 2.39.

2. *Select best interest points.* The best interest points are chosen (reject the rest) based on simple arithmetic to calculate the most extreme local maxima or minima as compared among the 26 adjacent pixels in the DoG images from the three adjacent octaves in the pyramid. In other words, the interest points are multiscale. The selected interest points are further qualified to achieve invariance by analyzing local contrast, local noise, and local edge presence within the local 26-pixel neighborhood. Various methods may be used.

3. *Feature descriptor creation.* Within the local region or patch surrounding the chosen interest points, the local magnitude of the gradients and the gradient orientation are calculated and stored in a HoG (histogram

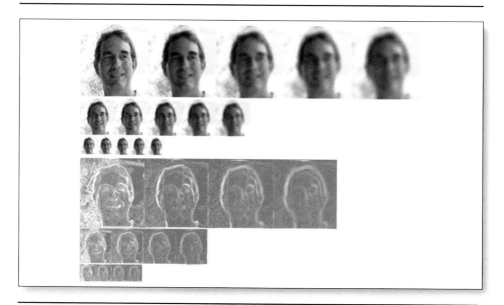

Figure 2.39 A Set of Gaussian Images (Top) Obtained by Convolution with a Gaussian Kernel and the Corresponding Set of *Difference* of Gaussian Images (Bottom) in Octave Sets. The DoG Function Approximates a Laplacian of Gaussian Gradient, or Tunable Bypass Filter. Matching Features Against the Various Images in the Scaled Octave Sets Yields Scale-Invariant Features.

of gradients) feature vector that is weighted in a circularly symmetric fashion to downweight points farther away from the center or interest point around which the HoG is calculated. The weighting is performed by multiplying points farther away using a Gaussian weighting function. HoG is reasonably invariant to scale, contrast, and rotation. SIFT can also be perform using a variant of the HoG descriptor called the gradient location and orientation histogram (GLOH), which uses a log polar histogram format instead of the Cartesian HoG format.

The calculations for the GLOH log polar histogram are straightforward as shown below from the Cartesian coordinates used or the Cartesian HoG histogram, where the vector magnitude is the hypotenuse of a right triangle and the angle is the arctangent of the right triangle.

$$m\,(x, y) = \sqrt{(L\,(x + 1, y) - L\,(x - 1, y))^2 + (L\,(x, y + 1) - L\,(x, y - 1))^2}$$

$$\theta\,(x, y) = \text{TAN}^{-1}\,(L(\,x, y + 1) - L\,(x, y - 1))\,/\,(L\,(x + 1, y) - L\,(x - 1, y))$$

ORB – Oriented Brief Descriptor

The *Oriented BRIEF* (ORB) descriptor is designed for rapid tracking & matching of features and is well suited for stereo mapping and possibly AR tracking and mapping applications where the features to be located have little affine or scale variation and do not move much from frame to frame. ORB is claimed to be 100x faster than SURF and 1000x faster than SIFT. ORB is available in OpenCV ™.

Note that ORB uses a variant of the BRIEF descriptor and adds orientation (*Oriented Brief - ORB*). The new ORB descriptor is called rBRIEF (for Rotationally Invariant BRIEF) which uses FAST corners followed by a HARRIS detector to qualify the FAST corners and adds orientation by finding the orientation of the corner as an intensity vector. rBRIEF uses a binary descriptor vector to describe local intensity over a set of local patches, where each bit in the vector represents a simple comparison with pixels in each patch (like an LBP, except uses a longer vector). Bits in the vector are set to '1' if first point is of higher intensity than the other, '0' otherwise, but BRIEF binary vectors can also be calculated using other comparison methods.

ORB has low tolerance for any variance in scale, affine, or perspective changes. According to ORB research is ongoing to improve the descriptor by perhaps using the BRISK descriptor in place of BRIEF to add more invariance.

How well does ORB do compared to SIFT and SURF? Depends on what you are trying to find. For example, to solve the object detection problem where we have same object under different scale, lighting and camera perspective, SIFT/SURF perform better than ORB. For stereo & image stitching, ORB and BRIEF can do much better and faster than SIFT and SURF. This is to be expected based on the goals of each descriptor method for speed and invariance for the particular applications intended.

In addition ORB research is also leading towards improvements in the scale space representation, where today ORB implements a simple method of scale invariance using FAST corners at a single scale with only small scale factor adjustments of 10% or 20% to assist in matching, in contrast to SIFT which is based on many years of research into scale space representations using octaves and performs much better.

Related to ORB is the BRISK descriptor which can be considered a more advanced version of ORB. Similar research on new descriptors is underway as well. DAISY is another option to replace the BRIEF descriptor used in ORB, since the DAISY descriptor more closely matches the human eye model of keeping the center of the field of view sharp, and allows sharpness to drop off as distance from the center of the field of view increases.

Variations on Feature Descriptor Methods

Table 2.7 provides summary information on a sampling of the vast field of feature description methods, and it is good to note that this is a very active area of research with great opportunity to advance the state of the art. In fact, consider customizing feature descriptors or creating new ones for your application.

Table 2.7   A Summary Comparison of Feature Descriptors

Feature Descriptor	Reference
PMK (Pyramid Match Kernel) – a novel Pyramid Match Kernel is proposed to create a histogram descriptor of regions at each scale in an image pyramid and concatenate all the histograms together to create a pyramid of *multiscale histograms* in the feature space. Weighted histogram intersection is used for correspondence. Note that methods like SIFT use a pyramid of images and a monoscale descriptor, while PMK takes the opposite view and creates the pyramid in the descriptor, so the descriptor contains multiscale information.	(Grauman and Darrell 2005)
Shape Context is based on the notion of spatial relationships between a set of interest points taken across an object (perimeter and interior points may be used) and uses log polar histograms for binning the spatial relationships in the final descriptor. Shape Context uses a log polar histogram derived from Cartesian histograms of point distances and angles between interest points as follows: 1. Define points on or within shape, record Cartesian coordinates 2. Measure distance between all points, normalize distance 3. Calculate angles between all points 4. Create point-to-point distance histogram into bins 5. Create point-to-point angle histogram into bins 6. Combine angle + distance histograms into a single log polar histogram descriptor (like a SIFT/HoG but in polar coordinates)	(Belongie, Malik, and Puzicha 2002)
SIFT/HoG descriptors (Scale-Invariant Feature Transform, Histogram of Oriented Gradient Magnitudes) as used in SIFT are essentially histograms of edge gradient magnitude and direction taken over patches surrounding a local interest point. The multiscale interest points are determined based DoG analysis on a pyramid set of images at multiple scales (See Figure 2.37). SIFT/HoG uses Cartesian coordinates for the histograms and may operate on patches of various sizes around an interest point to calculate gradients over the patch followed by a Gaussian weighting function for each point based on distance from the interest point and distance from bin boundaries to support *soft-binning*, making this method compute intensive.	(Lowe 1999, 2004)

SIFT is patented in the USA and owned by the University of British Columbia, Canada. A variant descriptor sometimes used in SIFT is the PHOG which uses log polar histograms, also LBP variants have been used in SIFT.

(*The SIFT Histogram Of Oriented Gradient Magnitudes is related but not to be confused with the HoG method of Dalal and Triggs (2006), where SIFT/HOG is computed at interest points, and the HoG (Dalal and Triggs 2006) is computed across a grid over the entire image or regions of the image with slightly different binning and weighting and size*)

HoG descriptors (Histogram of Gradients) use a gradient histogram very much like SIFT, except HoG and SWIFT/HOG descriptors are also calculated differently: SIFT/HOG is calculated in patches surrounding SIFT interest points, while HoG is calculated over an evenly spaced grid across the entire image and does not rely on any interest points. Note that slight variation on the HoG region are made by using other types of rectangular block regions (R-HoG) and circular block regions (C-HoG). In addition, a compressed version called CHoG is used to lower the bit rate for mobile applications (Chandrasekhar et al. 2009).	(Dalal and Triggs 2006)
PHoG descriptors (Pyramidal Histogram of Gradients) operate by dividing a region into a set of octave subregions, then calculating a set of Dalal style HoG descriptors over each subregion in the set, and finally a histogram is composed for HoG in the octave region set and all the histograms are concatenated together into a larger composite *multiscale descriptor*. This allows for scale invariance. PHoG is sometimes used in SIFT.	(Bosch, Zisserman, and Munoz, 2007)
GLOH descriptors SIFT can also be performed using a variant of the SIFT/HOG descriptor called the Gradient Location and Orientation Histogram (GLOH), which uses a Log Polar Histogram format instead of the Cartesian SIFT/HOG binning. GLOH descriptors are essentially histograms of gradient magnitude and direction taken over patches surrounding a local interest point and like HoG descriptors this requires gradient calculations over the patch, where the patch size may be of perhaps 16x16 pixels for a total of 256 gradient calculations, followed by a Gaussian weighting function for each pixel based on distance from the interest point and distance from bin boundaries to support *soft-binning*, with further processing using HYPOT and ATAN functions to convert to polar coordinates to bin into log polar histograms rather than Cartesian histograms as in HOG. Also the higher dimensionality of the GLOH descriptor is reduced using PCA (Principal Component Analysis) which adds more compute burden.	(Mikolajczyk and Schmid 2005)

Fourier descriptors – these can be created as 2D shape descriptors for any array or set of numbers using the properties of the Fourier Space as follows:

1. Calculate the centroid of an object shape
2. Calculate the perimeter of an object shape
3. Extend radii from the centroid to the perimeter at regular angle increments (say every 15 degrees)
4. Calculate the length of each radii and accumulate into an array
5. Calculate a 1D FFT across the array of radii lengths

6. Take the magnitude spectrum of radii lengths as the Fourier descriptor. This yields the shape of the object compared to a circle.

Note that the FFT descriptor is *rotation invariant* and can be calculated across any vector such as a histogram, and in fact the Fourier Descriptor is calculated across the 1D bins or vectors of LBP descriptors, SIFT, GLOH, and HoG descriptors, and the Fourier descriptor can be combined with said descriptors to create a multivariate descriptor with shape information and rotational invariance. See Figure 2.19.

Chain Code Histograms – this is based on the Freeman chain code representation of a polygon in Cartesian space where the chain is composed of the x,y coordinate move to trace the perimeter shape of the polygon: $x + 1$, $y = right, x − 1, y = left, x, y + 1 = down, x, y − 1 = up, x − 1, y − 1 = diagonal left up, x − 1, y + 1 = diagonal right up, x$ Chain Code Histograms1, y Chain Code Histograms1 = diagonal left down, $x + 1, y + 1 = diagonal right down$). For example, a square shape will have an equal number or left, right, up and down bins populated in the histogram. Tracing the perimeter involves morphology or segmentation to prepare them image for chain code tracing, so altogether this a compute-intensive descriptor.	(Bradski and Kaeler 2008)
Perimeter, Centroid, Area – these descriptors involve morphology or segmentation to prepare the image and note that both perimeter and centroid can be calculated together in a single pass over the object, since the process of tracing the perimeter can be used first to collect the length of the perimeter and collect the cumulative sum of all the perimeter points and average them into the centroid, where the centroid is the average value of each x,y coordinate pair of perimeter points. An alternative centroid method involves taking the average x, y value of each interior point of the region (area) which can be determined by using a flood-fill algorithm to fill in each point starting at the centroid up to the perimeter. This process is compute intensive and memory intensive, but the final descriptors sizes are of course small.	
Bag of Visual Words or Visual Vocabulary: there are a variety of such methods, and references are given in this table. These methods may be most relevant to scene classification and scene searching. Many of these methods start by detecting interest points and then calculating a set of multivariate descriptors about the interest points such as SIFT descriptors, color metrics and shape metrics. Next, the descriptor may be merged into a visual vocabulary of descriptors by grouping similar descriptor metrics using K-Means clustering or similar methods. The result is a high dimensional sparse matrix or vocabulary of visual words which can be search using the visual vocabulary. *Methods to reduce memory overhead are available using Fisher Vectors.	(Perronnin et al. 2010; Nister and Stewenius 2006; Muja and Lowe, 2009)
GIST – this method attempts to find the "gist" of the image in a perceptual rather than mathematical space by using a combination of multivariate features calculated from global, regional, and local metrics. The idea is that using local, regional, and global metrics together provides a better overall understanding of the "gist" of the image. GIST uses an aggregation of the saliency (Lowe 2004) model, intensity and color channels, and six feature maps for each descriptor expressed in a descriptor pyramid of six scales for each of the six feature maps combined with PCA and ISA feature dimension reduction.	(Siagian and Itti 2007; Oliva 2001)

Daisy Descriptor is inspired by SIFT and GLOH-like descriptors but is claimed to be about 40% faster to compute and designed for dense-matching applications such as stereo mapping and tracking for AR applications, relying on a set of radially distributed and increasing size Gaussian convolution kernels which overlap and resemble a flower-like shape (DAISY) rather than using the gradient magnitude and direction calculations used in SIFT and GLOH. DAISY uses overlapping patches blurred increasingly as the distance increase away from the center, which mimics the human eye and visual system to maintain sharpness and focus in the center of the field of view and decreasing focus and resolution farther away from the center of the FOV.	(Tola, Lepetit, and Fua 2010)
Haar Wavelets/SURF/Viola Jones – these descriptors are simply the sum of all pixel values in a rectangular region of an image. Adjacent sets of rectangles form a descriptor set which is compared to each adjacent rectangular feature by simple difference (sum of pixels in one rectangle subtracted from the sum of pixels in another rectangle), allowing sets of adjacent rectangles to be compared quickly and easily. A wide range of Haar-like wavelets can be designed and compared to find common features. The Haar wavelets can be quickly calculated from integral images, which are compact representations of the rectangular regions across each possible rectangle in an image. The well-known Viola Jones method makes use of tens and hundreds of thousands of Haar features and a complex matching, classification and training method, while SURF uses only tens or hundreds of Haar features to locate interest points. *An integral image is required to speed computation, and a large training set is used at runtime for matching.	(Viola and Jones 2004; Bay et al. 2008)
BRIEF – BRIEF is simple and fast to calculate and match, but has little tolerance for any variance in scale, affine, or perspective changes. For these reasons, BRIEF is most suitable for stereo correspondence. BRIEF uses a binary vector or bit string of some suitable size such as 128,256, or 512 where each bit represents a simple '>' comparison with the center key point in a patch (like an LBP, except uses a longer bit vector). The patches may be Gaussian smoothed to reduce noise.	
Steered BRIEF and rBRIEF – methods of improving the BRIEF descriptor to have rotational invariance, implemented as part of the ORB descriptor method.	(Rublee et al. 2011)
BRISK – method uses scale-space FAST keypoint detection with sub-pixel precision and floating point scale values, followed by a descriptor calculation using a binary vector or bit string of some suitable size such as 128, 256, or 512 where each bit represents a simple ">" comparison with the center key point in a patch (like an LBP, except uses a longer bit vector). The BRISK sampling pattern is similar to the DAISY method, but the sample regions do not overlap and the method is simpler to calculate.	(Leutenegger, Chli, Roland 2011)
ORB – ORB uses a variant of the BRIEF descriptor and adds orientation (Oriented Brief) , but has little tolerance for any variance in scale, affine, or perspective changes. The new ORB descriptor is called rBRIEF (*for Rotationally Invariant BRIEF*), which uses FAST corners followed by a Harris detector to qualify the FAST corners and adds orientation by finding the orientation of the corner as an intensity vector. rBRIEF uses a binary descriptor vector to describe local intensity over a set of local patches, where each bit in the vector represents a simple comparison with pixels in each patch (like an LBP, except it uses a longer	(Rublee et al. 2011)

vector). Bits in the vector are set to 1 if first point is of higher intensity than the other, 0 otherwise, but BRIEF binary vectors can also be calculated using other comparison methods.	
RIFF – Rotation-Invariant, Fast Feature (RIFF) descriptor is designed for mobile augmented reality (AR), and therefore designed for fast computation on slow compute devices. The method uses a histogram descriptor similar to a HoG with bins corresponding to *Radial Gradients*, and this method includes a *Radial Gradient Transform* (RGT) to assist with binning the radial gradients in a rotationally invariant manner, yielding a rotational invariant format similar to the Uniform LBP Patterns (same goal).	(Takacs et al. 2010)
PCA-SIFT – like the SIFT descriptor, except instead of using a histogram to contain the feature vector, PCA (Principal Component Analysis) is used to create a smaller feature vector from a smaller basis set of principal components.	(Abdel-Hakim and Farag 2006)
MSER or Maximally Stable Extremal Regions – The MSER method is compute intensive and involves sorting pixels into regions based on intensity, sort of like a *contour map*; regions with pixels whose intensity does not vary much (stable regions) are consider *maximally stable*. The MSER can be considered as the basis for a shape descriptor as an alternative to morphological methods of determining object shape. As such, MSER is only part of the compute needed to create such a feature descriptor.	(Matas et al. 2002)
Salient Regions - This method is calculated densely at each pixel in two parts: 1) pdf entropy is calculated over a set of three parametric ellipses centered at each pixel, locations with entropy extrema are selected for further processing, 2) the set of extrema locations are ranked based on magnitude of the derivative over the pdf scale, and the top ranked regions are considered salient regions. This method can detect objects or regions which show strong invariance to affine rotation, 2D translation, nonuniform warping, contrast and intensity changes, and perspective viewpoint variations, and these regions have shape. As such, Salient Regions are only part of the compute needed to create such a feature descriptor.	(Chun-Rong, Chu-Song, and Pau-Choo 2008; Kadir and Brady 2001; Kadir, Zisserman, and Brady 2004)
CCH Contrast Context Histogram-CCH represents the contrast distributions of a local region about a salient corner interest point, efficiently using subtraction of the interest point pixel value from set of regional pixel values to create the contrast metrics, provides rotation and illumination invariance, and uses separate log polar histogram bins for negative and positive contrast values. Accuracy is comparable to SIFT, but compute time is much reduced, about 3x–4x faster.	(Huang, Chen, and Chung 2008)
SUSAN - This is actually a method of finding connected corners and lines or edges, similar to the Canny detector or Harris corners, although SUSAN is referred to as a Two Dimensional Feature Detector in the original paper (Smith and Brady) and some other literature.	(Smith and Brady 1997)

LBP or Local Binary Patterns provide both statistical and structural information about local regions, compact bin-level coding, quick to calculate, and includes many variations including neighborhood topology variation via forming kernels, ternary levels of resolution range flexibility, and can be used with alternate comparison functions besides the original $n > p$ function. LBP can be made rotationally invariant and is naturally invariant to changes in illumination and contrast. LBPs are used in a wide range of applications. See (Pietikäinen et al. (2011) for a comprehensive treatment of LBP and variants.	(Pietikäinen et al. 2011)
LBP Variants *Many variations on the standard LBP method have been devised and are surveyed here.* *See* Pietikäinen et al. (2011) *for more detailed information on all the LBP variants listed here.* ULBP (Uniform LBP) uses only 56 uniform bins instead of the full 256 bins possible with 8-bit pixels to create the histogram. The Uniform patterns consist of contiguous segments of connected TRUE values. RLBP (ROBUST LBP) adds + scale factor to eliminate transitions due to noise (p[1] *Chain Code Histograms* p[2] + SCALE) CS-LBP Circle-symmetric, half as many vectors an LBP, comparison of opposite pixel pairs vs. comparison w/center pixel, useful to reduce LBP bin counts LBP-HF (Fourier spectrum descriptor + LBP) MLBP Median LBP (use area median value instead of center pixel value for comparison) M-LBP Multiscale LBP combining multiple radii LBP's concatenated together MB - LBP — Multiscale Block LBP: compares average pixel values in small blocks SEMB - LBP: Statistically Effective MB−LBP (SEMB−LBP) uses the percentage in distributions instead of the number of 0−1 and 1−0 transitions in the LBP and redefines the uniform patterns in the standard LBP after the percentage model. Used effectively in face recognition using Gentle ADA Boosting, (Schapire and Singer 1998) VLBP - volume LBP over adjacent video frames *or* within a volume—concatenate histograms together to form a longer vector, discussed in this chapter in the LBP section. LGBP (Local Gabor Binary Pattern) 40 or so Gabor filters are computed via convolution over a feature region, and then LBPs are extracted from the feature region and concatenated together to form a long feature vector, which is invariant over more scales and orientations. LEP - Local Edge Patterns: Edge enhancement (Sobel) prior to standard LBP EBP - Elliptic Binary Pattern, standard LBP but over elliptical area instead of circular region	(Pietikäinen et al. 2011)

EQP Elliptical Quinary Patterns - LBP extended from binary (2) level resolution to quinary (5) level resolution $(-2, -1, 0, -1, 2)$

LTP - LBP extended over Ternary range to successfully encode near constant contrast areas $(-1, 0, 1)$ rather than just edges and corners

LLBP Local Line Binary Pattern - calculates LBP over line patterns (cross shape) and then calculates a magnitude metric using square root of squares of each X/Y dimension

TPLBP- Three Pattern LBP, like FPLBP but uses three LBPs are calculated together: the basic LBP for the center pixel, plus two other LBPs around adjacent pixels, so the total descriptor comprises a set of overlapping LBPs

FPLBP- Four Pattern LBP, like TPLBP but uses four LBPs are calculated together: the basic LBP for the center pixel, plus three others around adjacent pixels so the total descriptor is a set of overlapping LBPs

*TPLBP and FPLBP methods can be extended to 3, 4, … n dimensions in feature space. Large vectors.

TBP - Ternary (3) Binary Pattern, like LBP, but uses three levels of encoding $(1, 0, -1)$ to effectively deal with areas of equal or near equal intensity, uses two binary patterns (one for + and one for -) concatenated together

ETLP - Elongated Ternary Local Patterns (elliptical + ternary [5] levels)

FLBP - Fuzzy LBP where each pixel contributes to more than one bin

PLBP - Probabilistic LBP computes magnitude of difference between each pixel and center pixel (more compute, more storage)

SILTP - Scale Invariant LBP using a 3-part piecewise comparison function to compensate and support intensity scale invariance to deal with image noise

tLBP - Transition Coded LBP, where the encoding is clockwise between adjacent pixels in the LBP

dLBP - Direction Coded LBP - similar to CSLBP, but stores both maxima and comparison info (is this pixel greater, less than, or maxima)

CBP - Centralized Binary pattern - center pixel compared to average of all nine kernel neighbors

S-LBP - Semantic LBP done in a colorimetric-accurate space (like CIE LAB) over uniform connected LBP circular patterns to find principal direction + arc length used to form a 2D histogram as the descriptor.

F-LBP - Fourier Spectrum of color distance from center pixel to adjacent pixels

LDP - Local Derivate Patterns (higher order derivatives instead of basic LBP compare function), where LBP is the first order directional derivative, which is combined with additional nth order directional derivatives concatenated into a histogram, more sensitive to noise of course

BLBP - Bayesian LBP - combination of LBP and LTP together using Bayesian methods to optimize towards a more robust pattern

MB-LBP - Multiscale Block LBP, compares average pixel values in small blocks instead of individual pixels, thus a 3×3 pixel LBP will become a 9×9 block LBP where each block is a 3×3 region. The histogram is calculated by scaling the image and creating a rendering at each scale and creating a histogram of each scaled image and concatenating the histograms together.

MSLBF - Multiscale Selected Local Binary Features

RILBP - Rotation-Invariant LBP rotates the bins (binary LBP value) until maximum value is achieved, the maximum value is considered rotationally invariant. This is the most widely used method for LBP rotational invariance.

ALBP - Adaptive LBP for rotational invariance, instead of shifting to a maximal value as is the standard LBP method, find the dominant vector orientation and shift the vector to the dominant vector orientation

LBPV - Local Binary Pattern Variance - uses local area variance to weight pixel contribution to the LBP, align features to principal orientations, determine nondominant patterns and reduce their contribution.

OCLBP - Opponent Color LBP - describes color and texture together—each color channel LBP is converted, then opposing color channel LBPs are converted by using one color as the center pixel and another color as the neighborhood, so 9 total histograms are computed but only six are used: R, G, B, RG, RG, and RB.

SDMCLBP - SDM co-LBP images for each color are used as the basis for generating occurrence matrices, and then Haralick features are extracted from the images to form a multidimensional feature space.

MSCLBP - Multiscale Color Local Binary Patterns (concatenate 6 histograms together) - Uses color space components.

Chapter 3

Face Detection: Overview and Accuracy Measurement

Once you eliminate the impossible, whatever remains, no matter how improbable, must be the truth.

—Sherlock Holmes (by Sir Arthur Conan Doyle)

In the previous chapter we described a variety of techniques from the field of computer vision that allow applications to interpret and understand visual information. While there are a variety of subfields of computer vision that focus on extracting or understanding specific types of visual data, one very popular area of research has been face detection which allows a computer to detect the position of human faces in an image. The popularity of face detection largely stems from the fact that it enables a variety of intelligent behaviors. For example, a face detection system is the first step of many surveillance or security solutions that may need to quickly find all faces in a scene in order to determine whether anyone matches a database of known subjects. Similarly, face detection can be used to build more intelligent video conferencing applications that can automatically pan or zoom the camera to focus on a specific speaker. Other uses for face detection include hands-free user interfaces that react to head and body motion, or viewership measurement systems that help marketers determine how long people are looking at billboards or digital advertising displays.

In this chapter we provide an overview of a frontal face detection system that operates in real-time using standard processing hardware and commodity cameras. We also present various metrics that can be used to measure the accuracy and performance of the face detection system.

Frontal Face Detection using Viola Jones

Since face detection potentially enables a variety of intelligent applications, it is not surprising that a large number of approaches have been proposed over the past two decades that attempt to solve the face detection problem. The approach that has received a significant amount of attention recently is the algorithm by Viola and Jones (2004) since it was one of the first algorithms that could detect faces in an image both quickly (in real-time) and reliably (with high detection and low false positive rates). Since its introduction, the Viola-Jones algorithm has effectively become the standard by which other face detection algorithms are often compared. For this reason, we will focus on providing a practical overview of the Viola-Jones algorithm in this chapter. Since we will not be going deep into the theoretical aspects of the algorithm, the reader is encouraged to refer to the original paper if more detail is required.

The Viola-Jones algorithm is technically not specific to finding faces. Instead, it is actually a general-purpose object detection framework that can be used to detect a variety of object classes. The primary requirement is that the class of objects that need to be detected should exhibit some common visual traits. For example, frontal human faces work extremely well since all faces have a similar set of features (such as two eyes, nose, mouth) and the relative position of these features does not vary significantly.

Training a Face Classifier

The Viola-Jones face detector uses a machine learning algorithm called AdaBoost (Viola and Jones 2004) in order to train a classifier that can be used to detect faces. The training process is typically performed offline as a time-consuming pre-processing step, and the resulting classifier can then be used in an intelligent system to detect faces at real-time rates. To train a classifier, the algorithm requires two inputs: 1) a large set of grayscale frontal face images that are similarly cropped and aligned (our positive examples); and 2) a large set of arbitrary grayscale images cropped to the same size as the face images, containing anything other than faces such as images of cars, trees, sunsets, and so on (our negative examples). In both cases, the positive and negative image sets should be as comprehensive as possible in order to capture the majority of variations that constitute a face or non-face. Table 3.1 lists a number of online resources containing image sets that can be useful for training a frontal face classifier.

Table 3.1 Publically Available Image Databases Useful for Training a Face Classifier

Database Name	Contents	URL
Labeled Faces in the Wild	Over 13,000 frontal faces labeled with the name of the individual.	http://vis-www.cs.umass.edu/lfw/
Color FERET	2,413 face images of 865 different individuals in various poses.	http://www.nist.gov/itl/iad/ig/colorferet.cfm
Yale Face Database	165 frontal faces of 15 different individuals with various facial expressions, lighting, and eyewear.	http://cvc.yale.edu/projects/yalefaces/yalefaces.html
Oxford VGG Data Sets	Various image sets of frontal faces, background scenes, vehicles, etc.	http://www.robots.ox.ac.uk/~vgg/data3.html
MIT CBCL Face Data	Over 2,500 face images and over 25,000 non-face images.	http://cbcl.mit.edu/software-datasets/FaceData2.html

Note: See http://www.face-rec.org/databases/ for an up to date list of more face databases.

Figure 3.1 shows four example face images from the Feret Face Database that could be used for training a frontal face classifier. Note that the faces are all cropped to the same size (32×32 pixels), and the positions of facial features are relatively aligned. Also note that the images capture many of the small variations between faces, such as glasses, moustaches, and different amounts of hair.

Figure 3.2 shows some sample face images which are not suitable for training. For example, side profile shots, unaligned faces, and tilted heads are

Figure 3.1   Example Face Images Used For Training a Face Classifier
SOURCE: NIST Color FERET Database

significantly different from frontal faces. If a profile face detector or a rotated face detector is required, then a training database consisting of only profile or rotated faces can certainly be created. However, attempting to mix unaligned images together will result in noisy data that negatively impacts the training algorithm and results in a poor frontal face classifier.

Figure 3.2   Unaligned Face Images Cause Problems During Training
SOURCE: NIST Color FERET Database

Haar Features

Figure 3.3 shows the types of visual features that are used by the Viola-Jones algorithm. These are known as Haar features, and they are simply rectangular regions that consist of two or more smaller subregions along with an operator and a threshold. For each subregion, the sum of pixel intensities is computed and the difference between the pixel sums in the white and black regions is compared to the predetermined threshold. If the difference is above the threshold, then the feature is considered to be valid. For example, the top-left Haar feature in Figure 3.3 consists of a left half and right half, where the pixel sum in the left half is higher than the pixel sum in the right half. Figure 3.4 shows this particular Haar feature overlaid onto a frontal human face near the bridge of the nose and the right eye. A common observation of frontal human faces is that the bridge of the nose is usually brighter than the eye sockets, so a two-rectangle feature positioned as shown in Figure 3.4 would be a strong indicator of this common visual trait. While this feature alone would be insufficient to differentiate between faces

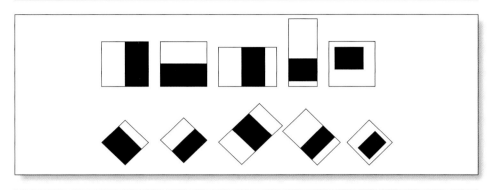

Figure 3.3   Rectangular Haar Features that Compare Sums of Pixel Intensities
Between the Black and White Subregions

Figure 3.4   A Haar Feature Overlaid Near the Bridge of the Nose and Right Eye
SOURCE: NIST Color FERET Database

and non-faces, it is certainly a starting point. By finding hundreds of such weak
features that capture various traits of human faces, we should be able to combine
these features together to create a single strong frontal face classifier.

The classifier that is output from the Viola-Jones training algorithm takes the form
of a chain of weak Haar features of various sizes that are selected from a very large set
of potential features, which is far larger than the number of pixels in each training
image. Mathematically, each level j of the classifier $hj(x)$ thus consists of a feature fj,
a threshold θj and a parity pj indicating the direction of the inequality sign:

$$h_j(x) = \begin{cases} 1 & \text{if } p_j f_i(x) < p_j \theta_j \\ 0 & \text{otherwise} \end{cases}$$

where x represents a sub-window of a training image.

To build a classifier, the AdaBoost training algorithm finds the optimal
weak Haar feature in a series of rounds $t = 1, ..., T$. For each round, the brute
force approach to find the optimal classifier involves searching all possible
sub-windows of a training image and evaluating every type of feature in each
of those sub-windows. For example, in Figure 3.4, the two-rectangle feature
would be evaluated across the training image size from the top-left location

to the bottom right, at every possible scale. At each round, a distribution of weights Wt is updated that indicates the importance of images in the training data set for the classification. The weights are initially set to be equal for each training image, and subsequent rounds result in the weights of each incorrectly classified example image to be increased (or alternatively, the weights of each correctly classified example are decreased) so that the features in the next round focus more on those incorrect examples. In other words, AdaBoost is adaptive in the sense that challenging training images are "boosted" so that subsequent features can be found to help classify those images correctly. The following steps formalize the AdaBoost algorithm for training our Haar classifier:

Step 1: Given training images $(x1,y1),..............(xn,yn)$ where

$$yi = 0 \text{ for negative images}$$

$$yi = 1 \text{ for positive images}$$

Step 2: Initialize the weights for our training images

$$\text{For } t = 1,$$

$$W_{t,i} = W_{1,i} ;$$

$$W_{(1, i)} = 1/2m \quad \text{if} \quad y_i = 0 ;$$

$$1/2l \quad \text{if} \quad y_i = 1 ;$$

where m and l are the number of negatives and positive images respectively.

Step 3: For $t = 1,...., T$, normalize the weights, so that wt is a probability distribution.

$$w_{t,i} \leftarrow \frac{w_{t,i}}{\sum_{j=1}^{n} w_{t,j}}$$

$$\epsilon_j = \sum_i w_i |h_j(x_i) - y_i|.$$

For each feature, j, train a classifier hj, which is restricted to using a single feature. The error is evaluated with respect to wt.

Choose the classifier *ht*, with the lowest error *εt*.
Update the weights:

$$w_{t+1,i} = w_{t,i} \beta_t^{1-e_i}$$

$$\beta_t = \frac{e_t}{1-e_t}$$

where $e_i = 0$ if example *xi* is classified correctly $e_i = 1$ otherwise, and

Step 4: The final strong classifier is:

$$h(x) = \begin{cases} 1 & \sum_{t=1}^{T} \alpha_t h_t(x) \geq \frac{1}{2} \sum_{t=1}^{T} \alpha_t h_t \\ 0 & \text{otherwise} \end{cases}$$

where

$$\alpha_t = \log \frac{1}{\beta_t}$$

The AdaBoost algorithm can also be extended by combining successively more complex classifiers in a cascade structure which dramatically increases the speed of the detector by focusing more time on promising face-like regions of the image and less time on those areas that are very unlikely to contain a face. In earlier stages of such a cascade, simple classifiers are used and the complexity increases for subsequent stages. As shown in Figure 3.5, the overall

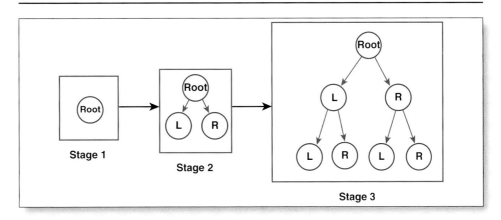

Figure 3.5   A Cascade of Classifiers Consists of Simpler Classifiers in Earlier Stages, and More Complex Classifiers in Later Stages. Complexity Is Determined by the Number of Features in the Decision Tree for a Particular Stage.

form of the detection process is that of degenerate a decision tree. A positive result from the first classifier triggers the evaluation of a second classifier which has been adjusted to achieve high detection rates. A positive result from the second classifier triggers a third classifier, and so on. A negative outcome at any point leads to the immediate rejection of the image sub-window. Stages in the cascade are constructed by training classifiers using AdaBoost and then adjusting the threshold to minimize false negatives. A lower threshold yields higher detection rates and higher false positive rates.

In practice, a reliable face detector that can achieve a 95–98 percent detection rate and a false positive rate of less than 5 percent can be achieved with a cascade consisting of 30–40 stages and roughly 6000 features. Training time is largely dependent on the number of images in the training set and can vary from a few hours up to a few days on current high-end CPUs. The accuracy of the classifier can vary based on the quality of images in the training set as described earlier.

Detecting Faces

Since the face training process is time-consuming, training is typically performed as an offline process with the resulting classifier being stored to disk. An intelligent application that requires face detection capabilities can therefore load the pre-trained classifier into system memory on startup and begin detecting faces immediately.

It is important to note that since the classifier is only trained to detect faces of a particular size (based on the size of each training image) we must first find a way to handle finding faces of arbitrary sizes. For example, if we used training images of 32×32 pixels, then by default our classifier will only be able find faces in images of size 32×32. In order to detect faces of an arbitrary size, there are two potential options:

1. Resize input images to the same size as the training images, and then apply the classifier on the resized image.

2. Rescale the Haar features in the classifier cascade so that they match the target image size, and adjust the feature thresholds accordingly.

In both cases, a search window of size $N \times N$ could be scanned across an input image, from left-to-right, top-to-bottom, in order to find all faces of size $N \times N$ in the image. For the first option, for every location of the $N \times N$ search window, we would first create a sub-image from the $N \times N$ region and resize that sub-image to our training size. The face classifier would then be evaluated on that resized image. For the second option, the classifier would first be rescaled to detect $N \times N$ faces, followed by evaluating the scaled classifier at every possible $N \times N$ location in the input image. As can be seen, the second option is potentially faster since it does not require sub-images to be constantly rescaled as we slide the $N \times N$ window across the entire input image. For this reason, the second option is preferred.

The final remaining task to enable face detection involves evaluating the actual classifier. This turns out to be a simple task, since we would simply be traversing the cascade and evaluating each Haar feature in the cascade at the appropriate location in the sub-image. Evaluating a Haar feature involves computing rectangular sums based on the type of feature being evaluated (number and arrangement of rectangles) and then comparing the differences between light and dark rectangular regions with the predetermined threshold for that feature. The cascade structure of the classifier implicitly focuses more processing time to promising candidate face regions and less to non-face regions. As shown in Figure 3.6, each stage of the cascade allows a decision to be made on the likelihood of the sub-window containing a face. Promising sub-windows are passed onto the next (more complicated) stage of the cascade will low-likelihood sub-windows are rejected early on without having to traverse the entire cascade. This allows the face detection process to be performed very quickly.

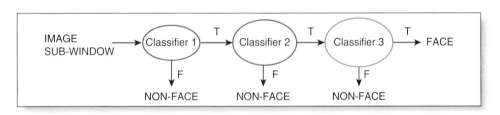

Figure 3.6   To Evaluate a Classifier, Each Sub-window Is Processed

A key contribution of the Viola-Jones framework involves the use of an image transformation known as an Integral Image, which is critical in providing a significant speed boost over other face detection techniques. An integral image is also known as a summed area table and it can be used for quickly and efficiently generating the sum of values in a rectangular subset of a grid. Since rectangular sums are the basic building block of our Haar features, integral images allow us to evaluate Haar features extremely fast.

The integral image representation of any grayscale input image simply consists of pixel values that represent the sum of pixels above and to the left of the same pixel in the input image (see Figure 3.7). The integral image I can be computed efficiently in a single pass over the input image i as follows:

$$I(x, y) = i(x,y) + I(x - 1,y) + I(x, y - 1) - I(x - 1,y - 1)$$

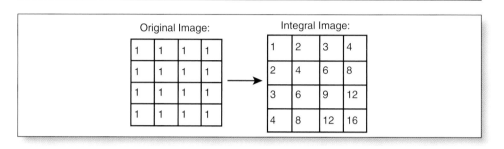

Figure 3.7 An Integral Image is a Transformation Where Any Point (x,y) in the Integram Image is the Sum of Pixels Above and to the Left of the (x,y) in the Original Image.

Once the integral image is calculated for a given input image, it is very easy to calculate the sum of pixel values for any rectangle ABCD in that input image (Figure 3.8) as follows:

$$sum(ABCD) = I(A) + I(C) - I(B) - I(D)$$

Figure 3.9 shows an example of how this equation could be used in practice.

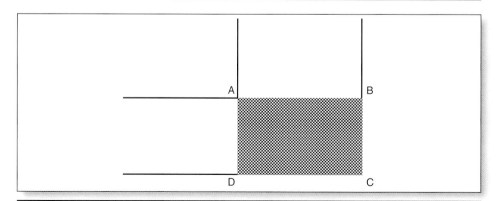

Figure 3.8 The Sum of the Rectangle ABCD Can Be Computed in Constant Time Using an Integral Image I. The Equation Is sum(ABCD) = I(A) + I(C) − I(B) − I(D).

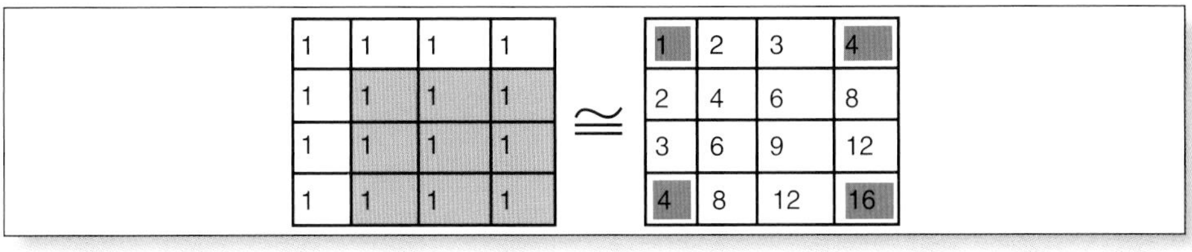

1	1	1	1
1	1	1	1
1	1	1	1
1	1	1	1

$\cong$

1	2	3	4
2	4	6	8
3	6	9	12
4	8	12	16

Figure 3.9 The Sum of Pixels in the Left Input Image Can Be Computed Using the Four Highlight Values from the Integral Image as $16 + 1 - 4 - 4 = 9$.

The overall algorithm to detect faces is shown in Figure 3.10. The pseudo code scans the input image from the top-left to the bottom right for all face sizes between a minimum and maximum face size, and the output of the algorithm is a set of rectangles representing valid face locations. Face sizes are traversed by using a scale factor after each pass over the image. A scale factor of between 1.1 and 1.2 works well.

```
void detectAllFaces(inputImage, inputWidth, inputHeight,
minSize, maxSize, scaleFactor)
{
    grayImage = convertToGray(inputImage);

    integralImage = computeIntegralImage(grayImage);

    for(n = minSize;n < maxSize;n *= scaleFactor)
    {
        for(y = 0;y < inputHeight;y++)
        {
            for(x = 0;x < inputWidth;x++)
            {
                // See if a face of size nXn exists at (x,y)
                if(evaluateCascade(integralImage, x, y, n))
                {
                    storeFaceRectangle(x, y, n);
                }
            }
        }
    }

    averageOverlappingFaces();
}
```

Figure 3.10 Pseudo Code for the Face Detection Algorithm. The Algorithm Searches for all Faces between *minSize* and *maxSize* by Scanning from the Top-Left to the Bottom-Right of the Input Image. All Candidate Face Regions are Stored in a List for Further Processing.

Since the face scanning process searches every possible sub-window of the input image, the algorithm will return a number of overlapping candidate face rectangles around a valid face as shown in Figure 3.11. This suggests that the Viola-Jones algorithm is somewhat tolerant of minor misalignments of features, which is desirable. However, in order to determine a single face rectangle from a set of overlapping rectangles, we will need to perform a post-processing step as shown by the call to `averageOverlappingFaces` in Figure 3.10. The averaging process can be implemented easily by simply comparing each face rectangle with all other rectangles and averaging those which have some minimum overlap and similar dimensions. A 30-percent overlap threshold and a 25-percent dimensional threshold work well in practice, but they can be empirically adjusted based on the needs of a specific application.

Figure 3.11 A Valid Face Will Often Result in a Large Number of Face Rectangles in the Vicinity of the Actual Face Location. Rectangles with Significant Overlaps and Similar Dimensions Can Be Averaged Together.

Algorithm Optimizations

Although the Viola-Jones algorithm is extremely fast when evaluating a cascade of Haar feature classifiers, the process of scanning every sub-window of an input image for candidate face regions is still very time-consuming. In order to speed up the detection process and reduce the CPU load of the face detector, there are a few simple adjustments that can be made:

Skipping Pixels

When scanning across the entire input image and applying the cascade to every sub-window, we can take advantage of the Viola-Jones algorithm's tolerance of small misalignments by skipping over pixels. For example, instead of evaluating the sub-window at every pixel location, we can skip over every other row and column instead to achieve a 4x speed improvement. Similarly, skipping over every fourth row and column would provide a 16x speed improvement. However, as we increase the number of rows/columns that are skipped, we may potentially begin to skip entire faces depending on the size of the face being searched for. To prevent this from happening, a better approach is to skip pixels based on the size of the face being scanned such as

$$\text{step} = \max(2, \text{search\_size/training\_size})$$

where *search_size* is the face width/height being scanned, and *training_size* is the width/height at which the cascade was trained. This approach forces the step size to be at least 2 pixels which works well for finding small faces, while larger faces can tolerate larger step sizes.

Adjusting Minimum and Maximum Face Sizes

In many applications, there may not be a need to search for a large range of face sizes. For example, a face recognition application that allows an authorized user to automatically login to a laptop will often only need to detect faces that are within 3 to 4 feet from the laptop's built-in camera. In such a situation, the face detector can significantly reduce the amount of time that is spent searching for extremely small or large faces that are outside the range of application usage scenarios.

Delaying Scans to Subsequent Frames

Many real-time intelligent applications that perform face detection on a live video stream may not necessarily require results at the video rate. For example, with a video rate of 30 Hz, if an application can tolerate finding a face in up to 1 second, then that allows the face detector up to 30 frames to find a face. This implies that the face detector can potentially defer searching for the entire range of face sizes to subsequent frames. In other words, rather than searching for all face sizes in each frame, the face sizes can be split into 30 groups and each group can be searched in 30 separate frames of live video. This approach prevents CPU resources from being exhausted on the face detection process by scheduling the search over a period of time instead of on every single frame of video.

Local Object Tracking

The face detection algorithm described thus far scans each input image from scratch without considering any information from previous frames. However, if we consider that people move from one position to another in a smooth manner at a certain velocity, we can use object tracking techniques to reduce the number of regions that we need to scan for faces. For example, consider a face rectangle A detected at frame t of an input video captured at 30Hz. At frame $t+1$ we know that face A will be in the vicinity of its position in frame t if we assume temporal and spatial coherence. Therefore, a simple object tracking technique would involve searching for face A in frame $t+1$ using a local search window around face A's position from frame t instead of scanning the entire frame. A local search window that is two times the width and height of face A, centered on face A's position in frame t, works well for most situations. More advanced tracking techniques could also be used that create a motion model which allows us to predict a better location for the search window or handle temporary face occlusions and other detection failures.

Global Motion Detection

Another optimization technique that is often used in conjunction with local object tracking is motion detection. The basic idea involves reducing the search space for faces by focusing only on regions of the input image where there is some significant motion, rather than searching the entire input image, under the assumption that human faces will be in areas of the scene that are not static. This approach is only beneficial if the motion detection algorithm is significantly faster than the time required for scanning the input image for faces. A simple and efficient motion detection algorithm can be implemented by performing an image subtraction operation between frame t and frame $t-1$, and thresholding the resulting image to remove noise. Any nonzero pixels in the resulting image will represent areas of motion, while zero values represent little or no motion. The integral image for the thresholded image can then be computed in order to quickly calculate sums on arbitrary rectangles, where zero sum rectangles represent regions with no motion and nonzero sums represent regions with some motion. This allows us to quickly discard zero motion sub-windows during the face scanning process. The motion detection process can be further optimized by using a lower resolution representation of the input image for image subtraction and integral image calculations. Motion checks can then be performed by scaling the sub-window coordinates down by the appropriate amount.

Training More Advanced Classifiers

Thus far we've shown how a cascade of classifiers can be used to detect faces. However, as discussed earlier, the AdaBoost algorithm can be trained to detect any class of objects that can be split into a positive and negative set. For example, a gender classifier could be created by simply taking a large number of frontal face images and splitting them into two sets, where one set contains all male faces and the other set contains all female faces. The male set becomes the positive examples, and the female set becomes the negative examples, and the AdaBoost algorithm could then be used to find a set of Haar features that strongly differentiates between the two sets. Such a gender classifier could then be applied as a post-process on a face rectangle after a valid face has been detected by the face classifier.

An age detector could be created in a similar manner by training a set of age-group specific classifiers. For example, if a face database could be split into child, teen, adult, and senior face groups, then four separate binary classifiers could be created to detect child/non-child, teen/non-teen, adult/non-adult, and senior/non-senior. An ethnicity detector could follow a similar approach where separate classifiers could be created for each ethnicity that an application might be interested in detecting. For classifications that contain more than two categories (such as age or ethnicity), the final classification can be determined by taking the maximum of the normalized output for each classifier that returns 1 for $h(x)$. The normalized output can be computed as follows:

$$\frac{\sum_{t=1}^{T} \alpha_t h_t(x)}{\frac{1}{2} \sum_{t=1}^{T} \alpha_t}$$

where

$$\alpha_t = \log \frac{1}{\beta_t}$$

Certain emotions could also be detected, such as a smile/no-smile detector or a frown/no-frown detector, by splitting the face database into separate training sets that capture the appropriate emotion.

Measuring the Accuracy of Face Detection

An important consideration when building a real-world face detection system is assessing how accurate the implementation is. Additionally, once a basic face detector is built, there must be a consistent way in which changes or optimizations of the algorithm can be assessed to determine whether the detector still performs as expected. In this section we describe some metrics that can be used to measure the performance of the face detection algorithm described thus far.

Ground Truth Data

The accuracy of a face detection algorithm can be determined by comparing the output of the detector against manually marked ground truth (GT) data. The preferred way to do this is to capture videos that mimic the various environments where the face detection application will be deployed. For example, if an application expects faces to be within 2 to 4 feet from the camera in a well-lit environment, then a set of videos containing faces in such a setting would be ideal. Similarly, an application which is expected to detect faces 15 to 20 feet away from the camera in low light environments should be tested with videos that consist of faces in a similar setting.

Since the output of the face detector is a rectangle consisting of the top-left (x,y) coordinate and the width/height of the face in the image, we can use this as the basis for developing ground truth data. In other words, for every frame of video, we need a corresponding data file that contains the *x, y, width, height* of every face in that frame. Such a data file could be represented in a simple comma-separated values (CSV) text format, where each line contains at least the following basic information: frame, *x, y, width, height*. A sample data file could consist of the following entries:

```
0,300,200,64,64

0,400,250,70,70

1,305,200,64,64

1,395,250,70,70
```

This sample data file consists of two faces in the first frame, and two faces in the second frame. In the first frame, one face is 64x64 in size with a top-left coordinate of (300,200), while the other face is 70x70 in size with a top-left coordinate of (400,250). In the second frame, the first face seems to have moved by 5 pixels in the positive x-direction, while the second face seems to have moved by 5 pixels in the negative x-direction. Note, however, that there is no correspondence between faces from frame to frame in this data file format, so it could be the case that the first face went from (300,200) to (395,250) and the second face went from (400,250) to (305,200). It could also be the case that the second frame contains two completely new faces. Nevertheless, if correspondences are required from frame to frame, they could certainly be made using local tracking techniques and unique IDs could then be appended to each entry in the CSV file. Other meta information such as gender, age, or emotion could also be added to the CSV format if required for a specific application.

Generating Ground Truth Data

Manually generating ground truth data from a video file is extremely time-consuming, since a human would need to mark every face rectangle in every frame of video. With a large set of videos captured at 30Hz, this could potentially be an intractable task. To expedite the process, the face detector itself could be used to bootstrap the generation of ground truth data. This can be accomplished by allowing the face detector to process a video file, and then outputting face rectangle information for each frame of video in the desired CSV format. An interactive tool could then be created which would allow a human to step through each frame of video and verify that the face rectangles that were output by the face detector were correct. Any errors or omissions could then be edited manually.

A more advanced approach that could be used to expedite both the ground truth generation process as well as the video capture process would be to create synthetic test videos. This would involve creating a custom tool that could use the large set of frontal face images from a face database as "actors" and automatically move/animate them in a virtual 3D scene. Since we are primarily interested in face detection accuracy, we would not need to concern ourselves with bodies and instead the face images could be treated as "floating heads". For example, a simple video could consist of hundreds of different frontal faces moving from left to right at a fixed speed, one after another, at a specific distance from the camera. For each frame of the video, the ground truth data could also be generated based on the position of the face rectangle in the virtual scene. This synthetic video generation approach could be extended with additional parameters such as multiple faces per frame to test the effect of occlusions, virtual 3D illumination to simulate different lighting scenarios, and orientation parameters to test the robustness of a face detector when heads are slightly tilted or rotated.

Accuracy Metrics

Once we have a set of testing videos and ground truth data, we can begin to measure the accuracy of the face detector. The basic idea is to compare the ground truth data, which corresponds to a particular video and has been verified by a human, with the raw frame-by-frame face rectangle output from the face detector when run with that same video.

False Positive Error

A false positive is a face that has been detected by the face detector but it is not in the ground truth data. This can happen due to an arrangement of pixel intensities that pass all stages of the classifier cascade, resulting in the face detector incorrectly believing that a particular sub-window in an input image contains a face. A false positive error (FPE) rate that measures the average number of false face detections per frame can be defined as follows:

$$FPE = \frac{\sum_{n=1}^{N} Pn}{N}$$

where N is the total number of frames being processed and Pn is the number of false positives in the nth frame.

The values for the FPE should be interpreted as follows:

- ◾ *Value range:* FPE can take any value greater than or equal to 0. The value 0 is assumed when there are no false positives in the output from the face detector. Higher values correspond to increasing false positive rates.

- ◾ *Best value:* 0. A face detection algorithm should target to achieve a FPE value close to 0. The further the FPE value is from 0, the higher is the chance of invalid detections.

False Negative Error

A false negative is a face that failed to be detected by the face detector but was present in the ground truth data. This can occur due to lighting variations, head tilt, or some other visual anomaly that causes an actual face to be rejected by the classifier cascade. The false negative error (FNE) rate, which represents the average number of faces missed by the face detection system per frame, can be defined as follows.

$$FNE = \frac{\sum_{n=1}^{N} Fn}{N}$$

where N is the total number of frames being processed and Fn is the number of false negatives in the nth frame.

The values for the FNE should be interpreted as follows:

■ *Value range*. FNE can take any value greater than or equal to 0. The value 0 is assumed when there are no false negatives in the output from the face detector. Higher values correspond to increasing false negative rates.

■ *Best value:* 0. All face detection systems should target to achieve a FNE value close to 0. The further the FNE value is from 0, the higher is the chance of missed detections.

Track Match Error

The Track Match Error (TME) metric assesses the accuracy of face position. It is the average Euclidean (root square) distance between the location of a face in the output from the face detector and the corresponding face in the ground truth data (see Figure 3.12). If correspondences are not being output by the face detector and/or ground truth data, a simple alternative is to generate correspondences on a frame-by-frame basis when computing the TME. This can be accomplished as follows:

■ For each face rectangle in a frame from the ground truth data, find a corresponding face rectangle in same frame from the face detector output by choosing the face rectangle that is the closest based on the centroids of the rectangles.

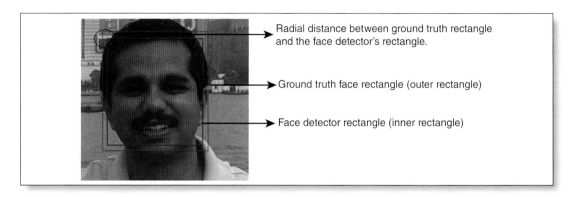

Figure 3.12 Viewer Matching Between Face Detection Data and Ground Truth Data Using Radial Distance

■ If no such unique correspondence can be found, then the face is designated as not having a correspondence and the face is ignored for TME computation purposes. Such failed correspondences will not be represented in the TME, but will result in a higher FNE rate.

The TME can therefore be computed as follows:

$$TME = \frac{\sum\limits_{n=1}^{N} \sum\limits_{i=1}^{On} Dni}{\sum\limits_{n=1}^{N} On}$$

where N is the total number of frames being processed, On is the total number of objects matched in the nth frame, and Dni is the Euclidean distance between the ith matched object in the nth frame. Lower values of the TME should be interpreted as more accurate face position estimation and tracking. The values for the TME metric should be interpreted as follows:

■ *Value range.* TME can take any value from 0 to D, where D is the diagonal dimension of the input video frame being processed. The value 0 is assumed when the face detector's output rectangles exactly match the ground truth output positions. This is the perfect tracking scenario. The value D is assumed when the face detector's output positions or tracks are offset from the ground truth output tracks by the maximum possible distance.

■ *Best value:* 0. All face detection and tracking systems should target to achieve a TME value close to 0.

Metrics for Additional Metadata

As we described earlier, additional data such as gender, age, ethnicity, and emotion can be determined for a face using the same Viola-Jones object detection framework. The accuracy of these additional parameters can be determined in a manner similar to the TME. For example, a gender match error (GME) could be used to assess how accurately the face detection system assigns gender to a particular face as follows:

$$GME = \frac{\sum\limits_{n=1}^{N} \sum\limits_{i=1}^{On} Gni}{\sum\limits_{n=1}^{N} On}$$

where N is the total number of frames being processed, On is the total number of objects matched in the nth frame, Gni is 0 if gender match happened for the ith object in the nth frame and 1 otherwise.

The values for the GME should be interpreted as follows:

■ *Value range.* GME can take any value from 0 to 1. The value 0 is assumed when the face detector's gender output exactly matches the ground truth gender output. This is the perfect gender detection scenario. The value 1 is assumed when for each face the face detector assigns gender differently from the corresponding assignment in the ground truth data.

■ *Best value:* 0. All face detectors with gender capabilities software should target to achieve a GME value close to 0. The further the GME value is from 0, the higher is the error in gender detection.

A similar approach could be used to detect age, ethnicity, and emotion error rates by simply substituting the Gni in the numerator from the GME equation with an appropriate value for the desired metric. Other application specific metrics can be measured in a similar manner as long as the ground truth data captures the desired information.

Summary

Face detection is an important enabling technology for many intelligent systems such as security applications, video cameras, and hands-free user interfaces. In this chapter we discussed the Viola-Jones object detection algorithm and how it could be used for the specific task of detecting frontal human faces as well as gender, age, ethnicity, and emotion. We also presented a variety of practical metrics that could be used to assess the performance of a face detector implementation and how to generate test videos and corresponding ground truth data.

Chapter 4

Object Detection Algorithms and Optimization

Try to learn something about everything and everything about something.

—Thomas Henry Huxley

Object detection is an important area of computer vision since it enables a variety of intelligent applications such as video surveillance and image retrieval. In the previous chapter we described the Viola-Jones object detection framework and showed how it could be used to solve the specific problem of frontal human face detection. In this chapter we describe an alternative object detection technique that is more suitable for detecting other classes of objects such as people, vehicles, and animals. We will also describe how the object detection algorithm can be optimized using advanced instruction sets found in many new processors.

Histogram of Gradients

The Histogram of Gradients, or HoG algorithm (Dalal 2006) is a popular and reliable object detection algorithm that can be used to detect objects such as cars, buildings, people, and animals from an image. The algorithm particularly classifies object into different classes such as humans or nonhumans, cars or non-cars, and so on. The algorithm takes a trained model for a specific object along with a test image as input, and the output is a set of bounding boxes representing areas of the image that contain positive (detected) objects. The algorithm relies on the simple observation that an object's appearance and shape can often be characterized rather well by the distribution of local intensity gradients or edge directions, even without precise knowledge of the corresponding gradient or edge positions. In practice this is implemented by dividing the image window into small spatial regions or cells, and for each cell accumulating a local 1-D histogram of gradient directions or edge orientations over the pixels of the cell. The combined histogram entries represent the features or descriptors used by the HoG algorithm. For better invariance to illumination or shadowing it is also useful to contrast-normalize the local responses before using them. This can be done by accumulating a measure of local histogram "energy" over somewhat larger spatial regions ("blocks") and using the results to normalize all of the cells.

Figure 4.1 shows the block diagram of the HoG algorithm, and Figure 4.2 represents the flow diagram of the algorithm. The input image is divided into a number of windows, and HoG descriptors are calculated for each window. These descriptors are passed through the linear SVM classifier. The classifier then checks the descriptors and detects if any objects are present in the window. The core of the algorithm is the computation of HoG descriptors, so we will describe each of the steps in more detail.

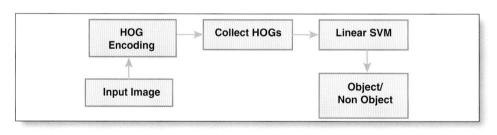

Figure 4.1   Block Diagram for the Histogram of Gradients Object Detection Algorithm

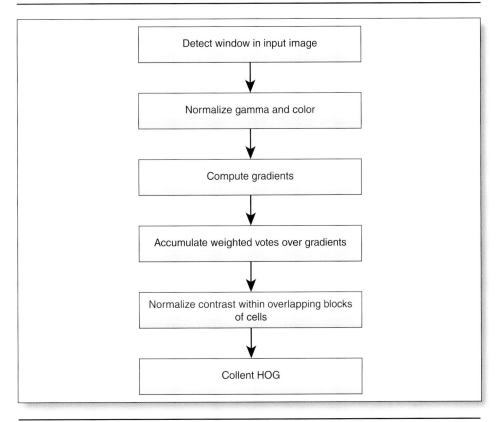

Figure 4.2   Flow Diagram for the Histogram of Gradients Object Detection Algorithm

Step A: Normalization of Gamma and Color

Global image normalization is applied to the image to reduce the influence of illumination effects. Gamma (power law) compression shown in Figure 4.3 is used, either by computing the square root or the log of each color channel. For practical implementations, computing the square root of each color channel is preferred. Note however that this step is optional as it only has a modest effect on performance.

Step B: Compute Gradients

First order image gradients are computed in this step as shown in Figure 4.4. Locally dominant color channel will be used for computation of the gradients. These gradients capture contour, silhouette, and some texture information, while

Figure 4.3   Gamma Compression and Normalization

providing further resistance to illumination variations. After the gradients are computed in X and Y directions, they are converted into a polar coordinate system.

For an image represented by an array A, in which each element of the array corresponds to the gray level of an image, the pixel values will range from 0 to 255 for an eight-bit per pixel image. The gradient is the change in gray level with direction. This can be calculated by taking the difference in value of

Figure 4.4   Compute Gradients

neighboring pixels. Let us construct a new array B that contains the values of the gradient from A.

The horizontal gradient is formed by taking the differences between column values:

$$B(j, k) = A(j, k + 1) - A(j, k)$$

where j represents the pixel location in horizontal direction and k represents the pixel location in vertical direction.

This can be represented by a filter array as shown below:

-1	1

A problem with this filter is that the location of the gradient in the array B is shifted somewhat to the left. With an even number of pixels in the computation it is impossible to locate the result in the center of the cells used to produce it. It is therefore most common to use an odd number of cells. This can be accomplished by doing the calculation over cells that are separated by step:

$$B(j, k) = A(j, k + 1) - A(j, k - 1)$$

This can be represented by the array shown below:

−1	0	1

However, this method is sensitive to noise and small fluctuations in image luminance. The effect of noise can be reduced by averaging the gradient calculations over the orthogonal direction.

We have represented the horizontal gradient computation by the mask

−1	0	1

Vertical averaging can be obtained by adding rows to the mask.

−1	0	1
−1	0	1
−1	0	1

The result produced by using the weights in the mask is placed in the location that is indexed by the center cell. The same logic is used for gradient computation in vertical direction.

The 3 × 3 mask is a basic form that can have many variations by changing the weights in the cells. Some of the popular gradient operators based on this form are shown in Table 4.1. The gradients can be computed by using Gaussian smoothing followed by applying some of the popular gradient masks listed in the table.

Table 4.1   Popular Gradient Operators

Uncentred	[−1, 1]
Centred	[−1, 0, 1]
Cubic Corrected	[1, −8, 0, 8, −1]

3 × 3 Sobel Masks	$[-1\ 0\ 1]$
	$[-2\ 0\ 2]$
	$[-1\ 0\ 1]$
2 × 2 Diagonal Masks	$[-1, 0]$
	$[0, 1]$

As per the results obtained by author of the algorithm (Dalal 2006). Using larger masks seems to decrease the performance, and smoothing damages it significantly. Hence, a simple 1-D mask $[-1, 0, 1]$ will be used without Gaussian smoothing.

Step C: Accumulate Weighted Votes for Gradients Orientation Over Spatial Cells

A dense grid of overlapping windows is taken over the image as shown in Figures 4.4 and 4.5. The further processing is done on each of these windows. Also a dense grid of overlapping *blocks* (groups of cells) is taken over the

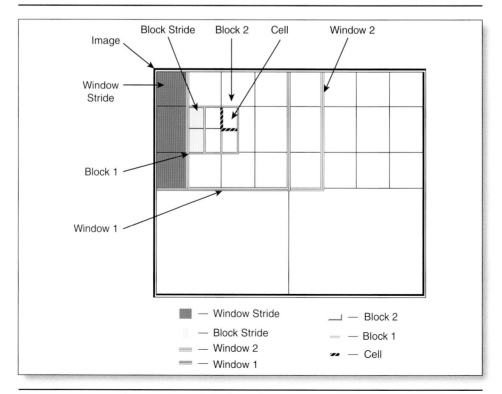

Figure 4.5   Window Stride and Block Stride

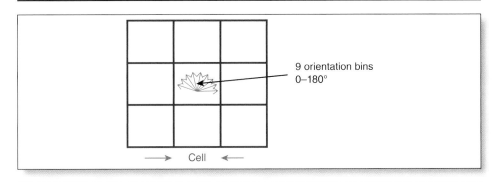

Figure 4.6   Cell and Orientation Bins

window. Using a block consisting of 3 × 3 cells, each of size 6 × 6 pixels, and a block consisting of 2 × 2 cells, each of size 8 × 8 pixels, gives the best performance. Here, the blocks of 2 × 2 cells, each of size 8 × 8 pixels will be used. The values to be considered as default values are: Window Size: 64 × 128 pixels, Window Stride: 8 pixels horizontal and 8 pixels vertical and Block Stride: 8 pixels horizontal and 8 pixels vertical.

Orientation Binning

An encoding that is sensitive to local image content while remaining resistant to small changes in poses or appearance is produced. The image window is divided into small spatial regions, called *cells*. For each cell we accumulate a local 1-D histogram of gradient or edge orientations over all the pixels in the cell. This combined cell-level 1-D histogram forms the basic *orientation histogram* representation. Each orientation histogram divides the gradient angle range into a fixed number of predetermined bins. The gradient magnitudes of the pixels in the cell are used to vote into the orientation histogram.

As per the results obtained by the authors of the algorithm (Dalal 2006), the bins spaced over signed gradients (angularly ranging from 0° through 360°) decreases the performance as compared to the bins spaced over unsigned gradients (angularly ranging from 0° through 180°). Hence the bins spaced over 0°–180° will be considered. Also increasing the number of bins improves the performance significantly up to 9 bins, but makes little difference beyond this. Hence 9 orientation bins in 0°–180° will be considered.

Step D: Normalize Contrast within Overlapping Block of Cells

In this step, the HOG descriptors from all the blocks of a dense overlapping grid of blocks covering the detection window are collected and are combined to form a feature vector as shown in Figure 4.7 for use in the window classifier (linear-SVM classifier). The bins of histogram of cells in each block are normalized by using an accumulated value of local histograms over all the cells in the block. The normalized block descriptors are referred to as the Histogram of Oriented Gradient (HOG). This normalization introduces better invariance to illumination, shadowing, and edge contrast. Although each cell is shared between various blocks, the normalized value of it in each block is different because of the trilinear interpolation of the pixel weight into the special orientation histogram. If h be the histogram with inter-bin distance (bandwidth) b, $h(X)$ denotes the value of the histogram for the bin centered at X. If the weight W is interpolated at point X into the histogram, and if X1 and X2 are the two nearest neighboring bins of the point X such that $X1 \leq X < X2$, linear interpolation distributes the weight W into the two nearest neighbors as follows:

$$_h(X1) \leftarrow {}_h(X1) + w\left(1 - \frac{x - X1}{b}\right)$$

$$_h(X2) \leftarrow {}_h(X1) + w\left(\frac{x - X1}{b}\right)$$

The cell thus appears several times in the final output vector with different normalizations.

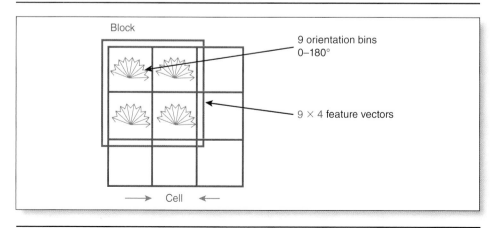

Figure 4.7   Block Used for Normalization

As per the results obtained by the authors of the algorithm (Dalal 2006) best results are obtained with the L2Hys (Lowe-style clipped L2 norm) Block Normalization. Hence L2Hys normalization will be used.

Feature Vector

The HOG descriptors from all the blocks of a dense overlapping grid of blocks covering the detection window are collected and are combined to form a feature vector for use in the window classifier as shown in Figure 4.8 (linear-SVM classifier).

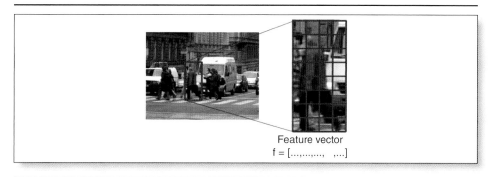

Feature vector
f = [...,...,..., ,...]

Figure 4.8   Feature Vector Representation for Detector Window

Training a HoG Model Using Latent SVM

In this section we describe how Latent SVM can be used to discriminately train deformable part models where the image features used for training and matching are histograms of oriented gradients. The training is performed on a set of images that contain positive marked bounding boxes on the images showing a particular object class. Many such images are given as input to the training algorithm, resulting in a trained model as output as shown in Figure 4.9. Such a trained model can be used as a classifier to detect the object instance in arbitrary images as described in the previous section.

The algorithm uses mixtures of multiscale deformable part models. The latent SVM model is trained by data mining hard negative examples. After training the model it is used for object matching. The training and matching is done using start structured part based models along with a root filter. The feature used for this purpose is HOG. The root filter is applied at each level of the multiscale pyramid and part filters are applied at twice the resolution compared to the root filter. The feature dimensions of HOG data have been reduced by taking into consideration the contrast-insensitive, contrast-sensitive,

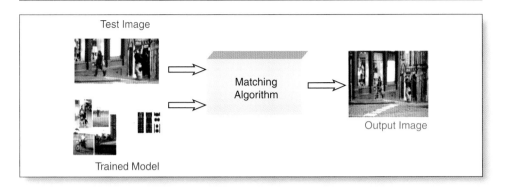

Figure 4.9   Algorithm Block Diagram

and texture features. During the training phase for each positive bounding box, the HOG features are calculated for root and part filters. A score is associated with each part position, which is called as deformation cost. The final feature vector is calculated as a concatenation of features of root filter plus features of part filters plus the deformation parameters. So, for all such positive examples Latent SVM is trained. Similar computation is applied for negative examples to get the final trained model. During the matching phase for a given test image a similar final feature vector is calculated at every scale and position of the pyramid. The SVM classifier is used to classify the given object as matching or not. Once a match is found then the bounding box for the detected instance is calculated by using root filter and part filters position. The Detailed Algorithm Diagram is shown in Figure 4.10.

Step A: Star-Structured Deformable Part Model

The Object Detection with discriminately trained deformable part models by using Latent SVM algorithm is based upon pictorial structure model. Rather than recognizing a specific object with specific orientation (detection of only side view of bicycle) pictorial structure model tries to detect entire object class (entire class of cycles with different poses). This is achieved by representing object class with parts and the connection between them. This is shown in Figure 4.11. This is achieved by assuming a star-like structure between the parts of object. Some spatial ordering is imposed on the parts in order to preserve object structure. Now we can use the parts along with a root for the description of object. The parts can be moved around keeping root filter constant.

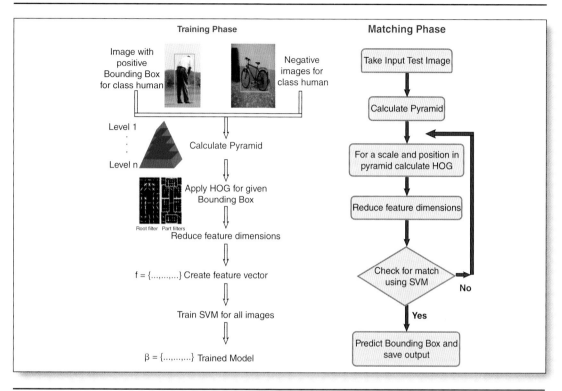

Figure 4.10 Detailed Algorithm Block Diagram

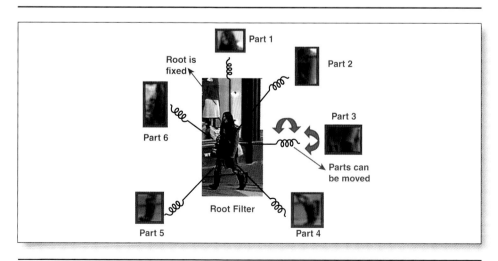

Figure 4.11 Star-Structured Deformable Part Model

Step B: Mixture Model and Intra-Class Variation

In order to take into consideration the intra-class variation (object with different poses and sizes) a multiscale pyramid approach with mixture models are used. Mixture model is a collection of more than one multiscale star model (as described above). Each such model is called as component of mixture model. Mixture model can effectively handle intra-class variation by incorporation of more information about the object model. In simpler terms, mixture models just combine different mutually exclusive information (in terms of parts, structure, and so on) about an object class puts that into an object representation.

Step C : HoG Feature

In order to take care of the variations in objects due to illuminations, object color changes, and so forth, the image data needs to be mapped into some kind of a robust feature that is invariant to such problems. The feature that is used here is called as HoG. A HoG computation follows the steps shown in Figure 4.13. The first step is to compute gradients of the input image. Gamma normalization can be performed beforehand, but it is optional. The typical mask used is a centered mask $[-1\ 0\ 1]$ and the transposition of it. Both these masks give gradient in X and Y direction. They are further converted into polar coordinates to get the orientations at particular pixels. The orientations calculated are between 0 to 360 degrees. The second step is to perform voting into orientation bins. The image is divided into blocks and cells. Cells typically contain 8×8 pixels, and four cells make one block. For each cell typically 18 orientation bins are used. The third step is normalization, which is applied to reduce local contrast effect and to make the descriptor robust. As shown in Figure 4.12, each cell is normalized four times per block. The accumulated value of orientation bins is used for normalization. Thus each cell will give 72 HoG descriptors. In order to reduce the dimensionality of the vector, a 31-dimensional vector will finally be computed by using 9 contrast-insensitive, 18 contrast-sensitive, and 4 texture sensitive features.

Step D: Multiscale Pyramid Approach

The procedure of calculating a feature vector is applied to the root as well as part filters in the algorithm. The root filter is applied at the coarse level of the image pyramid and part filters are applied at twice the resolution of the root

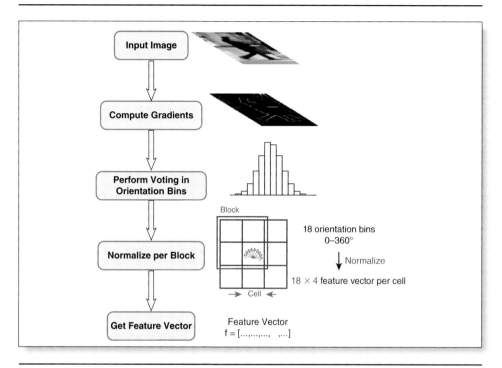

Figure 4.12 HoG Filter Calculation Steps

filters. Thus the root filter gives the initial guess at the object while part filters confirm the complete detection for the object. By applying this procedure at different scales of pyramid the objects of different sizes can be detected. For example, there are 25 levels of the pyramid. This is shown in Figure 4.13 Then root filters are calculated from 10 to 35 levels and part filters are calculated from 1 to 25 levels in the following pattern:

1, 11, 21, 31
2, 12, 22, 32
3, 13, 23, 33
4, 14, 24, 34
5, 15, 25, 35
6, 16, 26
7, 17, 27…

While scanning through the image, the root filter location is fixed and part filters can move around. Now, the root filters location can be defined

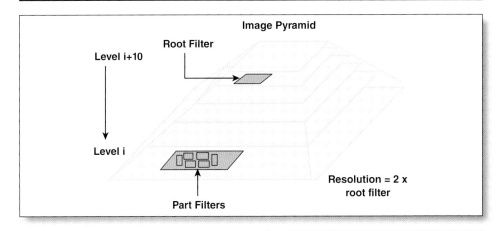

Figure 4.13 Multiscale Approach for Root and Part Filter Calculation

by $(x_1, y1, k1)$ where x, y are the positions on the kth level of pyramid. The part filters' movement is associated with a quadratic cost function. The more movement from its original position, the higher the cost. Figure 4.14 shows the typical cost function visualization. The darker the image, the lower the cost is, and vice versa. So, as the part moves away from its original location with respect to the root, the cost increases, and this cost is subtracted from the total score.

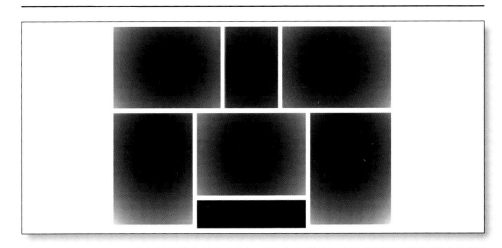

Figure 4.14 Cost Function for Part Visualization

Step E : Combining All Things Together

To get the maximum score, we need to compute the overall score of the root location with the best possible placement of the parts. In order to get a speedy solution for finding optimal part filters, a location distance transform with dynamic programming is used. The dynamic programming is a general method of solving complex problems by breaking them into overlapping subproblems. In the algorithm it is done by finding the optimal position of a part placement one by one. The generalized distance transforms are used to search all possible object configurations of a part without restricting the possible locations for each part. As shown in Figure 4.15, distance transform transforms the responses of part filters, which are then added to the root filter response to get the combined score. So, each part's optimal contribution is considered while calculating the final score.

In order to incorporate mixture models, we simply compute the models as described above and append them to the original model.

So, finally the complete description of model "feature map" is given by concatenation of the root filter's feature vector, followed by each part's feature vector, followed by deformation parameters for each part. This is shown in Figure 4.16. This representation is for one model; for a complete mixture model, each model is concatenated one after another.

Step F: The Training Procedure

For training a particular class of object, training images with marked positive bounding boxes are required. In the MATLAB implementation only two components per mixture model are considered. For handling intra-class variations, the aspect ratio of positive bounding boxes is used. The mean aspect ratio of the positive bounding boxes is considered as a decision boundary. Instances having a higher aspect ratio are grouped into one class and instances having a lower aspect ratio are grouped into a second class. The filter size in each category is considered 80 percent of largest bounding box. While in training to match the sizes of positive bounding boxes with filter size, the images are wrapped. Combine the initial root filters into a mixture model with no parts. Retain the parameters of the combined model. The part filters are initialized by interpolating the root filter to twice the spatial resolution. The parts are selected by fixing the number of parts to 6. These parts are placed one after another by selecting the highest energy regions. High energy is defined as positive weights/values in the HoG image. The parts are kept symmetric to the vertical axis or they are replicated along the vertical axis.

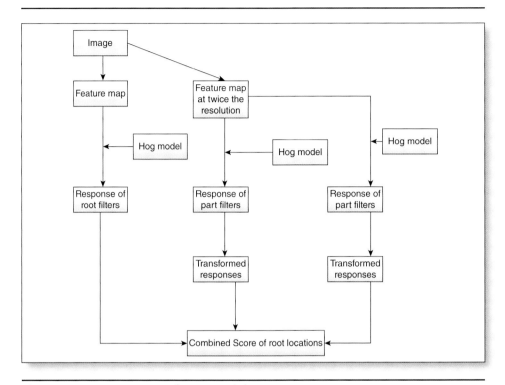

Figure 4.15 Cost Function for Part Validations

The training methodology used in the algorithm is latent SVM. For the training we get weakly labeled data as input; that is, only positive bounding boxes with no parts locations. So, the number of parts, their location size, and component label for mixture models are considered as latent (hidden) information while training. This latent information is provided during training to the algorithm. For training we are given a data set $D = (< x1, y1 > \cdots < xN, yN >)$ of N training examples. The ys are output specified such as -1 for negative examples and $+1$ for positive examples. Ultimately, the LSVM procedure will learn a linear classifier, β, from extracted feature vectors. The score of an example (positive or negative) x_i is given as

Equation 4.1:

$$f_\beta(x_i) = \max_{z \in Z(x_i)} \beta \cdot \varphi(x_i, z)$$

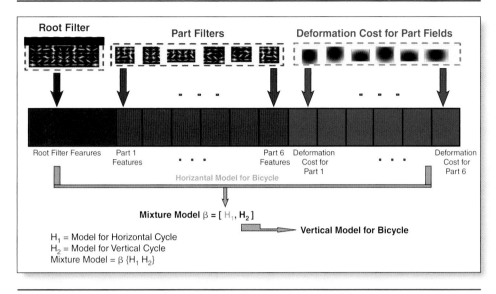

Figure 4.16 Formation of Feature Map for a Mixture Model

Here $Z(x_i)$ is the set of all valid values that the latent variables are allowed to take on, for example x_i. The function $\varphi(x_i, z)$ takes a particular setting of the latent variables z, which maximizes the above equation and computes a feature vector of the same dimension as β from the example x_i.

Let $q = \varphi(x_i, z)$.

The vector q is of same size that of β. But it is computed for a particular component in the mixture model. The entries corresponding to a particular model in q are filled and the rest of the vector is set to zero.

In the training $Z(x_i)$ is restricted to contain only one setting of the latent variables for each positive example x_i. So the solution becomes convex and we can iterate between the following steps.

1. Holding the model β fixed, solve the maximum problem in *Equation 1*. This will give the optimal latent values as output.

2. Holding the positive latent variables fixed, optimize the LSVM objective function, which is now convex in β.

For negative examples, component label and root filter locations are restricted but the part positions are unrestricted, provided they give a valid configuration. The root filters for each component are placed such that their geometric centers overlap as shown in Figure 4.17. This is done to select discriminative features for negative cases. For negative cases also Equation 4.1 is maximized and SVM is trained.

Model Update

Positive examples are the highest scoring placements with > 50 percent overlap with the bounding box. Negative examples are high scoring detections with no target object (add as many as can fit in memory).

- Train a new model using SVM

- Keep only hard examples and add more negative examples

- Iterate a number of times

Ultimately the algorithm will provide trained β as an output.

Figure 4.17 Selection of Negative Training Examples

Step G: Data Mining Hard Negative Examples

Typically a number of negative examples will be much larger than positive examples for any data set, as one negative example can be found for every nonpositive box location. In order to make the training procedure fast considering the large amount of data generated, the Data Mining Hard Negative Examples algorithm is used. For a given set of data, an SVM procedure is applied and the model is learned (Figure 4.18).

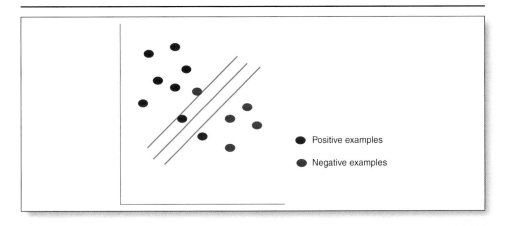

Figure 4.18 Data Mining Hard Negative Examples

The learned model is applied on the available data and the outputs are found out (Figure 4.18). After that the "hard negative" examples (that is, negative examples that score positive, or within the positive margin of the current classifier) are found out and kept for the next phase along with positive examples (Figure 4.18). The next set of data is added to it for another round of training (Figure 4.18). The new data will give another set of trained SVM classifiers as output, which is applied again on same data (Figure 4.18). This process is repeated until convergence is reached; that is, until no more hard negative vectors are found.

A stochastic gradient descent method is used to optimize β for a given data set. A learning rate α, which is based on iterations t is used for updating β. If f_β from Equation 4.1 correctly classifies the random example x_i (beyond the margin), β is shrunk by $\beta := \beta - \alpha\beta$. Otherwise β is shrunk and the scalar multiple of $\Phi(x_i, z_i)$ is added to it. The matching procedure usually returns multiple overlapping detections for each instance of an object. A greedy procedure is used for eliminating repeated detections via nonmaximum suppression, so that only local maxima are kept as a positive detection.

Optimization

This section focuses on optimization to be achieved by Intel performance primitives for Calpella and Sandy Bridge platforms. Intel® Integrated Performance Primitives (Intel® IPP) are an extensive library of multicore-ready, highly optimized software functions for multimedia, data processing, and communications applications. Intel IPP offers thousands of optimized functions covering frequently used fundamental algorithms. This chapter also contains examples about coding techniques illustrating how to take advantage of Intel® SSE and Intel® AVX for the AVA algorithms.

Optimizations Using Intel® IPP

This is achieved by integrating Intel IPP version 6.1 with selected base code. Depending upon the given platform (Calpella or Sandy Bridge), the Intel IPP library settings are configured. A suitable Intel IPP library is confirmed by calling the get_module_info() function.

In this type of optimization we will replace a block of OpenCV code with a block of optimized Intel IPP instructions. The example below shows the square root calculation.

Original Implementation

```
for( int i = 0; i < n; i++)
{
        a.val[i] = sqrt(a.val[i]);
}
for( int i = 0; i < n; i++)
{
        b.val[i] = sqrt(b.val[i]);
}
        for( k = 0; k <= n; k ++ )
            s += a.val[k] * b.val[k];
```

Possible Optimization

The above code can be directly replaced by following code:

```
ippsSqrt_32f (a, a, n);
ippsSqrt_32f (b, b, n);
        ippsDotProd_32s_32sc_Sfs (a, b, n, &s , 1)
```

Apart from the above-mentioned approaches, the following changes in the existing code without modifying the existing interfaces can be used.

Optimizations Using Intel® IPP/Intel® SSE/Intel® AVX

After generating a profiling report for Intel IPP integrated OpenCV code, further optimization can be achieved by directly calling an intrinsic for Intel SSE or Intel AVX, depending upon Calpella or Sandy Bridge platform respectively, at suitable places in the code. The Intel AVX intrinsic is supported by the Sandy Bridge platform only, so that is to be enabled as required.

Evaluating Code for SIMD Possibility

To use any of the SIMD technologies optimally, the code must be evaluated for fragments that are computationally intensive, that are executed often enough to have an impact on performance, or that have little data-dependent control flow. The code must also be evaluated for fragments that require floating-point computations, which can benefit from moving data 16 bytes at a time, those which can be coded using fewer instructions, and the ones that require help in using the cache hierarchy efficiently.

Coding Techniques

The SIMD features of Intel SSE3, Intel SSE2, Intel SSE, and MMX™ technology require new methods of coding algorithms. One of them is vectorization. Vectorization is the process of transforming sequentially executing, or scalar, code into code that can execute in parallel, taking advantage of the SIMD architecture parallelism. This section discusses the coding techniques available for an application to make use of the SIMD architecture. To vectorize code and thus take advantage of the SIMD architecture, we have to determine if the memory accesses have dependencies that would prevent parallel execution. We can "strip-mine" the inner loop to reduce the iteration count by the length of the SIMD operations (for example, four for single-precision floating-point

SIMD, eight for 16-bit integer SIMD on the XMM registers). Recoding the loop with the SIMD instructions also helps.

Coding Methodology

Coding methodology is based on the use of available intrinsics. The defined functions for Intel Streaming SIMD Extensions and Intel Streaming SIMD Extensions 2 are used for the Calpella platform. Intel AVX intrinsics are used for the Sandy Bridge platform.

The next step is to do stack and data alignment. This can be achieved by using padding to align data and using arrays to make data contiguous. The duplication and padding technique overcomes the misalignment problem, thus avoiding the expensive penalty for misaligned data access, at the cost of increasing the data size. When developing your code, you should consider this tradeoff and use the option that gives the best performance.

The following section demonstrates an example of the implementation.

Filter Convolution

This is a hotspot from the algorithm for object detecting using latent SVM, which takes around 85 to 90 percent of overall algorithm timing.

Purpose

In this algorithm, a feature map of the test image (Input A) gets convolved with a train model (Input B). The train model comprises 12 part filters and 2 root filters for a mixture model. This convolution has been done for every level of the pyramid to get a combine score for object detection as shown in Figure 4.19.

Function Description: OD_FconvProcess(thread_data *stThreadArg)

This function is implementation of convolution of part/root filters with the feature map of test image data for 31 feature dimensions.

Input

Input A buffer consists of a feature map of test image data whose dimensions are varying depending upon the levels of the pyramid. Input B buffer consists of Root/Part filter mask from train model.

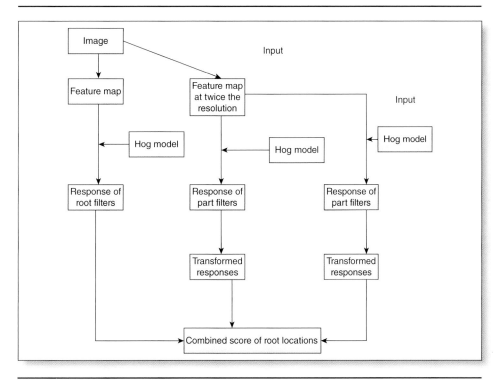

Figure 4.19 Pyramid wide Convolution

There are 2 root filters and 12 part filters whose dimensions are varying depending upon the object size and also depending upon the levels of the pyramid (for example: 5×10, 4×8, 7×10).

Output

Output C has convolution output of A and B and dimensions depend upon input data dimensions.

How Many Times Is the Filter Convolution Function Being Called?

It is called for every filter mask and each level of the pyramid.

There are 2 root filters and 12 part filters for each level of the pyramid. The number of pyramid levels varies depending upon the test image.

For example, with 31 pyramid levels this function is being called

(2 root filter + 12 part filter)* (31 pyramid levels) = 434 times (for test Image 2008_000185.jpg)

Base Code of Filter Convolution

```
void OD_FconvProcess(thread_data *stThreadArg)
{
// variables Declaration and function calls
Double *pf64A = stThreadArg->pf64A; // Feature map for test
image
Double *pf64B = stThreadArg->pf64B; // Train model from
training i.e. root or part filter
Double *pf64C = stThreadArg->pf64C; // Output of
convolution

int32 *pi32A_dims = stThreadArg->pi32A_dims; // Feature map
dimension
int32 *pi32B_dims = stThreadArg->pi32B_dims; // Train model
dimension
int32 *pi32C_dims = stThreadArg->ai32C_dims; // Output
dimension

int32 num_features = stThreadArg->pi32A_dims[2]; //HOG
Feature Dimension

/*Do convolution for 31 feature dimensions*/
for(int32 i32IndexI = 0; i32IndexI < num_features;
i32IndexI++)
{
   Double *strDst = pf64C;
//Intialize input for every feature
   Double *pf64A_src = pf64A + i32IndexI * pi32A_dims[0] *
pi32A_dims[1];
   Double *pf64B_src = pf64B + i32IndexI * pi32B_dims[0] *
pi32B_dims[1];

/*Output i32C_dims0 width and i32C_dims1 height */
   for(int32 i32IndexR = 0; i32IndexR < pi32C_dims[1];
i32IndexR++)
   {

for(int32 i32IndexC = 0; i32IndexC < pi32C_dims[0];
i32IndexC++)
{
```

```
   //Initializing variable for storing convolved output
   Double f64val = 0.0;
   /* Multiply and accumulate A and B and store results in C*/
   for(int32 i32RootRow = 0; i32RootRow < pi32B_dims[1];
i32RootRow++)
{
        /*Fetching the input A and B address locations*/
Double *pA_off = pf64A_src + ((i32IndexR + i32RootRow) *
pi32A_dims[0]) + i32IndexC;
Double *pB_off = pf64B_src + (i32RootRow * pi32B_dims[0]);
for (int32 i32RootCol = 0; i32RootCol < pi32B_dims[0];
i32RootCol++)
{
   f64val += *(pA_off++) * *(pB_off++);

   }/*End of for (int32 i32RootCol = 0; i32RootCol < pi32B_
dims[0]; i32RootCol++) */


   }/*End of for(int32 i32RootRow=0; i32RootRow<pi32B_
dims[1]; i32RootRow++)*/

*(strDst++) += f64val;  //Store output

}/*End of for(int32 i32IndexC=0; i32IndexC<pi32C_dims[0];
i32IndexC++) */


   }/*End of for(int32 i32IndexR=0; i32IndexR<pi32C_
dims[1]; i32IndexR++)*/


}/*End of for(int32 i32IndexI=0; i32IndexI<num_features;
i32IndexI++) */

   //Leaving function

}/*End of void OD_FconvProcess(thread_data *stThreadArg)*/
```

AVX Implementation

```
int32 innerloopcheck = i32B_dims0>>2;
int32 innerlooprem = i32B_dims0-innerloopcheck*4;
double setdat[4]= {0.0};
for(int i=0;i<innerlooprem;i++ )
```

```
{
   setdat[i]=1;
}
/*msetdata is used to multiply with the remainder part*/
__m256d msetdata = _mm256_loadu_pd(setdat);

/*Do convolution for 31 feature dimensions*/
for(i32IndexI = 0; i32IndexI < num_features; i32IndexI++)
{
strDst = pf64C;
pf64A_src = pf64A + i32Base_A;
pf64B_src = pf64B + i32Base_B;
/*Output i32C_dims1 width and i32C_dims0 height */
for(i32IndexR = 0; i32IndexR < i32C_dims1; i32IndexR++)
{
   for(i32IndexC = 0; i32IndexC < i32C_dims0; i32IndexC++)
//Point 1
   {
   Double dtemp[4] = {0.0};
   totalsum = _mm256_set1_pd(0.0);
   f64val = 0;
   i32RootRow = 0;
   int32 i32IndexAdimRR = (i32IndexR  * i32A_dims0);
   int32 i32BdimRR = 0;

   while(i32RootRow < i32B_dims1)
   {
   pA_off = pf64A_src + i32IndexAdimRR + i32IndexC;
   pB_off = pf64B_src + (i32BdimRR);
   i32RootRow++;
   __m256d sum=_mm256_set1_pd(0.0);
   m256f64val = _mm256_set1_pd(0.0);

   for(offset=0;offset<=i32B_dims0-4;offset+=4)    //Point 2
   {
m256f64val = _mm256_add_pd( m256f64val,(_mm256_mul_pd(_
mm256_loadu_pd(pA_off+offset),
_mm256_loadu_pd(pB_off+offset)))));
   }

m256f64val =
_mm256_add_pd(m256f64val,_mm256_mul_pd(msetdata,(_mm256_mul_
pd(_mm256_loadu_pd(pA_off+offset),
_mm256_loadu_pd(pB_off+offset)))));          //Point 3

   sum =
```

```
_mm256_add_pd(m256f64val,_mm256_permute2f128_
pd(m256f64val,m256f64val,1));

   totalsum =_mm256_add_pd(totalsum,_mm256_add_pd (sum,_
mm256_shuffle_pd(sum, sum, 1)));

i32IndexAdimRR += i32A_dims0;
i32BdimRR       += i32B_dims0;

}/*End of while loop*/
   _mm_store_sd(dtemp,_mm256_castpd256_pd128(totalsum));
   f64val+=(dtemp[0]);
   *(strDst++) += f64val;

   }/*End of for(int32 i32IndexC=0; i32IndexC<pi32C_
dims[0]; i32IndexC++) */

   }/*End of for(int32 i32IndexR=0; i32IndexR<pi32C_
dims[1]; i32IndexR++)*/
i32Base_A += i32MulAdim;
i32Base_B += i32MulBdim;
}/*End of for(int32 i32IndexI=0; i32IndexI<num_features;
i32IndexI++) */
```

Chapter **5**

Optical Flow and Patch Recognition

The power of accurate observation is frequently called Cynicism by those who don't have it.

— George Bernard Shaw

This chapter provides the reader with a practical guide for implementing optical flow algorithms such as Lucas Kanade (Lucas and Kanade 1981) for Feature Tracking. In this chapter we first describe the Lucas Kanade algorithm and then we move to patch recognition.

Optical Flow Algorithms

Optical flow is the pattern of apparent motion of objects, surfaces, and edges in a visual scene caused by the relative motion between an observer (an eye or an optical sensor such as a camera) and the scene. The analysis of scenes containing moving objects is complex since temporal variations in intensity needs to be considered. In order to track this moving object(s) through these images, we can employ various methods such as feature tracking and segmentation.

Some of the popular optical flow algorithms are Lucas Kanade, Horn and Schunck (1980), and Proesmans et al. (1994). Lucas Kanade is based on the assumption that the optical flow is constant in an area surrounding the pixel under consideration and solves the basic optical flow equations for all the pixels in that neighborhood by calculating the least squares. It is also less sensitive to image noise. Overall the Lucas Kanade algorithm provides good performance and is widely implemented. The other optical flow algorithm is the one developed by Horn and Schunck, which is based on the assumption that only considering neighboring points is not enough to calculate the optical flow, and that image brightness also plays an important factor. This algorithm did not become popular because it is very sensitive to noise as compared to Lucas Kanade. The other algorithm is the one that is proposed by Proesmans et al. This algorithm is similar to Horn and Schunck. The algorithm is based on using an image matching process while calculating the constraint equation. It also has a method for dealing with discontinuous flows. It performs fairly well and has good tolerance to noise, but might not be as popular as Lucas Kanade.

Lucas Kanade Implementation

Lucas Kanade is a very famous and widely used computer vision algorithm used for tracking features between images using the principle of feature tracking. Feature tracking is one of the methods used to detect motion between images. A feature, or a point of interest, is a point or a set of points where an algorithm can look and follow the motion through frames. There are several ways to select the features. They can be based on color and brightness or based on corner and edge detection. The specific features that are chosen are based upon the specific algorithm. The algorithm is coded using OpenCV, which is an open sourced computer vision library originally developed by Intel that is geared towards real-time capture, video file import, basic image treatment such as brightness, contrast, threshold, object and blob detection. In this section we discuss the algorithm in detail.

Figure 5.1 describes the basic flow for feature tracking. The input is a grayscale image that is decoded from input video. Good features to track block identifies the features to be tracked. Features (which are also known as corners) are found by computing second order derivatives of the image intensities and later by computing the needed eigenvalues. The algorithm follows two approaches for finding features: the approach of Harris, and that of Shi and Tomasi. (Proesmans et al. 1994). Either of the approach then returns list of the points/features. The stronger features are identified by finding the minimum distance between them. This integer corner location is passed to sub pixel

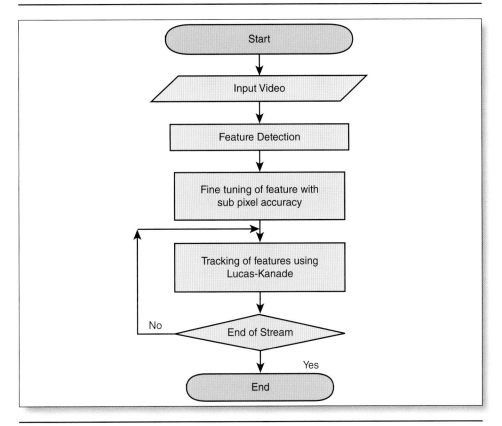

Figure 5.1 Feature Tracking Flow Diagram

accuracy and a refined set of corner location is obtained as an output. Motion tracking is done using the Optical Flow Pyramid LK algorithm.

The Feature Detection and Tracking Algorithm is divided into three submodules. They are, Good Features to Track, which will identify the good feature point to be tracked. Then this feature point is fine-tuned in the Subpixel Accuracy module.

Then the fine-tuned points are used for tracking of the feature. The detailed explanations of the three modules are given below.

I. Selecting Good Features for Tracking

This algorithm is processed frame level. It takes input as current input frame and gives output as detected features which are suitable for tracking for next frames. The features are the locations of pixels expressed in x and y coordinates. The output features generated by this algorithm are single precision floating point.

Steps involved are:

1. Calculation of eigenvalue by Harris or Shi and Tomasi method.

2. Calculation of threshold for noise removal

3. Applying dilation

4. Sorting of the features using quick sort algorithm

5. Calculation of the strongest features by comparing with the allowable minimum distance between two features

II. Fine-Tuning with Subpixel Accuracy

The following steps are used for fine-tuning the good feature. The input image is a single-channel, 8-bit, grayscale image. The corners structures contain the integer pixel location obtained from the routine cvGoodFeaturesToTrack(). Count holds the number of corners.

1. Determine the size of window (here it is window width = 10, window height = 10), then the search area is $10 \times 2 + 1 = 21$ pixels wide.

2. Calculate Mask. The size of Mask is 21×21.

3. Fine-tune the corners by extracting a rectangle and applying subpixel accuracy.

4. Calculate the derivative for both horizontal and vertical component.

5. Calculate the gradient for each feature and find out the inverse matrix.

6. After a set number of iterations, if the feature satisfies the criteria it will be accepted, otherwise rejected.

III. Feature Tracking Using Lucas Kanade Optical Flow

The fine-tuned points are then sent to Lucas Kanade Optical pyramid tracker module for tracking of the feature. The function cvCalcOpticalFlowPyrLK calculates the optical flow between two images for the given set of points. The function finds the flow with subpixel accuracy. Both parameters *pyrA* and *pyrB* comply with the following rules: if the image pointer is 0, the function allocates the buffer internally, calculates the pyramid, and releases the buffer after processing. Otherwise, if the image is large enough, the function calculates the pyramid and stores it in the buffer unless the flag CV_LKFLOW_PYR_A [B] _READY is set. After the function call, both pyramids are calculated and the ready flag for the corresponding image can be set in the next call. The function internally executes the Lucas Kanade optical flow algorithm. Both of the input images, that is, the current and previous frames, will get down-sampled as shown in the Figure 5.2. So the function is executing following the algorithm steps (Figure 5.3):

- ■ Process input current frame and previous frame.

- ■ Down-sample the image into various levels.

- ■ Set window size for each feature within the level of frame.

- ■ Apply subpixel accuracy for a set number of iterations for each feature.

- ■ Compare determinant with epsilon and select it as updated feature for current frame.

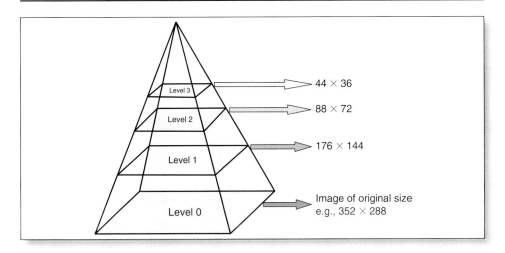

Figure 5.2 Optical Flow Pyramid

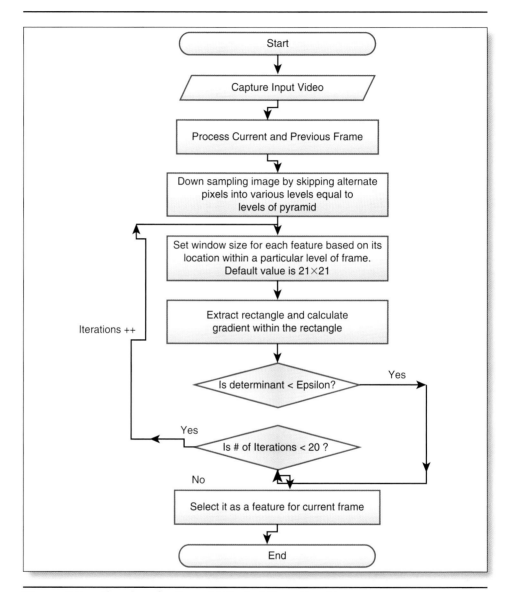

Figure 5.3   Flowchart for Pyramid Optical Flow Algorithm

Algorithm Accuracy Checker

The accuracy of the LK algorithm can be verified using Track Matching Error (TME). For calculating the Track Matching Error, we have track length of each feature (number of frames a particular feature was tracked). The TME is the average Euclidean distance (Euclidean distance is the root of square differences

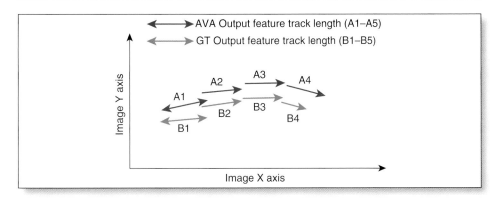

Figure 5.4   A Typical Example of AVA Data and GT Data After Matching Shown Pictorially

between coordinates of a pair of objects) of track length between the optimized and unoptimized code. The smaller the TME, the better the accuracy of the optimized code will be. Figure 5.4 shows the trajectory of a particular feature (locations of the feature over a sequence of frames, until it exists) for optimized and unoptimized code.

Patch Recognition

Even though feature point recognition is an important aspect of object detection, another equally important algorithm is the one based on patch-based object recognition. The principle of the algorithm is to build affine-invariant descriptors of local image patches and then to compare them across test images. The advantage of using affine-invariant descriptors is that it can be used to compare images even if the images are not in the same position/direction as the test image.

But before we do the matching, we have to perform an offline training phase during which multiple views of the patches to be matched are used to train randomized trees. Intensity-based comparison is carried out. One of the approaches can be to replace the tree by nonhierarchical structures that we refer to as *ferns* to perform the classification the patches.

Ferns Algorithm

The Ferns algorithm can be one way to perform patch recognition. In this section we are going to use it to perform logo detection. The algorithm can be split into two parts. The first phase is the training phase. During the training phase we train the algorithm by exposing it to various image patches and then during the testing phase we pass that test patch through this trained algorithm, which will classify the patch. The algorithm is explained in detail below.

Creating the Training Model

Figure 5.5 shows the training phase of the algorithm.

The training model is generated using logo images. These images are called as *model* images. Training starts by selecting a subset of the key points detected on these model images. This is done by applying different transformations like

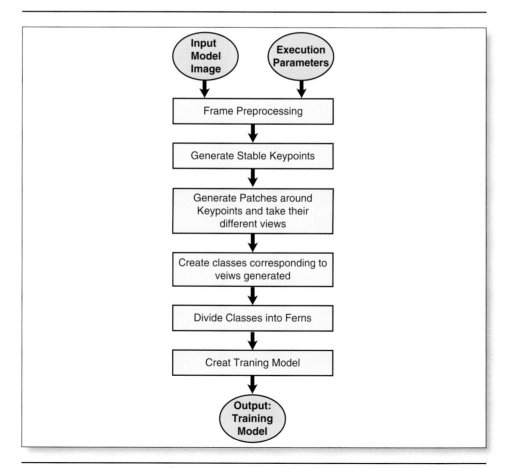

Figure 5.5   Generation of Training Model

blurring using Gaussian filter and affine transformation on the images many times, applying the key point detector, and keeping track of the number of times the same key point is detected. The key points that are found most often are assumed to be the most stable and retained. These stable key points are assigned a unique class number.

The training set for each class is formed by generating thousands of sample images with randomly picked affine deformations by sampling the deformation parameters from a uniform distribution, adding Gaussian noise to each sample image, and smoothing with a Gaussian filter of size 7×7. This increases the robustness of the resulting classifier to runtime noise, especially when there are features that compare two pixels on a uniform area.

The two main sections of training module are:

1. Generation of key points, which is explained in the section "Object Recognition"

2. Formation of classifier, which is in the section "Formation of Classes under Training"

Once the training model is generated, the same model is used to identify objects in the subsequent frames of the input video.

Object Recognition

With the help of model image, training model is generated. When the test image is provided as input, key points on the object frame are identified. Patches are generated around these key points. Therefore, given the patch surrounding a key point detected in an image, we assign it to the most likely class by using a set of binary features that will be calculated over the patch we are trying to classify. We will find the best match class for which we will calculate the homography matrix. Based on the homography, we will plot the points detected in the object frame (see Figure 5.6).

A homography matrix (HM) is, let's say, a 3×3 matrix that relates the pixels coordinates in the two images that we are comparing. So if we have an image with a point A and another image with a point B, then the relation is $B = HM \times A$. When this formula is applied to every pixel of image 2, then this image is the warped version of image 1.

Before the images can be used for training or testing purposes, they have to be preprocessed as described below.

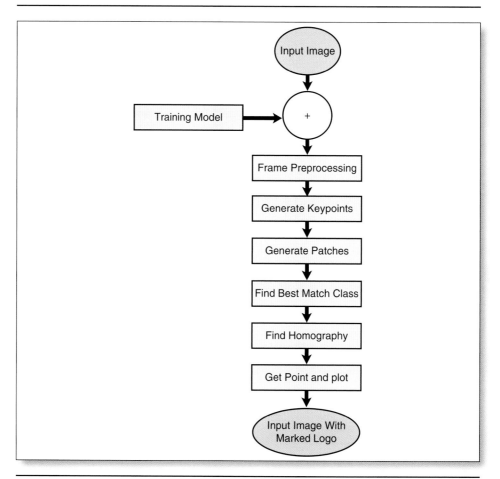

Figure 5.6   Finding Objects Using Homography

Frame Preprocessing

Application of a Gaussian filter and building an image pyramid are the two preprocessing techniques applied on both training frame and the input frames. Addition of Gaussian noise increases the robustness of the classifier to runtime noise, especially when there are features that compare two pixels on a uniform area. An image pyramid is used to form the different scaling levels of the image so that the key points are detected on every level, which results in scale-invariant key points (see Figure 5.7).

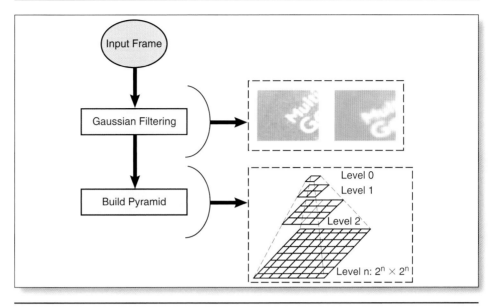

Figure 5.7 Frame Preprocessing

Key Point Generation

This section takes a different pyramid layer of the first frame as the input, along with the coordinates of the ROI in the same. The flow of events is shown in Figure 5.8

Training starts by selecting a subset of the key points detected on these model images. This is done by applying blurring and affine matrix on the images many times, applying the key point detector, and keeping track of the number of times the same key point is detected. The key points that are found most often are assumed to be the most stable and retained. These stable key points are assigned a unique class number. The training set for each class is formed by generating thousands of sample images with randomly picked affine deformations by sampling the deformation parameters from a uniform distribution, adding Gaussian noise to each sample image, and smoothing with a Gaussian filter of size 7×7 (see Figure 5.9). This increases the robustness of the resulting classifier to runtime noise, especially when there are features that compare two pixels on a uniform area.

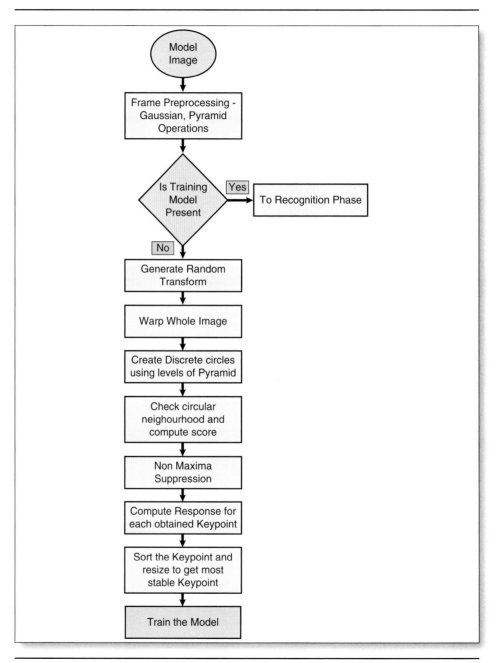

Figure 5.8   Generation of Key Points

Figure 5.9 New Views of a Key Point Detected in a Training Image Synthesized Using Warping and Affine Transformations

Mathematically, a warp-affine function applies an affine transform to an image by making use of a transformation matrix M, as defined by:

$$dst(x,y) = src(M11x + M12y + M13, M21x + M22y + M23)$$

For a given point in the training image, if the surface can be assumed to be locally planar, a new view of its neighborhood can be synthesized by warping using an affine transformation, that approximates the actual homography:

$$(n - n0) = A(m - m0) + t$$

Where $m0$ are the coordinates of the key point detected in the training image, $n0$ are the coordinates of the patch center, and n the new coordinates of the warped point m. The matrix A can be decomposed as:

$$A = R_\theta R^{-1}_\phi S R_\phi$$

where R_θ and R_ϕ are two rotation matrices respectively parameterized by the angles θ and φ, and $S = \text{diag} [\lambda_1, \lambda_2]$ is a scaling matrix; $t = [t_u; t_v]^t$ is a 2D translation vector. The view set is created by generating the views corresponding to a random sampling of the space of the $(\theta; \Phi; \lambda_1, \lambda_2; t_u; t_v)$ parameters.

The basic idea of key-point detection is to consider the intensities along a circle centered on each candidate key point. The concept of getting a key point is shown in Figure 5.10. It shows that if two pixels are diametrically opposed at distance dR from the center point m, then m is the key point only when intensity of these three pixels are different. Indeed, for points in a uniform area or along an edge, one can always find such a pair of diametrically opposed pixels. Therefore we scan the circle doing tests of type:

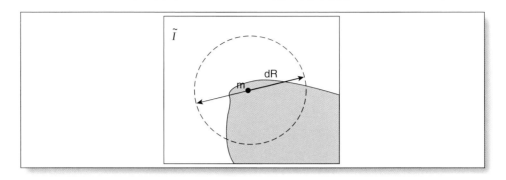

Figure 5.10 Key Point Detection Principle
SOURCE: Vincent Lepetit Pascal Fua

If $|\hat{I}(m) - \hat{I}(m + dR\alpha)| <= + \tau$ and
If $|\hat{I}(m) - \hat{I}(m - dR\alpha)| <= + \tau$ then m is not a key point

Where $dR_\alpha = (Rcos_\alpha; Rsin_\alpha)$, R being a chosen radius and varying in the range $[0; \pi]$. In practice we have to compare not only the diametrically opposed pixels but also their neighbors, to avoid responses near edges, as seen in Figure 5.11. Usually, non-key points are rejected very quickly, without scanning the whole circle.

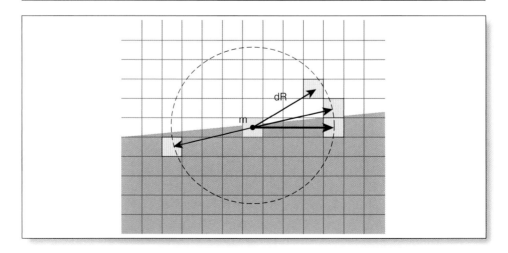

Figure 5.11 Neighborhood Comparison
SOURCE: Vincent Lepetit Pascal Fua

Formation of Classes under Training

This section takes the pyramid image of the object frame and key points generated in the previous step as input, along with the coordinates of the ROI in the model frame (see Figure 5.12). Preprocessing is done on the input in order to initialize the feature vectors with the random values. Further, random transform matrix is generated, which is used to perform the warp affine on the input. Using the random transformation matrix, we perform a affine and warping function (as described in the training section) on the image ROI in order to produce different angular rotations of the input ROI.

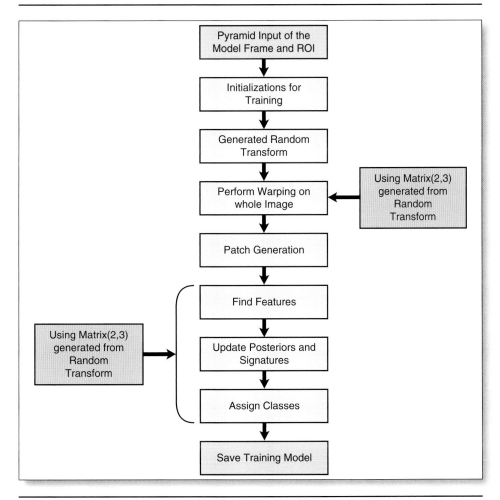

Figure 5.12 Formation of Classes

In the next step, patches are generated around the key points calculated previously. Generation of the patches is followed by finding features on these patches and updating of posterior probabilities and signatures for each class.

The features are grouped into M groups of size $S = N/M$. These groups are what we define as *ferns* and we compute the joint probability for features in each fern.

The conditional probability becomes:

Equation 5.1

$$P (f_1, f_2, \ldots f_N \mid C = c_i) = \prod_{k=1}^{N} P(f^k \mid C = c^i)$$

where $Fk = \{f(k,1), f(k,2), \ldots, f(k,S)\}$, $k = 1, \ldots, M$ represents the kth fern and (k, j) is a random permutation function with range $1, \ldots, N$.

The training phase estimates the class conditional probabilities $P(Fm \mid C = ci)$ for each fern Fm and class ci, as described in Equation 5.2. For each fern Fm we write these terms as:

Equation 5.2

$$p_{k, c_i} = P(Fm = k \mid C = c_i)$$

These probability distributions are calculated for each class and are used for the updating of posteriors and signatures that will make each class unique from each other. Finally the training model is stored as an XML file containing the following details about each of the class:

a. General information:

- Radius
- Threshold
- Octave
- Number of Views
- Base Feature size
- Clustering Distance

b. Information about the classes:

    1.   Number of structs

    2.   Structure Size

    3.   Signature Size

    4.   Features

    5.   Posteriors

Recognition Phase

In the recognition phase, initially the key points are calculated (as described in the training section) for different octaves of the input frame followed by sorting and resizing of the obtained key points (see Figure 5.13). Further, patches are generated around each of the key points. Features are extracted from the generated patches which are used to update posteriors and signatures, through which Max Log probability and best matches are found for the patches. Thus the conditional probabilities of the input patch and that of the classes generated in the training phase are compared to find the best matching class. In further processing, key points of the training model and that of the input frame are matched based on the response of the key points followed by finding the homography between the key points.

Mathematically, homography finds perspective transformation H, between the source and the destination planes as given below.

Given,

$$p_a = \begin{bmatrix} x_a \\ y_a \\ 1 \end{bmatrix}, p'_b = \begin{bmatrix} w'x_b \\ w'y_b \\ w' \end{bmatrix}, H_{ab} = \begin{bmatrix} h_{11} & h_{12} & h_{13} \\ h_{21} & h_{22} & h_{23} \\ h_{31} & h_{32} & h_{33} \end{bmatrix}$$

then,

$$p'b = H_{ab}p_a$$

where,

$$H_{ba} = H_{-1ab}$$

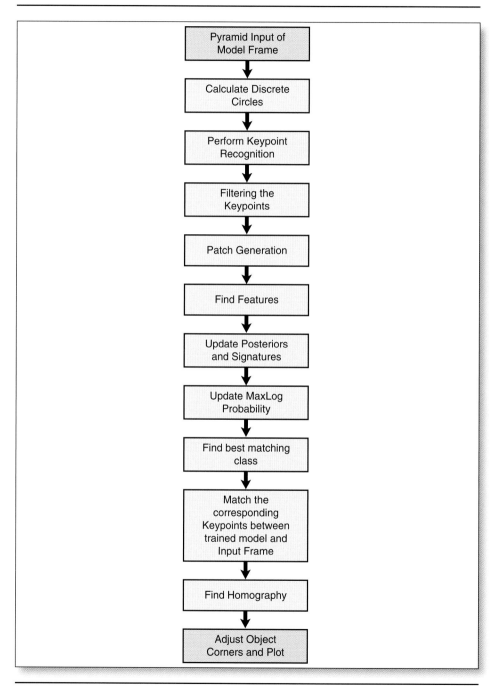

Figure 5.13 Object Recognition

Also

$$p_b = p'_b / w' = \begin{bmatrix} x_b \\ y_b \\ 1 \end{bmatrix}$$

By making use of the homography matrix, the object corners in the input frame are adjusted and plotted in the frame. At the end, a rectangle is drawn around the identified object, circles are drawn around the key points of the model and input frame and a connecting line is drawn between the object and model key points. Finally the output video file is stored in the form of an AVI file.

Checking Algorithm Accuracy

The performance analysis computation is done on the basis of how accurately the keypoints in ground truth (GT) data are matched with the key points in the logo detected output data. Figure 5.14 shows the flow of events used for checking the accuracy of the algorithm. The GT images are first marked and then the test images are compared against them. The True Positive (TP), True Negative (TN), False Positive (FP) and False Negative (FN) values for these two images are calculated. TP describes the situation where the keypoint was present in both GT and test images. TN means that key point exists in the GT image, but not in the test images. FN on other hand is the opposite of TN, it means that the key point does not exist in the GT image, but exists in the test images. Finally FP means that the keypoint does not exists in both the GT and test images. Refer to Figure 5.15 to help understand these concepts

If a pixel of "GT data" and "code output data" belong to a common area, then it is considered as a TP case. The area made up of TP cases mentioned in Figure 5.15 is shown with the green color.

If a pixel does not belong to the area of either "GT data" or "code output data," then it is considered as a TN case. The area made up of TN cases mentioned in Figure 5.15 is shown with the gray color.

If a pixel of "GT data" is not available but it is still detected in "code output data," then it is considered as an FP case. The area made up of FP cases mentioned in Figure 16.1 is shown with the blue color.

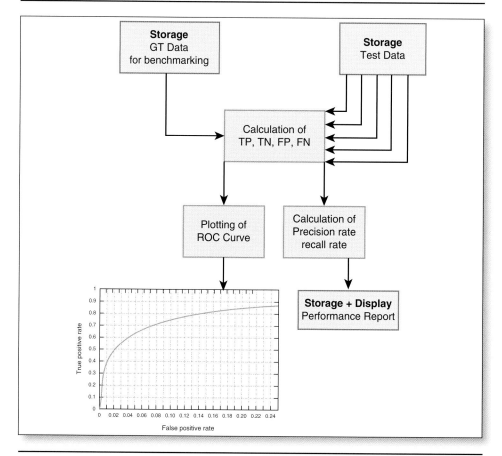

Figure 5.14 Feature Vector Representation for Detector Window

If a pixel of "GT data" is available but not detected in "code output data," then it is considered as an FN case. The area made up of FN cases mentioned in Figure 5.15 is shown with the yellow color.

The four outcomes can be formulated in a 2 × 2 *contingency table* or *confusion matrix*, as shown in Figure 5.16.

The results can be decided by following methods:

1. The pixel count will be kept for each of the TN, TP, FN and FP cases and count will be incremented on each successive occurrence of the case. These counts further use in calculations of TPR (True Positive Rate) and FPR (False Positive Rate).

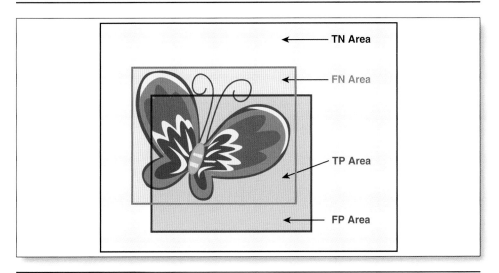

Figure 5.15 Visualization of Performance Values

Result	GT Data Available in Input	Detected data Detected In Output
TP	1	1
TN	0	0
FP	0	1
FN	1	0

Figure 5.16 Confusion Matrix

$$\text{TPR} = \frac{\text{TP}}{\text{TP} + \text{FN}}, \text{FPR} = \frac{\text{FP}}{\text{FP} + \text{TN}}$$

2. Effectiveness of the logo detection can be found by calculating overlap between the bounding boxes. The overlap area can be found by,

Area of Overlap = Area of Intersection/Area of Union of two bounding boxes.
$$= \text{area}(\text{BP} \cap \text{BGT})/\text{area}(\text{BP} \cup \text{BGT}),$$

where   BP = project code output bounding box
BGT = GT data bounding box

The higher the ratio the better is the logo detection. In Ideal cases the ratio will be equal to 1.

The precision rate and recall rate are calculated as follows,

$$P_{rate} = \frac{TP}{TP + FP}$$

$$R_{rate} = \frac{TP}{TP + FN}$$

The ROC curve will be plotted using TPR against FPR.

Chapter 6

An Overview of Data Mining

A mathematician is a device for turning coffee into theorems.

—Paul Erdos

This chapter provides an overview of the concept of data mining, various mining algorithms, as well as a privacy-preserving data mining approach. Then it describes how to implement a data mining process, including data collection, data preprocessing, tool selection, performance evaluation, and deployment. Lastly, this chapter depicts how to host and maintain data mining services in an Intel private cloud infrastructure to provision internal and external customers.

Data Mining Overview

A huge amount of data has been created due to the deployment of various information systems and the use of different web applications. Similar to the famous Moore's law, according to statistics, the scale of created data has continued to double every 18 months in the past several years. Table 6.1 shows the rough data volumes in some organizations several years ago. However, the data amount will dramatically increas in the future years along with the emergence and development of the Internet of Things (IoT). Stacy Collett, a Computerworld writer wrote "By 2020, the amount of data generated each year will reach 35 zettabytes, or about 35 million petabytes, according to market researcher IDC. That's enough data to fill a stack of DVDs reaching from the Earth to the moon and back, according to John Gantz, chief research officer at IDC. Demand will be high for IT workers with the ability to not only analyze dizzying amounts of data, but also work with business units to define what data is needed and where to get it." (Collett 2010)

Table 6.1   The Data Scale of Common Organizations

Organization	Content	Scale (per month)
Telecom company	Phone bill record	Billions
Bank	Business data	Tens of millions
Stock exchange	Daily data	Hundreds of thousands
Cigarette factory	Production data	Millions
Supermarket	Sales data	Millions
Environmental protection bureau	Pollution data	Hundreds of thousands
Search service provider	Web page	Tens of billions
E-mail service provider	Email	Tens of millions
Online retailer	Transaction	Millions

Although a huge amount of data has been collected and stored within various enterprises and organizations, they don't know how to make full use of the data to help their business. They are in the situation referred to as "rich in data, but poor in knowledge and valuable information." How to mine the nuggets from the mass business data to improve satisfaction of customers, reduce inventory, optimize manufacturing process, as well as support decision making has become a key research problem in many corporations. With this background, with the combination of traditional data analysis techniques and modern artificial intelligence, database and statistics, emerges this cross-discipline: knowledge discovery and data mining (KDD).

Knowledge discovery and data mining was first proposed at the first KDD workshop in 1989. In 1995, the first international conference on knowledge discovery and data mining sponsored by the American Association for Artificial Intelligence (AAAI) was held in Montreal, Canada, which indicated the research on KDD had entered a new stage. After that, KDD-related specialties and subjects were set up in many famous universities. And various KDD applications started to spread across a broad field of interests including finance, telecommunication, insurance, retail, sports, manufacturing, and science. With more and more

KDD application, data mining tools are increasingly prevalent. Besides data mining tools provided by the traditional statistical software vendors, such as SAS and SPSS, the main database vendors including Oracle, IBM, Microsoft, and Teradata also released their data mining tools based on their database products.

In the academic literature, there are multiple definitions for knowledge discovery and data mining. One popular definition is given by Usama M. Fayyad et al. as follows:

KDD is a nontrivial process for discovering novel, valid potentially useful and understandable patterns from a very large dataset (Fayyad et al. 1996).

From this definition, KDD has several characteristics described below.

- *A Huge Amount of Data.* KDD deals with a huge amount of data, which is one way in which KDD methods differ from previous data analysis methods. For KDD algorithms, compute complexity is a key factor, and the algorithms with high compute complexity will heavily constrain the scale of the problem.

- *Novel and Useful Patterns.* The patterns or rules discovered by KDD algorithms should not be obvious and useless. On one hand, the patterns hide in the mass data and cannot be found by simple observation or statistics. On the other hand, the patterns should be able to benefit the business, such as increase revenue, reduce cost, or improve decision making. The patterns or rules discovered by KDD algorithms are also called data mining models.

- *A Nontrivial Process.* KDD is not a magic box and cannot immediately output amazing results once fed with raw data. On the contrary, it needs a series of steps including business understanding, data understanding, data preprocessing, modeling, evaluation, and deployment. The ability of business understanding and analytics play an important role for the success of KDD.

KDD is an interdisciplinary field of study based on statistics, machine learning, databases, and so on. It has some connection with, but is also different from these disciplines.

Statistics is a main source of KDD algorithms. Many KDD algorithms, such as regression, Bayesian classifiers, and clustering are based on statistics. But KDD is significantly different from the common simple statistical queries. Simple statistical queries usually have a clear objective and can get clear results. For example, a statistical query could be "list the people having bad credit records in the database". KDD tasks usually are not explicit and cannot get definite results. For example, a KDD task could be to determine "what type of people would have bad credit records." The answers to the question are usually correct under some specified conditions and in some confidence interval, not at 100 percent.

Machine learning is another main source of KDD algorithms. Many KDD algorithms, such as rule induction method, decision tree, and artificial neural network, are from machine learning community (Mitchell 1997). Traditionally, machine learning focuses on problems with a smaller data scale and attempts to enable the machines with better intelligence through learning from cases prepared by the human. It emphasizes the completeness and convergence of the algorithms. KDD deals with a huge amount of business data, attempts to discover valuable information and knowledge to benefit the business. It focuses more on the applicability of the algorithms to mass data related and ambiguously defined problems.

On-line analytical processing (OLAP) has similar analytical objectives to KDD, finding useful knowledge or information from a dataset. But OLAP is essentially a statistical analysis from multiple dimensions, focusing on the analysis of the aggregated attributes at different granularities. It is realized by manual OLAP operations (drill down/through, roll up, slice/dice, rotate, and so on). KDD is able to analyze and model the relation among multiple attributes; it can execute automatically or semi-automatically to discover the hidden patterns from the dataset. OLAP and KDD can be combined to find the anomalies with OLAP and then to discover the causes or reasons for the anomalies with KDD algorithms.

KDD is an application-oriented subject, which has been successfully applied to many industries. Some typical KDD applications are as follows:

■ *Customer segmentation.* Partition the customers into different groups using clustering methods and then perform targeted marketing for each customer group according to its features.

■ *Customer churn prediction.* Predict the list of customers with high churn possibility through modeling the customers' behaviors and then perform targeted customer maintenance actions.

■ *Customer value analysis*. Find the potentially best (most-contributing) customers of the enterprise in order to invest the resources in these customers.

■ *Outlier analysis*. Find and analyze the outliers in the business data, which is widely used for fraud detection, protection against money laundering, tax evasion analysis, intrusion detection, and so on.

■ *Cross-selling and bundle sales*. Find the good tie-in sale among the sold products and services and then design and perform cross-selling and bundle sales policy accordingly.

■ *Personalized services*. Analyze the personal consumption or usage behaviors and discover personal distinctive consumption custom, provide personalized services or promotion.

■ *Process optimization*. Analyze the daily business data to improve production efficiency and business process, such as finding the optimal operation mode of a supply chain, the best work schedule, or the optimal production process flow.

■ *Scientific discovery*. Mining the mass scientific experimental data could lead to new scientific discovery, such as discovery of a new star, new gene and protein folding, a molecule with a good medicinal property, a relation between medicine and disease.

■ *Early warning*. Analyze the trend existing in the dataset and give early warnings of future possible events, which is often used in proactive management to prevent major issues or incidents from happening.

Data Mining Algorithms

This section describes the most popular data mining algorithms. According to the data mining tasks, they can be categorized as classification and prediction algorithms, regression algorithms, clustering algorithms, association analysis algorithms etc. Most of the algorithms described in the section are summarized from a Chinese book (Keyun Hu et al. 2008) coauthored by an author of this book.

Classification and Prediction

Classification and prediction is the most common data mining task. And many algorithms were proposed and studied in the past years, including decision tree, rule induction, neural network, Bayesian classifier, support vector machine, K nearest neighbors, and so on (Duda and Hart 1973).

Decision Tree

A decision tree is commonly used tool for decision analysis and support (Murthy 1998). Based on the concept of "divide and conquer," it learns a tree-like graph. With this graph it outputs the classification result given the inputs. A decision tree algorithm is of low complexity and can handle a high dimensional dataset. It can usually achieve very high classification accuracy and is one of the most popular data mining algorithms.

Use of a Decision Tree. Figure 6.1 is a decision tree used to predict if a person will buy a computer or not given the inputs including the person's age, credit rating, and whether the person is a student or not. For given inputs, it will match the inputs with the branches and take the value of the leaf node of the matched branch as the output. For example, given a young student, it will output as "yes," which means the person will buy a computer; given a senior whose credit rating is fair, the output is "no," which means the person will not buy a computer. It is very easy to convert the decision tree to a set of decision rules.

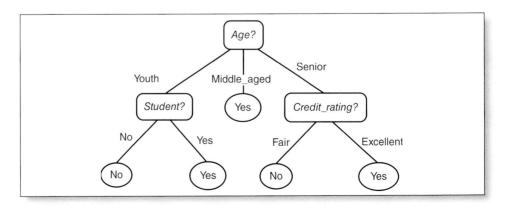

Figure 6.1   A Sample Decision Tree

Learn a Decision Tree from a Training Dataset. The decision tree algorithm learns a tree structure based on the concept of "divide and conquer." It first selects the best attribute (for example, age) to partition the training dataset into several subsets according to its values. Regarding each subset, it selects the best attribute (for example, student or credit rating) among the remaining attributes and do further partitioning. Repeat this partitioning process until reaching some stop criteria. Some stop criteria are as follows: the node only includes data having one class label, the number of cases of the node reaches the predefined minimum, or the depth of the node reaches the predefined maximum.

In a decision tree, the number of cases of each leaf node is regarded as its support. The bigger the support, the stronger the rule generated from the root to the leaf node. Strong rules have strong predictive capability. It is critical to learn a tree with an appropriate size, rather than a big and complex tree, which usually results in over-fitting. Usually a small and simple tree has better capability of generalization and prediction. To avoid over-fitting, one way is to stop its growth before a tree grows too big and complex. Another way is to prune it after a tree fully grows. An evaluation will be made regarding the tree before and after the pruning. The decision on pruning or not is made according to the evaluation result.

Regarding the selection of the best attribute, the common used methods include information gain in ID3 algorithm, gain ratio in C4.5 algorithm (Quinlan 1993), Gini coefficient in the CART algorithm (Breiman et al. 1984), and Chi-square test in the CHAID algorithm.

The decision tree algorithm can make use of both discrete and continuous attributes to partition the training dataset. Regarding continuous attributes, it finds multiple split points and splits the data range of the continuous attribute into multiple intervals with these splitters. Then each interval can be regarded as one discrete value. This is actually a discretization process.

Extension of Decision Tree. To further improve the performance of the decision tree algorithm, many extensions were proposed.

■ *Multivariable Partition.* The traditional decision tree algorithm uses one attribute for each partition, which actually partitions the training dataset vertically or horizontally. To improve the performance, a linear combination of multiple attributes could be used for partition, which means partitioning the dataset askew. But it is very hard to find the best combination of the attributes. Some heuristic methods (such as hill-climbing in the CART algorithm) are usually used for this purpose. The decision tree with multivariable partition can usually achieve higher classification accuracy than traditional decision trees, but its complexity is also much greater than traditional ones.

■ *Mass Dataset.* The traditional decision tree algorithm stores the whole training dataset in main memory, but it is not practical for a very large dataset. When the dataset is too large to be stored in main memory, the traditional algorithm has to swap the data frequently, which significantly increases the training time of the decision tree. One method to attempt to solve this problem is to sample the original dataset. Another method is to reduce the number of the scans of the data on the disk. SLIQ (Mehta, Agrawal, and Rissanen 1996) makes use of presorting and breadth first search to reduce the data scan to at the most twice for each level of the tree. It can handle much more data stored on disk.

■ *Cost Matrix.* In many cases, the costs of misclassification regarding different classes are different. For example, in disease diagnosis, misclassification of a healthy person into a patient doesn't cost much; but misclassification of a patient into a healthy person may cost a lot, perhaps losing the best treatment opportunity. A cost matrix can be used to capture such kinds of cost differences. It defines the costs of all the misclassification from each class into another. The decision tree algorithm can make use of the cost matrix for real applications by some extensions.

Artificial Neural Network

An artificial neural network (ANN) is a type of model simulating the stimulation and response mechanism of organisms. It is composed of a set of units and connections among them. Each unit simulates a neuron and is fully connected to every unit in the next layer, and each connection is attached with a weight to indicate its strength. An ANN has many different connection styles for various usages. The most commonly used is called a *feed-forward neural network*, which is a layered ANN, mainly used for classification and regression. Figure 6.2 shows an example of a feed forward ANN.

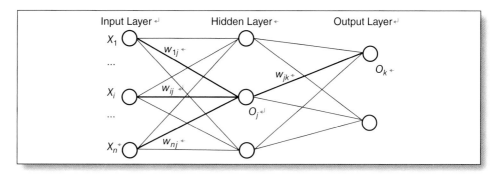

Input Layer   Hidden Layer   Output Layer

Figure 6.2   An Artificial Neural Network

Usage of a Trained ANN. If the inputs are provided to a well-trained ANN, it can calculate the output as follows. Let's discuss the calculation process with the feed-forward neural network shown in Figure 6.2.

First, the number of units in the input layer and output layer depends on the number input attributes and output attributes.

Step 1. Calculate the input of each unit except for those in the Input layer with Equation 6.1.

$$I_j = \sum_{p=1}^{n} O_p * W_{pj} + B_j \tag{6.1}$$

where I_j means the input of node j, O_p is the ouput of node x_p, W_{pj} is the weight attached to the connection between node x_p and j, B_j is the bias of node j.

Step 2. Calculate the output of each unit in each layer. The output of each unit is determined by its activation function. The most common activation function is the sigmoid function. One sigmoid function is a logistic function:

$$f(x) = \frac{1}{1 + e^{-\alpha x}} \tag{6.2}$$

where $\alpha > 0$, is a constant, determining the slope of the curves, as those shown in Figure 6.3. The data range of a logistic function is $(0, 1)$.

Another sigmoid function is a hyperbolic tangent function:

$$f(x) = \beta \frac{1 - e^{-\alpha x}}{1 + e^{-\alpha x}} \tag{6.3}$$

where $\alpha, \beta > 0$ are constants, determining the slope of the curves. The data range of a hyperbolic tangent function is $(-\beta, \beta)$.

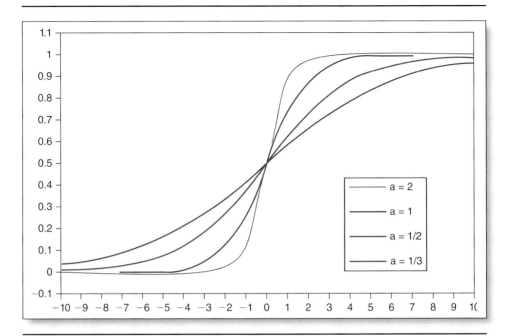

Figure 6.3   Logistic Function with Different α Parameter

Sometimes a threshold function is also used.

$$f(x) = \begin{cases} 1 & x \geq 0 \\ 0 & x < 0 \end{cases} \tag{6.4}$$

A feed-forward neural network (FNN) could have multiple hidden layers. But it is provable that a FNN with a single hidden layer can approximate any continuous functions. In real applications, a three-layer FNN is the most common FNN. Sometimes FNNs with more than three layers are also used due to network complexity, training difficulty, or over-fitting.

Training an FNN. After the determination of the network structure (number of hidden layers, number of units in each layer), the training process of the FNN is to finalize the weights attached to all the connections. The common training algorithm is the back propagation (BP) algorithm (Haykin 2001). For each training case, the BP algorithm modifies the weights so as to minimize the mean squared error between the network's prediction and the actual target value. These modifications are made in the reverse direction, that is, from the output layer back to the input layer. The training process stops after the training error is below a predefined threshold or reaching a certain number of iterations. The algorithm is summarized in Algorithm 6.1.

Algorithm 6.1: Back Propagation (BP)

1.   Determine the structure of the FNN.

2.   Initialize all the weights and biases in Net to small random numbers (for example ranging from -0.5 to 0.5).

3.   While training termination condition is not satisfied,

   For each training case:

   a.   Calculate the output of each unit from Input layer till Output layer with Equations 6.1–6.4. The selection of the activation function should be finished in advance;

   // Back propagate the errors:

   b.   For each node k in the output layer, let $E_k = O_k (1 - O_k) (T_k - O_k)$; E_k is the error for node, k, T_k is the actual value of node k;

   c.   For each unit j in the hidden layers, from the last to the first hidden layer, $E_j = O_j (1 - O_j) \sum_k E_k W_{jk}$;

   d.   For each weight W_{jk} in the network, $W_{jk} = W_{jk} + \eta * E_k O_j$, where η is the learning rate;

   e.   For each bias B_j in the network, $B_j = B_j + \eta * E_j$

■   *Number of Nodes in Hidden Layer.* Only the number of nodes in hidden layers needs to be determined since that for Input and Output layers is determined by the number of input and output variables. Till now, there is no theoretical method to determine the best number, and it is usually determined by experiences and trials. For example, we can start from two hidden nodes and gradually increase the number until reach the best performance. Or start from a larger number of hidden nodes and gradually reduce the number. Usually the number of hidden nodes is less than that of input nodes.

■ *Learning Rate.* Usually both learning rate η and momentum constant α take values within interval [0, 1]. Smaller η results in slow convergence of training process, but tends to find better results than bigger η. If smaller η is used, then larger α should be used to accelerate the convergence. Otherwise if larger η is used, smaller α should be used to avoid the instability of the network.

Usually α is constant during the training process; η may vary as the below equation:

$$\eta(n) = \eta(n-1) \exp\left(\frac{\log \frac{\eta_{min}}{\eta_{max}}}{d}\right) \tag{6.5}$$

where $\eta(n)$ and $\eta(n-1)$ respectively mean the values of η for the nth iteration and $(n-1)$-th iteration. η_{max} and η_{min} are the predefined maximum and minimum of η. The denominator d is the predefined loss of each iteration. Specify an initial η and then modify η using Equation 6.5; when η reaches η_{min}, then set η as η_{max} and continue the modification using Equation 6.5.

Rule Induction Method

In data mining, rules refer to if/then rules, such as "*if* it is gloomy and sweltering, *then* it will probably rain." Rule induction methods try to directly induce classification rules from training data. In fact, each training case can be regarded as a piece of classification rule: the combination of the values of the input attributes is the rule premise; the value of the output attribute is the rule conclusion. But these kinds of rules are usually not strong since their supports (actually the number of reduplicate cases) are usually very low. Hence, they are not good representatives and not capable of generalization to make accurate prediction. Rule induction methods focus on inducing a set of strong rules with high support and good generalization. The typical rule induction methods include AQ, C45rules, and Ripper.

AQ Algorithm. The algorithm quasi-optimal (AQ) is based on the cover algorithm or star algorithm (Hong, 1997). Assume we have the following binary class training data shown in Table 6.2. The instances with class label "P" are called positive instances and the instances with class label "N" are called negative instances. The star of a positive instance over negative instances is a set of rule premises that cover the positive instance and exclude all the negative instances.

Table 6.2   An Example of Binary Class Training Data

Case ID	A	B	C	Class
1	0	0	0	P
2	1	2	0	P
3	1	0	0	P
4	0	0	2	P
5	1	0	1	N
6	0	1	0	N
7	1	1	0	N
8	1	1	2	N
9	0	0	1	N

For example, instance #1 in Table 6.2 is a positive case, whose star over the negative instances is "(B = 0 or B = 2) and (C = 0 or C = 2)" or "B ≠ 1 and C ≠ 1". It is easy to verify that all the negative instances cannot satisfy this rule premise, but instance #1 can. So a star is a set of rules that can distinguish at least one positive instance from the negative instances. The AQ algorithm is tasked to find such a star.

According to Boolean algebra, the star of a positive instance l over the negative instances is

$$l(A) \wedge l(B) \wedge l(C) \wedge \neg (f_1 \vee f_2 \vee \ldots \vee f_n) \tag{6.6}$$

where $\wedge$, $\vee$, and $\neg$ are operators representing conjunction, disjunction, and negation respectively, f_i ($i = 1, \ldots, n$) represents the conjunction of all the input attribute values in the ith negative instance. Transform the above formula into a disjunction normal form, which is the star of instance l. To reduce compute complexity when a large number of input attributes are involved, the AQ algorithm picks up part of the disjunction normal form (a "shrunken" star) for the further calculation. Besides, all the positive instances can be covered by generalization, such as removing some conjunctions during the transformation. Finally, we can get a star covering all the positive instances and excluding all the negative instances. The AQ algorithm uses the following procedure to find the best star.

Algorithm 6.2: Algorithm Quasi-optimal

1. Initialize the rule set as an empty set;

2. Pick a positive instance from training dataset;

3. Construct "shrunken" stars of the positive instance over the negative instances, select the stars following some criteria, such as those with the least attributes, and rank them regarding the number of covered positive instances;

4. Add the star covering the most positive instances to the rule set;

5. Delete all the positive instances covered by this star;

6. If there are still positive instances in the training dataset, then go to step 2;

7. Return the rule set.

C45rules. This algorithm is a rule induction method based on a decision tree. It first creates an unpruned decision tree and then transforms the tree to a set of rules. Each path from the root node to the leaf node of the tree generates a rule. Since the rule set has lots of redundancy, it must be simplified and consolidated.

C45rules checks each rule's premise and calculates its pessimistic error rate (the pessimistic error rate is the maximum error rate under a specified confidence interval estimated using binomial distribution and the error rate of the rule on the training dataset as prior probability). Then the algorithm separately deletes each element from the rule premise and calculates the pessimistic error rate of the remaining elements in the rule premise. That, along with the minimum pessimistic error rate, will be selected for further calculation. Repeat the above deletion until no remaining element can be found whose pessimistic error rate is less than that of the complete original premise.

After simplifying all the rules, categorize the rules according to the rule conclusion (that is, the class label). For each category, select the subset of rules having shortest coding length according to the MDL (Minimum Description Length) principle. The coding length of a rule set is the sum of the coding length of each rule plus that of the exceptions, including false positive and false negative instances.

Ripper. This is a rule induction algorithm with approximate linear time complexity. It has advantages in the analysis of mass data. For a dataset with n cases, the complexity of AQ algorithm is $O(n^2)$; that of C45rule is $O(n^3)$ at worst. For binary class tasks, the Ripper algorithm is as follows.

Algorithm 6.3: Ripper

1. Initialize the rule set as a null set;

2. While the set of positive instances is not null:

   a. Partition the training data into a Growth set and a Prune set (saying two thirds into Growth set, and one third into Prune set);

   b. Generate a piece of rule from the Growth set.

   c. Prune the rule according to the Prune Set.

   d. Add the pruned rule to the rule set;

   e. Calculate the MDL of the rule set. If the termination condition is met, then terminate the process.

   f. Delete the positive instances covered by the rule from training dataset.

3. Go to Step 2.

4. Optimize the obtained rule set.

The termination condition is as follows. After a new rule is added to the rule set, the sum of the rule set's MDL and the instances' MDL is greater than the previous rule set's MDL plus d. By default, d is set as 64. Here MDL means the same thing as it does with C45rules.

Support Vector Machine

Support Vector Machine (SVM) (Cristianini and Shawe-Taylor 2000) is a classification algorithm based on statistical learning with a solid theoretical foundation and excellent characteristics. SVM mainly deals with continuous

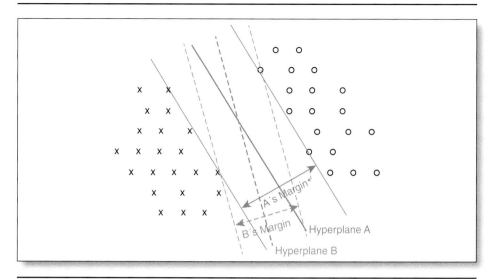

Figure 6.4   An Example of Hyperplanes

attributes. Discrete attributes need to be preprocessed before being fed into SVM classifier.

The Optimal Separating Hyperplane. Regarding a linearly separable, binary classification task, there exist infinite hyperplanes to separate the two classes. Figure 6.4 shows an example of such hyperplanes. In the figure, *o* and *x* represent the two different classes of cases. Both hyperplane A and hyperplane B can separate the two classes. So which is a better hyperplane?

Let's examine the margin of each hyperplane. Moving a hyperplane in both directions perpendicular to the hyperplane until reaching some case of each class, then getting two hyperplanes, the margin of the original hyperplane is defined as the distance between the two hyperplanes close to each class. For example, the margin of hyperplane A is the distance between the two solid lines, and the margin of hyperplane B is the distance between the two dot lines. Obviously A's margin is larger than B's margin. That indicates hyperplane A is less likely to misclassify new coming cases than hyperplane B. So hyperplane A has better generalization performance than hyperplane B and is better than hyperplane B. Among all the hyperplanes, the one with the largest margin is called the *optimal hyperplane*.

Each case can be represented as a pair (x_i, y_i)·where x_i is a vector with k dimensions composed of k values of k input attributes. Assuming the class attribute is binary, it takes value 1 or -1. A separating hyperplane can be written as

$$WX + b = 0 \tag{6.7}$$

where W is a weight vector, namely, $W = \{w1, w2, \ldots, wn\}$; n is the number of input attributes; and b is a scalar, referred to as a bias. Thus, any point that lies above the separating hyperplane satisfies, $WX + b > 0$. Similarly, any point that lies below the separating hyperplane satisfies $WX + b < 0$. The weights can be adjusted so that the hyperplanes defining the two sides of the margin can be written as

$$H1: WX + b \geq 1 \text{ for } y_i = +1 \tag{6.8}$$

$$H2: WX + b \leq -1 \text{ for } y_i = -1 \tag{6.9}$$

That is, any case that falls on or above $H1$ belongs to class $+1$, and any case that falls on or below $H2$ belongs to class -1. Combining the two inequalities of Equations 6.8 and 6.9, we get

$$y_i (WX + b) \geq 1 \tag{6.10}$$

Any training cases that fall on hyperplanes $H1$ or $H2$ (that is, the sides of the margin) satisfy Equation 6.10 and are called *support vectors*, which are equally close to the maximum margin hyperplane. It is easy to verify that the optimal hyperplane is that satisfying 6.10 and at the same time minimizing Equation 6.11 (maximizing the margin).

$$f(w) = \frac{\|w\|^2}{2} \tag{6.11}$$

The solution of Equation 6.10 is a constrained convex quadratic optimization problem, which can be resolved with a Lagrangian function. The solution can be found by maximizing α_i and minimizing w and b in the below Lagrangian function.

$$L(w,b,\alpha) = \frac{\|w\|^2}{2} \sum_{i=1}^{N} \alpha_i ((wx_i + b) y_i - 1) \tag{6.12}$$

where α_i is the Lagrangian multiplier and N is the number of the training cases. Computing the derivative of Equation 6.12 with respect to w and b, and using Kühn-Tucker condition, we can transform w into a function of α:

$$w(\alpha) = \sum_{i=1}^{N}\alpha_i - \frac{1}{2}\sum_{i,j=1}^{N}\alpha_i\alpha_j y_i y_j \langle x_i x_j \rangle \text{ and } \sum_{i=1}^{N}\alpha_i y_i = 0 \tag{6.13}$$

So $\alpha_i \geq 0$ can be resolved by maximizing the above formula. It can be proved that if the training case is a support vector, then $\alpha_i = 0$. The resolving of α_i can be achieved through numerical methods. We use $\alpha^0 = (\alpha_i^0, ..., \alpha_N^0)$ as the calculated α_i, then w and b can be calculated with Equations 6.13 and 6.14.

$$w^0 = \sum_{i=1}^{N} y_i \alpha_i^0 x_i$$

$$\tag{6.13}$$

$$b^0 = \frac{1}{2}(\langle w^0 x_{y=1}^* \rangle + \langle w^0 x_{y=-1}^* \rangle) \tag{6.14}$$

where $x_{y=1}^*$ and $x_{y=-1}^*$ represent any positive case and negative case.

After getting a trained support vector machine, the optimal hyperplane can be rewritten as

$$h(x) = \sum_{i=1}^{l} y_i \alpha_i^0 x_i x + b_0 \tag{6.15}$$

where y_1 is the class label of support vector x_i, x is a test case; i and b_0 are numeric parameters that were determined as above; and l is the number of support vectors. The classification result of x is indicated by the sign of Equation 6.15. If the sign is positive, then x falls on or above the optimal hyperplane, and so x belongs to class $+1$; otherwise it falls on or below the optimal hyperplane, and is predicted as class -1.

The optimal hyperplane is a linear class boundary, and so the corresponding SVM can be used to classify linearly separable data. Such SVMs are called *linear SVMs*.

Linearly Inseparable Data. When the training data is linearly inseparable, whatever hyperplanes are used, there always exist some training cases falling into the other side of the hyperplane. For this problem, one solution is to find some nonlinear mapping, and map each training case into a higher dimensional space, in which the previously linearly inseparable cases become linearly separable. At last, figure out the optimal hyperplane in this new space.

But the dimensionality of the new space could be very high, which sometimes renders further calculation almost impossible. If using a polynomial as the nonlinear mapping function, then the construction of dth order polynomial in k-dimensional space will create $(k/d)^d$ attributes. Obviously, this will result in the curse of dimensionality.

Kernel Function. This function can be used to avoid the dimension explosion issue. From Equation 6.15, calculation of the optimal hyperplane only needs to calculate the dot product of the support vectors and the test case in the transformed space. Kernel functions can be applied to the data in the original space to substitute the computation of the dot product in the transformed space, which is mathematically equivalent.

A kernel function is a type of special function, which satisfies

$$K(x, z) = \langle \phi(x) \bullet \phi(z) \rangle \tag{6.16}$$

Where x and z are two input vectors and $\phi(x)$ is a mapping from the input space to another high dimensional feature space, and $\bullet$ represents the dot product. Using the kernel function $K(x, z)$, the optimal hyperplane can be calculated with Equation 6.17.

$$h(x) = \sum_{i=1}^{l} y_i \alpha_i^0 K(x_i, x) + b_0 \tag{6.17}$$

The commonly used kernel functions include the polynomial kernel function, the Gaussian radial basis function, and the Sigmod kernel functions.

The complexity of SVM is dependent on the number of support vectors rather than the dimensionality of the attributes. Hence, SVMs tend to be less prone to over-fitting than other methods. The support vectors are the essential or critical training cases, since they lie closest to the optimal hyperplane and dominate the decision boundary. Moreover, A SVM with a small number of support vectors can have good generalization, even when the dimensionality of the data is high.

Bayesian Classifiers

Bayesian classification is based on statistics and probability theory. It assumes the attributes or variables follow some probabilistic distribution, the best decision can be inferred from the distributions and observed data. Bayesian classifiers (Friedman, 1997) try to infer the conditional probability of the class variable given the observed values of the input variables. Now Bayesian classifiers have been used in text classification, pattern recognition, economic forecasting, and so on. They usually show very high classification accuracy and efficiency.

Naïve Bayes Classifier. This is a very simple, effective, and commonly used classifier. Its performance is often comparable with that of ANN, decision tree (saying C4.5), and better than other classifiers in many cases.

The Naïve Bayes (NB) classifier assumes that the input variables are independent of each other given the value of the class variable, which is called the conditional independence (CI) assumption. Figure 6.5.a shows an example of a NB classifier. Where C is the class variable, X_1, X_2, …, X_n are the input variables.

Bayesian classifiers try to infer the conditional probability of the class variable given the observed values of the input variables; that is, $P(c_j|x_1, …, x_n), j=1, …, m$, here c_j is the jth value of class variable C and x_1, …, x_n is the observed input value. Based on the m conditional probabilities, the Bayesian classifier picks the class with the maximum conditional probability as the predicted class label. Because of this, the Bayesian classifier is also called an optimal classifier.

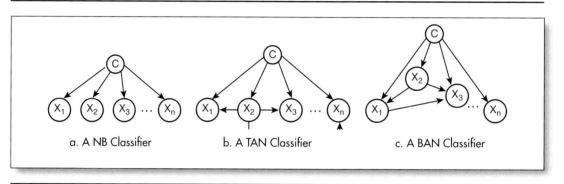

a. A NB Classifier   b. A TAN Classifier   c. A BAN Classifier

Figure 6.5   Several Bayesian Classifiers

Using Bayes theory and the CI assumption,

$$P(c_j|x_1, …, x_n) = \frac{P(x_1, …, x_n|c_j)P(c_j)}{P(x_1, …, x_n)} = \alpha * P(c_j) * \prod_{i=1}^{n} P(x_i|c_j) \qquad (6.18)$$

where α is a standardization constant. Then the predicted class label is that having the maximum class post probability.

$$arg\ max_{c_j \in C} P(c_j) * \prod_{i=1}^{n} P(x_i|c_j) \qquad (6.19)$$

In real application, $P(c_j)$ and $P(x_i|c_j)$ are proximated with the frequency observed from the training dataset (Observed Frequency Estimation).

The problem of the NB classifier is that the CI assumption does not always hold in reality. Recently, many researchers have been making efforts to improve the NB classifier. One type of methods is to introduce feature selection. Another is to weaken the CI assumption.

Tree Augmented Naïve Bayes (TAN) Classifier. This classifier was proposed by Nir Friedman. The basic idea is, in a NB classifier, to add arcs among the input variables, and create a tree structure on the input variables. Doing this weakens the CI assumption to some extent. Figure 6.5.b shows an example of a TAN. In the figure, there are arcs from X_2 to X_1, X_3 and X_n. That means X_1, X_3 and X_n are not only dependent on class variable C but also input variable X_2. But each input variable can depend on at most one other variable besides the class variable. This guarantees all the input variables form a directed tree.

Friedman proposed an algorithm for learning TAN based on the tree learning algorithm by Chow and Liu (1968).

Algorithm 6.4: Tree Augmented Naïve Bayes (TAN)

1. Calculate the CMI (Conditional Mutual Information) of each pair of input variables given the class variable:

$$I(X_i, X_j \mid C) = \sum_{x_i, x_j, c} P(x_i, x_j, c) \times \log \frac{P(x_i, x_j \mid c)}{P(x_i \mid c) \, P(x_j \mid c)} \tag{6.20}$$

2. Construct an undirected complete graph with the input variables X_1, X_2, ..., A_n, and attach the CMIs to the corresponding edges in the graph as the weights.

3. Build a maximum spanning tree regarding the weights;

4. Select an input variable as the root of the tree, and set the direction of each edge, as pointing out from the root. Then get a directed tree;

5. Add the class variable C and the arcs pointing to each input variable X_i from C to the above tree.

TAN has the same advantages, such as simplicity and robustness, as the NB classifier, but can usually achieve higher accuracy.

Bayesian Network Augmented Naïve Bayes (BAN) Classifier. This is another augmented classifier based on the NB classifier. BAN further weakens the CI assumption and allows that all the input variables compose a Bayesian network (a directed acyclic graph), so it can represent any dependency among the input variables. Figure 6.5.c shows an example of BAN.

Since all the input variables compose a Bayesian network, the learning process of BAN is quite similar to the process of learning a Bayesian network. First, learn a Bayesian network upon all the input variables; then, add the class variable as well as the arcs pointing to each input variable from a class variable.

Bayesian Multi-Net (BMN) Classifier. BMN (Geiger and Heckerman 1996) is an extension of TAN or BAN. TAN or BAN has the same structure regarding different class labels, which means the relationships among the input variables are constant for different class values. While in BMN, the relationships could vary with different class labels, which means each class label can have its own structure. So BMN is actually a set of TAN or BAN; each corresponds to one class label. Figure 6.6a shows an example of BMN composed of BAN.

Regarding the learning process of BMN, first separate the training dataset into m subsets according to the m values of the class variable. Then learn a TAN or BAN from each subset. The learned TAN or BAN for a particular class label is named a local classifier. With these local classifiers plus the prior probability of class variable, all the post probabilities regarding class variable can be calculated.

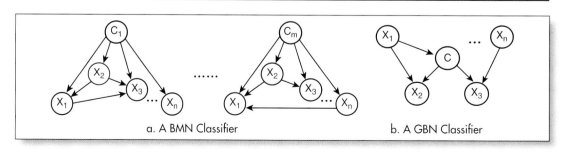

a. A BMN Classifier   b. A GBN Classifier

Figure 6.6   BMN Classifier and GBN Classifier

General Bayesian Network (GBN) Classifier. GBN is a general classifier completely discarding the CI assumption. In GBN, the class variable is just a general node, not a special node any more. Figure 6.6b shows an example of GBN.

The learning of GBN is exactly the same as the learning process of a Bayesian network. After a GBN is learned from the training data, it can be used for classification. Since it is not necessary to have an arc between the class variable C and each input variable, usually only a subset of input variables around C is used, which is called a *cut set* of C. The classification task turns to calculate the class post probability given the observed values of the cut set. The classification performance of GBN is dependent on the gradual correctness of Bayesian network learning. The more the training cases, the more accurate the learned GBN, so as the classification.

Rough Set

The rough set, proposed by the Polish mathematician Zdzislaw I. Pawlak (1991), is a new mathematical tool for dealing with uncertain concepts and knowledge. A rough set for a given class C, is defined by two sets—a lower approximation of C and an upper approximation of C. The lower approximation of C consists of all of the data cases that are certain to belong to C without ambiguity based on the current attributes. The upper approximation of C consists of all of the cases that cannot be described as not belonging to C. The lower approximation is also called the *positive region*. The area beyond the upper approximation is called the *negative region*. The difference between upper approximation and lower approximation is called a border, which describes the roughness of the rough set. When lower approximation and upper approximation are the same, the border disappears and the rough set turns to an exact set. An example of the lower and upper approximations for a class C is shown in Figure 6.7, where each rectangular region represents an equivalence class.

An equivalence class is a set of cases that are indiscernible with the current attributes, which means these cases are identical with respect to the attributes describing the data. In many real applications, some classes cannot be exactly defined by the available attributes. Rough sets can be used to approximately or "roughly" define such classes.

Generation of Rough Set for Attribute Reduction. Rough sets can be used for attribute subset selection or feature reduction (where attributes that do not contribute toward the classification of the given training data can be identified

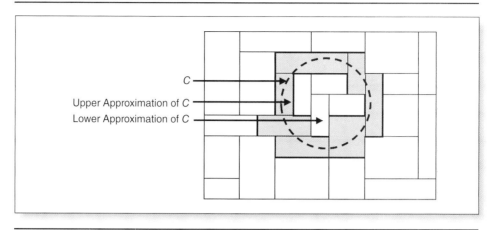

Figure 6.7   The Lower and Upper Approximations of a Class C

and removed). A *reduct* is a set of such attributes; if any of them is removed, the positive region will change. The attributes not in any reduct are abundant and can be deleted. The problem of finding the minimal reducts of attributes is NP-hard. A method based on a discernibility matrix and some heuristic methods can be used to find the minimum reducts.

Table 6.3 shows a training dataset, $U = \{x1, x2, x3, x4, x5, x6, x7, x8\}$, which contains eight applicants, in which {Diploma, Experience, French, Reference} are the input attributes, and {Decision} is the decision or class attribute.

Table 6.3   An Example of a Training Dataset

	Diploma	Experience	French	Reference	Decision
$x1$	Ba	M	y	e	Accept
$x2$	Sc	H	y	n	Accept
$x3$	Sc	H	y	e	Accept
$x4$	Ba	H	n	g	Accept
$x5$	Ba	L	y	n	Reject
$x6$	Ce	L	y	g	Reject
$x7$	Sc	M	y	n	Reject
$x8$	Ce	L	n	e	Reject

Regarding this example, the discernibility matrix for the training cases from the two classes is shown in Table 6.4, where each cell shows a set of attributes in which the two cases take different values. For simplicity, we use {D, E, F, R} to represent {Diploma, Experience, French, Reference} respectively.

Table 6.4   The Discernibility Matrix Used for the Training Cases

	x1	**x2**	**x3**	**x4**
x5	E,R	D,E	D,E,R	E,F,R
x6	D,E,R	D,E,R	D,E,R	D,E,F
x7	D,R	E	E,R	D,E,F,R
x8	D,E,F	D,E,F,R	D,E,F	D,E,R

The discernibility function of the two classes regarding the training data is defined as shown in Equation 6.21:

$$f(s) = \bigwedge \left(\bigvee_{k \in c_{ij}} a_k \right) \tag{6.21}$$

Then the discernibility function of Table 6.4 is

$$f(S) = (E \vee R) \wedge (D \vee E) \wedge (D \vee E \vee R) \wedge (E \vee F \vee R) \wedge (D \vee E \vee F) \wedge (D \vee R) \wedge E \wedge (D \vee E \vee F \vee R)$$

$$= (E \vee R) \wedge (D \vee E) \tag{6.22}$$

That means we can get two reducts, {E, R} and {D, E}; they have the same equivalence classes regarding calss attribute as all the four input attributes.

Generation of Classification Rules. Rough set theory can also be used for classification to discover structural relationships within imprecise or noisy data. It applies to discrete-valued attributes. Continuous-valued attributes must therefore be discretized before their use. Classification rules can be generated from both the positive region and the border area for a given class. The rules created from the positive region are certain, holding in 100 percent, but those created from the border area are uncertain, holding at some probability less than 1. A method based on a discernibility matrix can be used to create the rules holding in 100 percent. Typically, the rules are represented as a decision table.

Regarding the above example training cases, each class has one discernibility matrix for rule generation, which is very similar to that for reduct calculation, which would just need to replace the attributes in Table 6.4 with an equation, like attribute = value. Each cell in the matrix indicates the different values between a pair of cases. And the discernibility functions are defined as shown in Equation 6.23:

$$f(d = d_m) = \vee\,(\wedge_{c_i}\,\vee_{ak\in cij}\,a_k) \tag{6.23}$$

Tables 6.5 and 6.6 show the discernibility matrices for the two classes, decision = Accept and decision = Reject.

Table 6.5   The Discernibility Matrix Class Decision = Accept

	x5	x6	x7	x8
x1	E=m, R=e	D=mba, E=m, R=e	D=mba, R=e	D=mba, E=m
x2	D=msc, E=h	D=msc, E=h, R=n	E=h	D=msc, E=h, R=n
x3	D=msc, E=h, R=e	D=msc, E=h, R=e	E=h, R=e	D=msc, E=h
x4	E=h, R=g	D=mba, E=h	D=mba, E=h, R=g	D=mba, E=h, R=g

Table 6.6   The Discernibility Matrix Class Decision=Reject

	x1	x2	x3	x4
x5	E=l, R=n	D=mba, E=l	D=mba, E=l, R=n	E=l, R=n
x6	D=mce, E=l, R=g	D=mce, E=l, R=g	D=mce, E=l, R=g	D=mce, E=l
x7	D=msc, R=n	E=m	E=m, R=n	D=msc, E=m, R=n
x8	D=mce, E=l	D=mce, E=l, R=e	D=mce, E=l	D=mce, E=l, R=e

Then the discernibility function for class decision = Accept is:

f(decision = Accept) = ((E = m V R = e) ∧ (D = mba ∨ E = m ∨ R = e) ∧ (D = mba ∨ R = e) ∧ (D = mba ∨ E = m)) ∨ ((D = msc ∨ E = h) ∧(D = msc ∨ E = h ∧ R = n) ∧ E = h ∧ (D = msc ∨ E = h ∨ R = n)) ∨ ((D= msc ∨ E = h ∨ R = e) ∧ (E = h ∨ R = e) ∧ (D = msc ∨ E = h)) ∨ ((E= h ∨ R = g) ∧ (D = mba ∨ E = h) ∧ (D = mba ∨ E = h ∨ R = g)) = (E = m ∧ R = e) ∨ (D = mba ∧ R = e) ∨ (D = mba ∧ E = m) ∨ E = h

And the discernibility function for class decision = Reject is:

f(decision = Reject) = ((E =l ∨ R = n) ∧ (D = mba ∨ E = l) ∧ (D = mba ∨ E = l ∨ R = n)) ∨ ((D = mce ∨ E = l ∨ R = g) ∧ (D = mce ∨ E = l)) ∨ ((D = msc ∨ R=n) ∧ E = m ∧ (E = m ∨ R = n) ∧ (D = msc ∨ E = m ∨ R = n)) ∨ ((D = mce ∨ E = l) ∧ (D=mce ∨ E=l ∨ R=e)) = E=l ∨ (R=n ∧ D = mba) ∨ (R = n ∧ E =m) ∨ D = mce

Taking into consideration the dependcy between the attribute values, and taking use of one reduct {E, R}, then we can get the following simple rules:

Experience = m *and* Reference=e => Decision=Accept;

Experience = h = > Decision = Accept;

Experience = l = > Decision = Reject;

Experience = m *and* Reference = n = > Decision = Reject;

KNN Classifier

The *k* nearest neighbors (KNN) algorithm is a typical classification algorithm based on lazy learning. It doesn't construct a classification model actively (or beforehand), but directly classifies the unknown test cases using the training cases.

KNN assumes "things of one kind come together," that is, the adjacent cases have the same class label. So it uses *k* nearest training cases (named neighbors) of a test case to classify this case. Figure 6.8 shows an example of the KNN algorithm. For a test case *x*, KNN finds three nearest neighbors (here *k* = 3), and uses them to classify *x*. KNN is quite straightforward, as depicted in Figure 6.8.

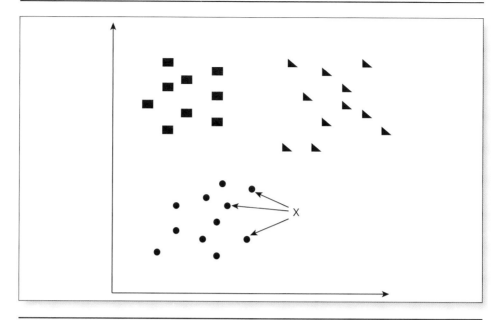

Figure 6.8   An Example of KNN

Algorithm 6.5: *k* Nearest Neighbors (KNN)

1. Set the value of parameter *k*;

2. For each test case,

    a. Calculate the distance from each training case to the test case;

    b. Find the *k* training cases with the shortest distance to the test case;

    c. Determine the class label according to the vote of the *k* training cases.

Usually, the distance regarding a numerical attribute is measured by Euclidean distance. To avoid the influence of the difference of different data ranges of the attributes, standardization regarding each attribute is usually required before the distance calculation. For the distance regarding a discrete attribute, a simple method is to define the distance as 0 if the two cases have the same value regarding the attribute, as 1 otherwise. Another method is to calculate the distance with VDM (value difference metric), which is defined in Equation 6.24.

$$vdm\_dist\,(i_a, j_a) = \sum_{k=1}^{c} |\frac{count(i_a, c_k)}{count(i_a)} - \frac{count(j_a, c_k)}{count(j_a)}|^2 \qquad (6.24)$$

where i_a and j_a respectively represent the values of case i and j regarding the discrete attribute a, $count(i_a)$ and $count(j_a)$ represent the counts of i_a and j_a in the training cases, count (i_a, c_k) and count (j_a, c_k) represent the counts of (i_a, c_k) and (j_a, c_k) in the training cases, c_k is a class label and c is the number of class label. Actually, the formula in Equation 6.24 defines the distance between two cases regarding a discrete attribute is a quadratic sum of the difference of the two class post probabilities, $P(c_k|i_a)$ and $P(c_k|i_a)$.

Regarding mixed attributes (containing both continuous and discrete attributes), mixed Euclidean distance can be used, where VDM is applied to the discrete attributes, and squared Euclidean distance is applied to the continuous attributes.

Regarding the vote of the k nearest cases, the simplest method is majority-dominant (each training case has the same weight), which means the test case will be classified to the dominant class label regarding the k nearest training cases. A more reasonable method is weighted voting, in which each training case has different weight according to the distance to the test case: the further the distance, the smaller the weight. The parameter k has significant influence on classification performance. The KNN classifier with too small a k value is apt to be influenced by noise. That with too large a k value tends to increase the misclassification rate.

Ensemble Classifier

Ensemble classifier learning is to learn multiple classifiers and then use all the classifiers for classification and get a combinational classification result. In most cases, an ensemble classifier can achieve higher classification accuracy than a single classifier. A typical structure of an ensemble classifier is shown in Figure 6.9.

Ensemble classifier learning does not simply repeat the learning process on the same training dataset with multiple algorithms; it interferes with the training dataset during the learning process. Furthermore, the training errors of one classifier can be leveraged by the next classifier. One reason of misclassification is that the distribution of test cases is different from that of the training cases. By introducing interference to the training dataset, it helps to eliminate the bias of a single classifier and gets more accurate and general classification models.

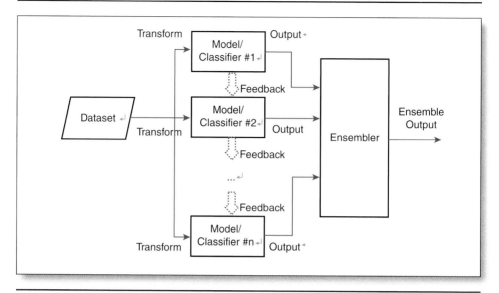

Figure 6.9   A Typical Structure of an Ensemble Classifier

Generally speaking, there are two types of ensemble classifier learning methods. One type interferes with training cases. By changing the composition of the training cases, we can learn a group of classifiers, each called a *base classifier*. Through the combination of the outputs of all the base classifiers, the final classification result will be obtained. This type of method requires that the base classifiers are unstable (that is, sensitive to small changes in the training dataset). The typical algorithms include *bagging* and *boosting*. The other type of method interferes with the input attributes. First select a different attribute subset from input attributes and then learn one base classifier for each subset. This type of method is suitable for the training datasets with many redundant input attributes. One typical algorithm is *random forest*.

Bagging and Boosting. Bagging (Breiman 1996) first performs multiple sampling with replacement upon the original training dataset and gets multiple new training datasets, each having the same number of training cases as the original dataset. According to the sampling principle, for a large training dataset, the number of distinct cases in the new datasets is around 63.2 percent of that in the original training dataset. The next step is to earn k base classifiers with the k new created datasets (k is a predefined parameter). The classification result is obtained by the combination of the votes of all the base classifiers, each with one dataset.

In bagging, each training case has the same weight, and each base classifier also has the same weight. It reduces the misclassifications caused by the sensitivity of the base classifier with respect to the training dataset and is usually able to improve the performance of the unstable classifiers.

Boosting is a more elaborate ensemble learning method. It assigns each training case a weight. It increases the weights of the training cases misclassified the last time when creating a new training dataset so as to force the classifier to pay more attention to the misclassified cases. It also uses weighted voting, assigns good classifiers larger weights, and assigns bad classifier smaller weights. There exist various implementations of the boosting algorithm, AdaBoost is the most common.

Algorithm 6.6: AdaBoost

1. Initialize the weights of the training cases as the reciprocal of the training case number;

2. Assume k is the number of the base classifiers;

3. Repeat the below steps for k times:

    a. Perform a sampling with replacement according to the weights upon the original training dataset and get a new training dataset;

    b. Learn a base classifier with the new dataset;

    c. Calculate the weighted classification error of the base classifier;

    d. If the classification error is beyond 50 percent, then go to step 1.

    e. Calculate the significance of the base classifier according to its classification error;

    f. Recalculate the weights of the training cases according to their classification correctness and the significance of the base classifier.

4. Regarding an unknown test case, its class label is determined by the weighted vote of all the base classifiers.

The weighted error of a base classifier c_j, denoted as $E_{(weighted)}(C_j)$, is the sum of the weights of all the misclassified cases. And the significance of a base classifier C_j is calculated as shown in Equation 6.25:

$$Sig(C_j) = \frac{1}{2} \ln \left| \frac{1 - E_{weighted}(C_j)}{E_{weighted}(C_j)} \right| \tag{6.25}$$

The update of the weight of training case x_i is relevant to its classification correctness and the significance of the base classifier.

$$w_{j+1}(x_i) = \frac{w_j(x_i)}{Z} \times \begin{cases} e^{-sig(C)_j} & \textit{if classification is correct} \\ e^{sig(C)_j} & \textit{if classification is incorrect} \end{cases} \tag{6.26}$$

where Z is a normalizing factor, to ensure the sum of the updated weight $w_{j+1}(x_i)$ equals 1. It is obvious that this formula increases the weights of the misclassified training cases, and enables the classifier to pay more attention to the misclassified cases. It helps improve the classification accuracy, but sometimes risks over-fitting.

In AdaBoost, the voting of the base classifiers is influenced by their significance, which enables classifiers with better performance to dominate the classification result.

Random Forest. This is a combination of the bagging algorithm and random subspace sampling. Usually decision tree classifiers are used as the base classifiers. Random forest performs sampling regarding both training cases and input attributes. It learns multiple decision trees and then uses decision trees to vote. A typical learning process of the random forest algorithm is as follows.

Algorithm 6.7: Random Forest

1. Set the number of used attributes as m (smaller than the size of the input attribute set);

2. Repeat the below process until reaching the predefined number of iterations:

    a. Perform multiple sampling with replacement upon the original training dataset. The sampling size is N.

    b. Construct decision trees. When calculating the best partitioning attributes, randomly select m attributes from

> the input attributes as the candidates rather than using all the input attributes.

c. Don't prune the above trees.

3. Regarding an unknown test case, its class label is determined by the voting of all the decision tree classifiers.

The advantage of random forest is that not only can it improve the classification accuracy, but it is also not sensitive to noises and missing values. Owing to using less attributes to construct the decision trees, its learning speed is also improved. The value of parameter m has significant influence on the random forest algorithm. A good reference value of m is $m = \log_2 k + 1$, where k is the number of all the input attributes.

Regression

Regression is a mathematical modeling method used for data mining. This section gives a brief description of Linear Regression and Logistic Regression.

Linear Regression

Linear regression tries to discover the linear relation between the input attributes and output attribute. Figure 6.10 shows an example, where a straight line is used to fit the linear relation between X and Y.

In linear regression, both the input attributes and output attribute should be continuous. Assume a_1, ..., a_k are input attributes and d is the output attribute, then linear regression is used to find the best solution for Equation 6.27 using the training data.

$$d = \beta_0 + \beta_1 a_1 + \beta_2 a_2 + \cdots + \beta_k a_k \tag{6.27}$$

Assume there are n cases in the training dataset, and a_{ij} is the value of attribute a_j in the ith case and d_i is the value of attribute d in the ith case. Then Equation 6.27 can be represented in a form of matrix.

$$D = A\beta$$

$$\text{Where } D = \begin{pmatrix} d_0 \\ d_1 \\ \cdots \\ d_n \end{pmatrix}, A = \begin{pmatrix} 1 & a_{11} & \cdots & a_{1k} \\ 1 & a_{21} & \cdots & a_{2k} \\ \cdots & \cdots & \cdots & \cdots \\ 1 & a_{n1} & \cdots & a_{nk} \end{pmatrix} \text{ and } \beta = \begin{pmatrix} \beta_0 \\ \beta_1 \\ \cdots \\ \beta_k \end{pmatrix}$$

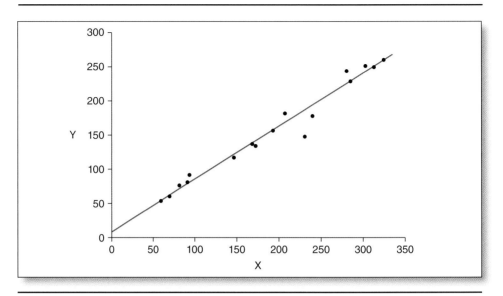

Figure 6.10 An Example of Linear Regression

Coefficient matrix β can be estimated with the least square method, and the estimation, demoted as β^*, can be calculated with the formula shown in Equation 6.28.

$$\beta^* = (A^{\mathrm{T}}A)^{-1}A^{\mathrm{T}}D \tag{6.28}$$

where A^{T} is the reverse matrix of A.

The sum of squares of errors (SSE) of the estimation is represented as:

$$\text{SSE} = \sum (d_j - d^*_{\ j})^2 \tag{6.29}$$

where $d^*_{\ j}$ is the predicted value of the output using β^*. SSE represents the fitness of the linear regression model. The smaller the SSE, the more accurate the model is.

The sum of squares of regression (SSR) of the estimation is:

$$\text{SSR} = \sum (d^*_{\ j} - \bar{d})2 \tag{6.30}$$

where $\bar{d}$ is the mean of d. The larger the SSR, the more accurate the model is.

To quantify the performance of the model, we can compute the discriminant coefficient R^2:

$$R^2 = \frac{SSR}{SSR + SSE} \qquad (6.31)$$

The closer to 1 R^2 is, the better the model.

For example, if we build a linear regression model for the dataset shown in Table 6.7, we can get

$d^* = 62.4 + 1.55a_1 + 51a_2 + 0.1a_3 - 0.144a_4$
And $R^2 = 0.9824$, so the above model is a good model.

In linear regression, if some input attributes are not relevant to the output attribute, then the created linear model will suffer over-fitting and has not good predictive power. Using the F-distribution (Johnson, 1995), we can test whether an attribute is effective or not in the final created model.

Table 6.7   An Sample Dataset

a_1	a_2	a_3	a_4	d
7	26	6	60	78.5
1	29	15	52	74.3
11	56	8	20	104.3
11	31	8	47	87.6
7	52	6	33	95.9
11	55	9	22	109.2
3	71	17	6	102.7
1	31	22	44	72.5
2	54	18	22	93.1
21	47	4	26	115.9
1	40	23	34	83.8
11	66	9	12	113.3
10	68	8	12	109.4

The method is first calculating the SSE and SSR of the created model including attribute a_t and then calculating SSE and SSR of the created model after excluding a_t, denoted as SSE_t and SSR_t. Then the F statistic can be defined as:

$$F_t = \frac{SSR - SSR_t}{SSE/(n - k - 1)} \qquad (6.32)$$

Where F_t follows $F_{(1, n - k - 1)}$ distribution.

The above method can be used for attribute selection. According to the direction of the attribute selection, there are forward regression, backward regression, and stepwise regression.

Forward regression starts from an empty model. It calculates the F statistic of all the remaining attributes and selects the attribute having the largest F statistic. Repeat this process until the maximum F statistic value is smaller than a specified threshold.

Backward regression first creates a complete regression model. It gradually deletes the trivial attributes (those that have the minimum F statistic values). Repeat the process until the minimum F statistic value is larger than a specified threshold.

Stepwise regression is the combination of forward regression and backward regression. First perform a forward regression, then add a new attribute, and finally perform a backward regression. Repeat the process until you cannot add and delete an attribute any more.

Linear regression requires the input attributes are linearly independent of each other. If some input attributes are not linearly independent of each other, then the estimation using the least square method will become inaccurate.

Logistic Regression

The linear regression algorithm is only applicable to the scenario in which the output attribute is continuous. But in many cases, the output attribute is discrete. Logistic regression is applicable to these cases.

Logistic regression is most used for a binary output attribute. It doesn't directly predict the value of the output attribute, but predicts the probability of each value of the output attribute. The binary attribute has only two values, saying $d = 0$ and $d = 1$, if the predicted probability of $d = 1$ is p, then the probability of $d = 0$ is determined, saying $1 - p$. So logistic regression is essentially to predict the continuous value p and therefore can be represented as a linear regression expression.

$$p = \beta_0 + \beta_1 a_1 + \beta_2 a_2 + \cdots + \beta_k a_k \qquad (6.33)$$

where p is the probability of $d = 1$ given the input attributes taking some combinatory value l, which is approximated with the count of cases having value $(l, d = 1)$ divided by the count of cases containing value l. But the expression cannot be resolved with the least square method, since p's value is constrained and within the interval $[0, 1]$. To resolve this, we can use the below transformation, which is called the Logit transformation of p.

$$f(p) = \ln\left(\frac{p}{1-p}\right) \tag{6.34}$$

Since the data range of $f(p)$ is the whole field of real number, we can apply linear regression to $f(p)$.

$$f(p) = \beta_0 + \beta_1 a_1 + \beta_2 a_2 + \cdots + \beta_k a_k \tag{6.35}$$

Suppose we have the following statistics about a training dataset shown in Table 6.8, where only one input attribute exists, a.

Based on this table, we resolve Equation 6.35 and get a regression equation, $f(p) = -17.2086 + 0.5934a$. Regarding a new input value, we first get $f(p)$ using this equation, and then figure out the value of p with the formula in Equation 6.36, which is the reverse function of Equation 6.34.

$$p = \frac{e^{f(p)}}{1 + e^{f(p)}} \tag{6.36}$$

Given the intimate connection between logistic regression and probabilistic theory, Equation 6.35 is usually estimated with the maximum likelihood method. Similar to linear regression, logistic regression can also be used for attribute selection.

Table 6.8   Statistics of a Training Dataset

a	Count	Count for d=0	Count for d=1	p	f(p)
28	6	4	2	2/6	−0.6931
29	5	3	2	2/5	−0.4055
30	9	2	7	7/9	1.2528
31	9	2	7	7/9	1.2528
32	20	4	16	16/20	1.3863
33	15	1	14	14/15	2.6391

Since logistic regression is used for classification tasks, its performance can be assessed with the metrics for classification algorithms, such as classification accuracy or those from statistical methods, such as −2 log likelihood (−2LL), R-Square by Cox and Snell, and R-Square by Nagelkerke.

Clustering

In machine learning, clustering is called unsupervised learning, and classification called supervised learning. The commonality of these two is that both group the training cases into two or more classes. The difference lies in the fact that, during learning process, the classification algorithms are provided training cases with class labels, but clustering algorithms are provided cases without class labels.

Since no class label can be used, clustering algorithms group training cases into clusters following the below criterion. The training cases within the same cluster have high similarity, and the training cases in different clusters have low similarity. The similarity between two cases is usually measured by distance. The further the distance, the lower the similarity is.

Clustering algorithms can be used as a standalone data mining tool for the purpose of data distribution understanding or even classification. They can also be used as a preprocessing step of other data mining algorithms, such as data discretization. Clustering has been widely used in customer classification, market segmentation, pattern recognition, bioinformatics, spatial data analysis, Web document classification, animal and plant categorization, disease classification, image processing, and so on.

The main clustering algorithms include the partitioning method, hierarchical method, density based method, and Kohonen clustering.

Partitioning Method

The partitioning method requires specifying the cluster number k beforehand. It first creates k initial partitions (or clusters), and then based on some score function, tentatively moves the training cases among the clusters to optimize the k clusters. A common score function is the SSE (sum of squares of errors) function. The partitioning method can only obtain the globally optimal clusters after enumerating and comparing all the possible partitions. But this enumeration will result in very high time complexity. In real applications, the following two heuristic methods are commonly used:

■ k-*Means*. Each cluster is represented by the mean of all the cases in the cluster.

■ k-*Medoids*. Each cluster is represented by the case closest to the cluster center.

These two heuristic methods are suitable for finding spherical and similarly sized clusters from medium-sized and small datasets. For finding clusters with complicated shape or from large datasets, they need to be extended further.

k-**Means**. This algorithm can be depicted as follows.

Algorithm 6.8: *k*-Means

1. Specify parameter k, the number of created clusters;

2. Randomly select k cases, each representing a cluster center;

3. Partition all the remaining cases to k clusters. According to the distances (usually Euclidean distance) between each case and the cluster centers, allocate it to the cluster represented by the closest cluster center;

4. Compute the mean of the cases in each updated cluster as the new cluster center;

5. Repeat steps 3 and 4 until any of the k means doesn't change any more or the score function converges.

A commonly used score function is the square error score function:

$$J_e = \sum_{i=1}^{k} \sum_{X \in C_i} |X - m_i|^2 \qquad (6.37)$$

where X is a training case, C_i is the ith cluster, and m_i is the mean of cluster C_i.

The complexity of the k-means algorithm is $o(nkt)$, where n is the number of training cases, k is the cluster number, and t is the number of iteration. Usually $k<<n$, and $t<<n$. So the algorithm is very efficient and quite scalable for a large dataset.

Nevertheless, the k-means algorithm has several disadvantages. First, it is only applicable to the situation where the means of clusters are definable and not applicable to dataset containing non-numerical attributes. Second, it requires the user to specify in advance the number of the clusters to be created. But it is usually not easy to find an appropriate value for this number, especially when there is no useful prior classification information. Third, k-means usually converges to a local maximum, and sometimes it cannot get good clusters. At last, it is sensitive to noises and outliers, and cannot find clusters with nonconvex shapes or clusters of very different size. Figure 6.11 shows an example of this case, where k-means resulted in two clusters represented by the arrowheads and asterisks respectively, rather than the true clusters depicted by the curves.

Some variants of the k-means algorithm have been proposed to address these disadvantages. They use a different method to calculate similarity and

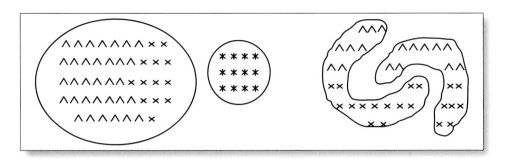

Figure 6.11 A Bad Example of *k*-Means

cluster means, as well as for selecting the initial cluster means. Another effective method is a combination of *k*-means and hierarchical clustering, to determine the appropriate *k* and the initial clusters using hierarchical clustering, and then further optimize the clusters with *k*-means.

***k*-Medoids.** To reduce the sensitivity of *k*-means to the outliers, *k*-medoids doesn't use cluster means as cluster representatives, but instead uses the real cases closest to the cluster center, the *medoids*. The basic process of the *k*-medoids algorithm is as follows.

Algorithm 6.9: k-Medoids

1. Arbitrarily choose *k* cases as the initial cluster representatives (or medoids);

2. Assign each of the remaining cases to the cluster with the nearest representatives;

3. Randomly select a nonrepresentative case *or*

4. Compute the total cost *S* of swapping representative case *oj* with *or*;

5. if *S* < 0 then swap *oj* with *or* to form the new set of *k* representatives;

6. Repeat steps 2 through 5 until he *k* representatives no longer change.

The total cost *S* is defined as the sum of square error after swapping minus that before swapping. After a representative is replaced by a nonrepresentative case, all the cases excluding the *k* current representatives need to be reassigned.

For datasets with noise and outliers, *k*-medoids is more stable than *k*-means, since the medoids are not influenced by anomalies as much as the means. But *k*-medoids has higher time complexity than *k*-means.

Hierarchical Clustering Method

Hierarchical clustering methods group training cases into a tree of clusters. They can be further classified as *agglomerative* and *divisive* hierarchical clustering, depending on whether the hierarchical decomposition is formed in a bottom-up (merging) or top-down (splitting) fashion.

Agglomerative hierarchical clustering uses a bottom-up strategy. It first treats each training case as a cluster and then merges these atomic clusters into larger and larger clusters, until all the training cases are in a single cluster or certain termination conditions are satisfied. Most hierarchical clustering methods belong to this category. The process of agglomerative hierarchical clustering is described in Algorithm 6.10.

In an opposite approach to agglomerative hierarchical clustering, divisive hierarchical clustering uses top-down strategy. It first puts all the training cases in one cluster and then subdivides the cluster into smaller and smaller pieces, until each single case forms a cluster, or until certain termination conditions are satisfied, such as a desired number of clusters are obtained, or the diameter of each cluster is within a certain threshold.

Figure 6.12 shows the process of both *agglomerative* and *divisive* hierarchical clustering for a dataset including five training cases {a, b, c, d, e}.

Algorithm 6.10: Agglomerative Hierarchical Clustering

1. *Initialization.* Regard each single case as a cluster. Compute the similarity matrix, where each cell is the reciprocal of the distance (usually Euclidean distance) between any two training cases.

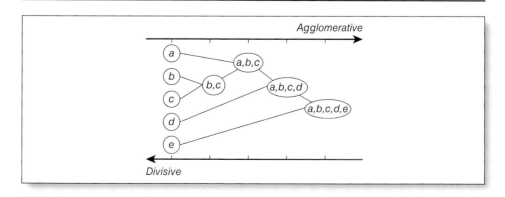

Figure 6.12 The Process of *Agglomerative* and *Divisive* Hierarchical Clustering on a Small Dataset

2. *Selection.* Find the two clusters most similar to each other using the similarity matrix.

3. *Update.* Merge these two clusters into one cluster. Update the cluster number and the similarity matrix, where two previous rows will be replaced by one row.

4. Repeat 2 and 3, until all the training cases are in a single cluster or certain termination conditions are satisfied.

The hierarchical clustering method is a simple and flexible way to change the granularity of the created clusters. But it has disadvantages. First, during the hierarchical clustering process, once a merge or split operation has been executed, even though it is later turns out to be a bad operation, it cannot be backtracked and corrected. This results in poor clustering results. The hierarchical clustering method also does not scale well, since a large number of similarity calculations between cases and clusters are required for each merge or split operation.

One promising direction for improving hierarchical clustering methods is to integrate hierarchical clustering with other clustering techniques and form multiple-phase clustering. BIRCH, CURE, ROCK, and chameleon algorithms are all such methods. BIRCH (Balanced Iterative Reducing and Clustering using Hierarchies) hierarchically partitions the cases using tree structures, which describe the summary of the created clusters, and then applies other clustering algorithms to the summary to create final clusters. CURE (Clustering Using REpresentatives) represents each cluster with a fixed number of cases and shrinks the clusters along the direction to their cluster centers according to a ratio so as to find nonspherical and different sizes of clusters. ROCK (RObust Clustering using linKs) measures the similarities among the clusters and merges the clusters based on their interconnectivity. It overcomes CURE's inability to deal with categorical attributes.

Chameleon was proposed with respect to the shortcomings of CURE and ROCK. It first groups the training cases into a large number of smaller sub-clusters with a graph partition algorithm, and then repeatedly merges the sub-clusters and gets the final clusters with an agglomerative hierarchical clustering algorithm. All the above four algorithms were well described in (Han and Kamber 2006).

Density-Based Clustering Method

Density-based clustering methods regard clusters as dense regions of cases in the data space separated by regions of low density (representing noise). This type of method can filter out noise and discover clusters of arbitrary shape.

DBSCAN (Density-Based Spatial Clustering of Applications with Noise) is a typical density based clustering algorithm, which uses a density threshold to control the growth of the clusters. The algorithm grows regions with sufficiently high density into clusters and defines a cluster as a maximal set of *density-connected* points. The cases not included in any cluster are regarded as noise or outliers.

The process of DBSCAN algorithm can be described as follows.

Algorithm 6.11: Density-Based Spatial Clustering of Applications with Noise (DBSCAN)

1. Initialize the parameters *Eps* and *MinPts*,, where *Eps* represents the radius of a neighborhood and *MinPts* represents the minimum number of points or cases in the *Eps* neighborhood;

2. Arbitrarily select a point *p* not included in any cluster from the training dataset;

3. Retrieve all points density-reachable from *p* with respect to *Eps* and *MinPts*.

4. If *p* is a core point, then create a cluster containing *p* and all the above points.

5. Repeat steps 2 through 4 until no point can be added into any cluster.

Figure 6.13 shows an example of a clustering result of DBSCAN. There two clusters and an outlier are discovered. In general, the computational complexity of DBSCAN is $O(n^2)$, where *n* is the number of cases in the dataset. If a spatial index is used, the computational complexity of DBSCAN can be reduced to $O(nlogn)$. DBSCAN is very sensitive to the parameters defined by the users, and a slight variation of them could result in very different clusters. The parameters are usually set according to experiences.

OPTICS (Ordering Points To Identify the Clustering Structure) is an extension of DBSCAN. It does not explicitly produce clusters, but computes an augmented *cluster ordering* for automatic and interactive cluster analysis. This ordering represents the density-based clustering structure of the training dataset, and can be used to extract basic clustering information as well as provide the intrinsic clustering structure.

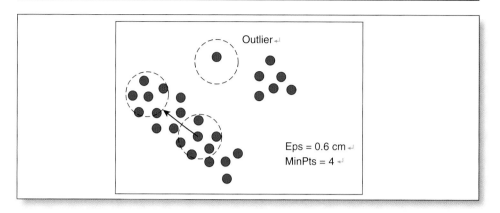

Figure 6.13 An Example Clustering Result of DBSCAN

Outlier Analysis

In the process of data analysis, very often a small number of cases are significantly different from the remaining (or most of the) cases. These cases are called *outliers*. Outliers are generated for many different reasons, sometimes due to measurement or recording errors. For example, air temperature being 230 degrees is probably due to a malfunctioning thermometer or a clerical error during recording. Sometimes, outliers are generated due to inherent data variability, such as, for example, when the cases are created by a totally different mechanism.

In many data mining tasks, outliers are regarded as noise and are removed from the training cases. However in some other applications (such as fraud detection, intrusion detection, and medical diagnosis), outliers are much more important than the general cases. In these applications, outliers may indicate fraud behaviors, intrusion behaviors, or disease, and need to be further analyzed, even though they are rare cases in the training dataset. Thus outlier detection and analysis is a very interesting and meaningful type of data mining task.

The commonly used outlier detection methods include the *statistical approach*, the *distance-based approach*, and the *deviation-based approach*. After being automatically detected, the outliers should be verified by users to confirm they are real outliers. Clustering algorithms can also be used for outlier detection in that the cases not included in any cluster are regarded as outliers.

Association Rules

The association rule was proposed by Agrawal et al. (1993). It originally focused on shopping basket analysis to discover the patterns and rules on customers' purchase behaviors in the transaction database. The well-known story of "diapers and beer" tells a successful application of the association rule. The story tells that a major US retailer Wal-Mart mined its transaction data warehouse and found that the most frequent product bought together with diapers is beer. Through further analysis, the data miner found that when some young fathers went off duty and bought diapers for their children in Wal-Mart, they usually bought some beer while they were there for themselves for the football game. Then Wal-Mart repositioned the shelf and put beer next to diapers. The sales volume was increased significantly. Now the association rule is used for not only shopping basket analysis, but for many other applications, such as classification, sequence pattern discovery, and so on.

Basic Concepts

Let's discuss the relevant concepts with an example. Table 6.9 shows a simple transaction dataset, where each transaction has an ID, and each transaction contains the purchased products (or items); all the items form the entire itemset $I = \{$beer, jelly, bread, milk, peanut butter$\}$.

Table 6.9   A Simple Transaction Dataset

ID	Transaction
1	bread, jelly, peanut butter
2	bread, peanut butter
3	bread, milk, peanut butter
4	beer, bread
5	beer, milk

Definition: the support of an itemset X, denoted as *Support(X)*, is defined as the ratio of the number of transactions containing X to the total number of transactions in a transaction dataset D.

$$Support(X) = \|\{d \in D \mid X \subseteq d\}\| \Big/ \|D\| \tag{6.38}$$

Then the supports of all the sub-itemsets formed by I can be determined, as shown in Table 6.10.

Table 6.10 The Supports of All the Sub-Itemsets Formed by *I*

itemset	Support (%)	itemset	Support (%)
beer	40	beer, bread, milk	0
bread	80	beer, bread, peanut butter	0
jelly	20	beer, jelly, milk	0
milk	40	beer, jelly, peanut butter	0
peanut butter	60	beer, milk, peanut butter	0
beer, bread	20	bread, jelly, milk	0
beer, jelly	0	bread, jelly, peanut butter	20
beer, milk	20	bread, milk, peanut butter	0
beer, peanut butter	0	jelly, milk, peanut butter	0
bread, jelly	20	beer, bread, jelly, milk	0
bread, milk	20	beer, bread, jelly, peanut butter	0
bread, peanut butter	60	beer, bread, milk, peanut butter	0
jelly, milk	0	beer, jelly, milk, peanut butter	0
jelly, peanut butter	20	bread, jelly, milk, peanut butter	0
milk, peanut butter	20	beer, bread, jelly, milk, peanut butter	0
beer, bread, jelly	0		

Definition: if the support of an itemset *X* is not less than the minimum support *Minsup*, that is, Support(*X*) ≥ *Minsup*, then *X* is called a frequent itemset (or large itemset). Where *Minsup* is a user-defined threshold on the frequency of itemsets.

Definition: the maximum frequent itemsets are defined as the frequent itemsets that are not contained by other frequent itemsets.

If *Minsup* is set as 40 percent, then we can get all the frequent itemsets as shown in Table 6.11 and the maximum frequent itemsets as shown in Table 6.12.

Table 6.11   All the Frequent Itemsets and Their Supports

itemset	Support (%)	itemset	Support (%)
beer	40	peanut butter	60
bread	80	bread, peanut butter	60
milk	40		

Table 6.12   All the Maximum Frequent Itemsets and Their Supports

itemset	Support (%)	itemset	Support (%)
beer	40	bread, peanut butter	60
milk	40		

Definition: The support of a rule *X*→*Y* is defined as the support of *X* ∪ *Y*, the union set of *X* and *Y*.

Definition: The confidence of a rule *X*→*Y* is defined as the ratio of the support of *X* ∪ *Y*, support(*X* ∪ *Y*) to the support of *X*, support(*X*).

$$\textbf{\textit{Confidence}}(X \rightarrow Y) = \textbf{\textit{Support}}(X \cup Y) \Big/ \textbf{\textit{Support}}(X) \tag{6.39}$$

Based on the frequent itemsets in Table 6.11, we can generate association rules as shown in Table 6.13.

Table 6.13 Rules Generated Based on the Frequent Itemsets

$X \rightarrow Y$	Support (%)	Confidence (%)
bread → peanut butter	60	75
peanut butter → bread	60	100

Definition: if the confidence of a rule $X \rightarrow Y$ is not less than the minimum confidence *minconf*, that is, *Confidence*($X \rightarrow Y$) ≥ *minconf*, then rule $X \rightarrow Y$ is called a strong association rule, where *minconf* is a user-defined threshold on the confidence of association rules.

Mining Association Rules

To mine association rules is to find strong association rules from the dataset based on the user-defined minimum support and minimum confidence. This process can be divided into two sub-problems. The first is to mine frequent itemsets. The second is to generate interesting association rules based on the frequent itemsets.

The performance of mining association rules is dominated by the first sub-problem given; it is quite easy and straightforward to generate association rules based on the frequent itemsets, so most association rule mining algorithms focus on the first sub-problem, how to efficiently mine frequent itemsets. Assuming all the frequent itemsets have been discovered, we can use the following steps to generate all the strong association rules:

1. For each frequent itemset l, generate all the nonempty subsets of l;

2. For each nonempty subset s of l, if

$$\frac{Suppot(l)}{support(s)} \geq minconf$$

then output an association rule $s \rightarrow (l - s)$, where *minconf* is the user specified minimum confidence.

Usually frequent itemsets and their supports are stored in a hash table so as to be accessed quickly.

Apriori Algorithm. This algorithm was proposed by R. Agrawal and R. Srikant in 1994 for mining frequent itemsets (Agrawal and Srikant 1994). The basic process of this algorithm is as follows.

Algorithm 6.12: Apriori

1. Construct candidate 1-itemsets (the itemsets containing only 1 item) C_1 based on the entire itemset I, assume $I = \{a_1, a_2, \ldots, a_n\}$, then $C_1 = \{\{a_1\}, \{a_2\}, \ldots, \{a_n\}\}$. Find frequent 1-itemsets F_1 from C_1 using user-defined minsupp;

2. For ($k = 2$; $F_{k-1} = $ NULL; $k++$),

   a. Construct the set of candidate k-itemsets (itemsets containing k items) C_k based on F_{k-1};

   b. For each transaction t in database, increase the count of the itemsets in C_k if it is contained by t;

   c. Let F_k be the set of the k-itemsets in C_k, whose supports are greater than *minsupp*;

3. Return $\cup F_k$.

Apriori makes use of a breadth-first search. Where the core step is to construct C_k based on F_{k-1}, it is realized by these two steps:

1. Join: join each pair of frequent ($k - 1$)-itemsets in F_{k-1}. The join condition is that the first $k - 2$ items in the two itemsets are same (the items are sorted beforehand);

2. Prune: remove the itemsets if one of those subsets is infrequent. This takes use of the contrapositive of the monotonic property: all the nonempty subsets of a frequent itemset are frequent. Its contrapositive is that all the supersets of an infrequent itemset are infrequent.

The apriori algorithm has to execute multiple scans of the dataset. Each scan creates a set of longer frequent itemsets. If there exists a long frequent itemset, the I/O overhead of the apriori algorithm is very heavy. Besides, a huge number of candidate itemsets are usually generated during the apriori process, and the update of the candidate itemsets' counts requires match operations between the itemset and the transactions; this causes heavy computing overhead.

Frequent pattern growth (FP-growth) algorithm. FP-growth is a method of finding all the frequent itemsets without generating candidate itemsets. It first compresses the dataset into an FP-tree, which also stores the association and counts of the items. Then it mines the FP-tree regarding each conditional FP-tree. In this way, mining frequent patterns in the dataset is transformed to mining the FP-tree.

Sequential Rules

Traditional association rules don't take into account the sequence among the transactions. In real applications, sequential patterns are usually required to describe customers' purchase behavior varying with time. Sequential rules were proposed to address this request.

In sequential transactional datasets, each transaction has a time stamp, and all the transactions of a customer form a sequence of transactions according to the time stamp. Then a sequential transactional dataset is composed of multiple sequences of transactions generated by customers. Table 6.14 shows a simple example of a sequential transactional dataset, where CID is the customer ID, the itemset in one pair of parentheses represents one transaction (the itemset is called an element), and each row shows a sequence of transactions of one customer.

Table 6.14 A Simple Example of a Sequential Transactional Dataset

CID	Sequence of transactions
1	(30) (90)
2	(10, 20) (30) (40, 60, 70)
3	(30, 50, 70)
4	(30) (40, 70) (90)
5	(90)

The sequential association rule mining algorithm is to discover the common or frequent purchase sequences of multiple customers (Agrawal, 1995). The frequent sequence is defined as the sequence whose support is greater than the predefined minimum support threshold. For example, if the minimum support threshold is 25 percent, then both <(30) (90)> and <(30) (40,70)> are frequent sequences. The sequence <(30) (40,70)> is frequent since customer #2 purchased <(30) (40,60,70)> , which contains <(30) (40,70)> .

The mining process of sequential association rules is similar to that of traditional association rules. But the number of candidate itemsets created for sequential association rules is much larger than that for traditional association rules, given the sequence of itemsets matters. For example, <(30) (90)> is different from <(90) (30)> and <(30,90)>. Besides, sequences like <(30) (30)> could also be appear in the set of candidate itemsets.

When constructing longer candidate itemsets from frequent itemsets, the join operation of two frequent sequences requires that the first sequence removing the first item is the same as the second sequence removing the last item. The result of the join operation is the first sequence added by the last item of the second sequence. If this item is a separate element in the second sequence, then it is added into the first sequence as a separate element. Otherwise, it can be merged into the last element in the first sequence.

Privacy-Preserving Data Mining Approaches

The problem of privacy-preserving data mining has become more important in recent years because of the increasing ability to store personal data about users, and the increasing sophistication of data mining algorithms to leverage this information. Data mining techniques have been developed successfully to extract knowledge in order to support a variety of domains such as marketing, weather forecasting, medical diagnosis, and national security. But it is still a challenge to mine certain kinds of data without violating the data owners' privacy. For example, how to mine patients' private data is an ongoing problem in health care applications. Data mining has been viewed as a threat to privacy because of the widespread proliferation of electronic data maintained by corporations and governments. This has led to increased concerns about the privacy of the underlying data.

Privacy-preserving data mining finds numerous applications in surveillance that are initially supposed to be "privacy-violating" applications. The key is to design methods that continue to be effective without compromising security. A number of techniques have been proposed for modifying or transforming the data in such a way as to preserve privacy. Most methods for privacy computations use some form of transformation on the data in order to perform the privacy preservation. Typically, such methods reduce the granularity of representation in order to reduce the sensitivity to privacy. This reduction in granularity results in some loss of effectiveness of data management or mining algorithms. This is the natural tradeoff between information loss and privacy. A survey of some of the techniques used for privacy-preserving data mining is presented here.

Anonymization

When releasing microdata for research purposes, one needs to limit disclosure risks to an acceptable level while maximizing data utility. To limit disclosure risk, Samarati and Sweeney introduced the k-anonymity privacy requirement, which requires each record in an anonymized table to be indistinguishable from at least *k* other records within the dataset, with respect to a set of quasi-identifier attributes. To achieve the *k*-anonymity requirement, techniques such as generalization and suppression are used for data anonymization. Figure 6.14 shows an example of data generalization. Unlike traditional privacy protection techniques such as data swapping and adding noise, information in a *k*-anonymous table through generalization and suppression remains truthful. In particular, a table is *k*-anonymous if the quasi-identifier values of each tuple are identical, to those of at least *k* other tuples. In general, *k* anonymity guarantees that an individual can be associated with his real tuple with a probability of at most 1/k. While *k*-anonymity protects against identity disclosure, it does not provide sufficient protection against attribute disclosure. Limitations of the *k*-anonymity model stem from the two assumptions. First, it may be very hard for the owner of a database to determine which of the attributes are or are not available in external tables. The second limitation is that the *k*-anonymity model assumes a certain method of attack, while in real scenarios there is no reason why the attacker should not try other methods.

Randomization

The randomization method is a technique for privacy-preserving data mining in which noise is added to the data in order to mask the attribute values of records. The noise added is sufficiently large so that individual record values cannot be recovered. Therefore, techniques are designed to derive aggregate distributions from the perturbed records. Subsequently, data mining techniques have to be developed in order to work with these aggregate distributions. Two kinds of perturbation are possible with the randomization method:

ViewerID	DeviceID	Age	Gender	Date
1	Bangalore	25	Male	11/11/2011
2	Bangalore	24	Male	11/11/2011
3	Bangalore	22	Female	11/12/2011
4	Beijing	44	Female	11/11/2011
5	Beijing	8	Male	11/11/2011
6	Beijing	7	Male	11/12/2011

ViewerID	DeviceID	Age	Gender	Date
1	Bangalore	Young Adult	Male	11/11/2011
2	Bangalore	Young Adult	Male	11/11/2011
3	Bangalore	Young Adult	Female	11/12/2011
4	Beijing	Senior	Female	11/11/2011
5	Beijing	Child	Male	11/11/2011
6	Beijing	Senior	Male	11/12/2011

Figure 6.14 Data Generalization Technique

1. *Additive Perturbation.* In this case, randomized noise is added to the data records. The overall data distributions can be recovered from the randomized records. Data mining and management algorithms are designed to work with these data distributions.

2. *Multiplicative Perturbation.* In this case, the random projection or random rotation techniques are used in order to perturb the records.

Condensation

Condensation constructs constrained clusters in the dataset and then generates pseudo-data from the statistics of these clusters .We refer to the technique as condensation because of its approach of using condensed statistics of the clusters in order to generate pseudo-data. The constraints on the clusters are defined in terms of the sizes of the clusters, which are chosen in a way so as to preserve *k*-anonymity. This method has a number of advantages over the randomization model in terms of preserving privacy in an effective way. In addition, since the approach works with pseudo-data rather than with modifications of original data, this helps in better preservation of privacy than techniques that simply use modifications of the original data. Furthermore, the use of pseudo-data no longer necessitates the redesign of data mining algorithms, since they have the same format as the original data. In contrast, when the data is constructed with the use of generalizations or suppressions, we need to redesign data mining algorithms to work effectively with incomplete or partially certain data. It can also be effectively used in situations with dynamic data updates such as the data stream problem.

Downgrading Application Effectiveness

In many cases, even though the data may not be available, the output of applications such as association rule mining, classification, or query processing may result in violations of privacy. This has led to research in downgrading the effectiveness of applications by either data or application modifications. Some examples of such techniques include association rule hiding, classifier downgrading, and query auditing.

Cryptographic Techniques

In many cases, the data may be distributed across multiple sites, and the owners of the data across these different sites may wish to compute a common function.

In such cases, a variety of cryptographic protocols may be used in order to communicate among the different sites, so that secure function computation is possible without revealing sensitive information. This technique became hugely popular for two main reasons: first, cryptography offers a well-defined model for privacy, which includes methodologies for proving and quantifying it. Second, there exists a vast toolset of cryptographic algorithms and constructs to implement privacy-preserving data mining algorithms. However, recent work has pointed that cryptography does not protect the output of a computation. Instead, it prevents privacy leaks in the process of computation. Thus, it falls short of providing a complete answer to the problem of privacy-preserving data mining.

Data Mining Process

CRISP-DM (Cross-Industry Standard Process for Data Mining) is an industry standard methodology for data mining and predictive analytics (Shearer, 2000). It makes data mining and predictive analytics projects more efficient, better organized, more reproducible, more manageable, and more likely to yield business success. Although CRISP-DM 2.0 is under investigation due to many changes occurring in the business application of data mining, CRISP-DM 1.0 is still the golden rule to be followed before CRISP-DM 2.0 is published. CRISP-DM 1.0 has been adopted in various industries and business problems, including marketing analysis and management, customer relationship management, risk analysis and management, fraud and unusual pattern detection, and social media analysis.

Figure 6.15 shows the CRISP-DM 1.0 process model, which is a popular process followed by most of data mining applications. It provides an overview of the life cycle of a data mining project, wherein are included six phases, business understanding, data understanding, data preparation, modeling, evaluation, and deployment. Each phase completes specific tasks depending on the data mining problem and the characteristics of the data. The arrows in Figure 6.15 indicate the sequence of the phases in the process model. From the figure, we can see that data mining is a multiple-phase, iterative, and spiral process, and it is never done by one-off execution from first phase (business understanding) to last phase (deployment). Actually, a lot of moving back and forth between different phases is always a must for improving the modeling accuracy. That is a very critical point that one should keep in mind always.

The outer circle in Figure 6.15 symbolizes the cyclic nature of data mining itself again. The lessons learned during the process can trigger new, often more focused business questions that need to be addressed in a new cycle of modeling. Besides, the business requirements may change with time, and the models could be out of date after a period of time of creation due to the change of the pattern within the data. All these will request to retrain and update the existing models and may trigger a new modeling iteration. During this continuous evolution, subsequent data mining processes will benefit from the experiences of previous ones.

Given its widespread use in various industries, CRISP-DM is adopted and adapted to realize data mining capability. Since data understanding and data preparation are correlated very closely, for simplicity we combine them into one phase, data understanding and preparation. We also combine modeling and evaluation into modeling and evaluation for the same purpose. The details on modeling practice within each phase are as follows.

Business Understanding

This initial phase focuses on understanding the project objectives and requirements from a business perspective, converting this knowledge into a data mining problem definition, and designing a preliminary plan for achieving the objectives.

Business Objective and Requirement

The objective of targeted advertising in digital signage is to play relevant advertisements to the audience in front of the digital sign. This requires correlating the displayed advertisement with demographic information (such as age and gender) and context information (such as time, location, and weather), and on this basis training advertising models that are used for advertisement recommendation. Corresponding to the three different targeting modes, seeing-based targeting, prediction-based targeting, and context based-targeting, three types of models or rules need to be trained as described before. It should be noticed that we cannot use a passer prediction rule like "a kid followed by a young couple" to target the young couple, since there could be some others, such as three seniors walking together with them. We need to predict the distribution of the audience or the dominant audience type in a particular timeslot instead.

Data Mining Problem Definition

Within these rules, some predicted attributes have continuous values, some have discrete values, and some could have continuous values or discrete values

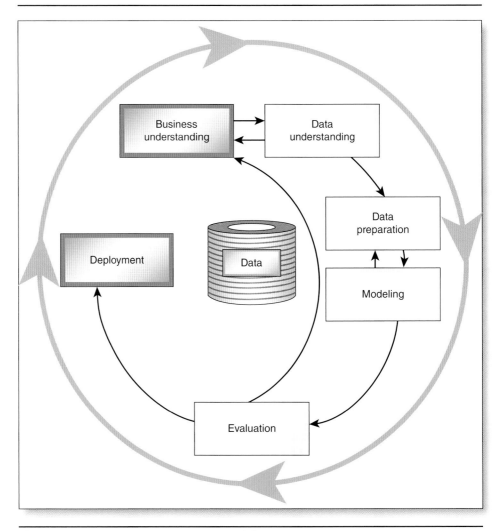

Figure 6.15 CRISP-DM 1.0 Process Model

after being discretized. From the perspective of data mining, the above training tasks require both classification and regression. Therein, classification is used for prediction on categorical or discrete predicted variables, and regression is used for prediction on continuous predicted variables. That means both classification and regression algorithms are needed. Regarding the predicted attribute that can be discretized, both of these two algorithms could be used from functionality, but which should be used finally also depends on other factors, such as the form of the explanatory or input attributes.

Research Method

The research is carried out by the combination of domain knowledge and experimental analysis. Based on domain knowledge and expert experiences, a number of modeling experiments were designed. Then analysis was conducted based on the experimental results. Upon the analysis, new experiments were designed accordingly. The iteration will continue until obtaining satisfying modeling results.

Data Understanding and Preparation

Data understanding starts with an initial data collection and proceeds with activities in order to get familiar with the data, identify relevant data sources and attributes, investigate data quality problems, discover first insights into the data (statistics of the variables), or detect interesting subsets to form hypotheses for hidden information. Based on the understanding of the data and the business problem, data preparation covers all activities to construct the final dataset (data that will be fed into the modeling tool) from the initial raw data. Main activities include data extraction, data preprocessing, such as normalization, transformation, data cleaning, and data discretization (Dorian, 1999). Table 6.15 shows the typical preprocessing requirements of different algorithms. There "Yes" means the corresponding preprocessing operation is needed by the algorithm, and "No" means the corresponding preprocessing operation is not needed by the algorithm.

Data Understanding

Relevant Attributes. Based business understanding and requirement, some possible relevant attributes are identified and collected, including date, time, location, weather, temperature, gender, age, device, and advertisement profile.

Basic Data Understanding. Understand the distribution of the values of each attribute with simple statistics or distribution chart. Understand the quality of the collected data, including existence of missing values, outliers and anomalies. Understand the relevance and dependency among the input attributes as well as output attribute and input attributes.

Data Quality Analysis. Confirm that the key data items are collected that are critical for the success of the data mining project. If missing, the project most probably will fail. Examine the existence and volume of missing values, invalid values, and anomalies to determine the required data preprocessing. Determine the data volume or date scope required for full training of advertising models. A reasonable amount of training data with a reasonable quality is the basis of the data mining task.

Data Preparation

Feature Selection. Based on understanding of the problem and the relevant data source, several tables are joined to collect the relevant features (or attributes). On one hand, feature selection is based on existing knowledge and experience about which attributes possibly influence the dwelling time as

Table 6.15   The Typical Preprocessing Requirements of Different Algorithms

Algorithm name	Handling Missing values	Handling outliers	normali-zation	Numerali-zation	discreti-zation	transfor-mation	Feature selection
Decision Tree	No	No	No	No	No	Yes	Yes
ANN	Yes	Yes	Yes	Yes	No	Yes	Yes
Rule induction	Yes	No	No	No	Yes	Yes	No
SVM	Yes	Yes	No	Yes	No	Yes	Yes
Naïve Bayes	Yes	No	No	No	No	Yes	Yes
Rough set	Yes	No	No	No	Yes	Yes	No
Regression	Yes	Yes	No	Yes	No	Yes	Yes
KNN	Yes	Yes	Yes	No	No	Yes	Yes
Clustering	Yes	Yes	Yes	No	No	Yes	Yes
Association Rules	Yes	No	No	No	Yes	Yes	No

well as some relevance tests between the input and output attribute (Liu and Setiono 1995; Kohavi and John 1997). This selected set of attributes will be filtered later on per the modeling experimental results. So selecting a relative larger attribute set is not a bad idea.

New Attribute Derivation. A new attribute named TargetPotential is created to describe the level of interest of an audience in a particular advertisement or advertisement category. Since it is hard to determine if one audience type is interested in one ad or not accurately, five values (very weak, weak, likely, strong and very strong) are assigned to TargetPotential according to the dwelling time of the audience type. Also two other attributes, FromMediaStart and TillMediaEnd are created if the audience watched the advertisement from its very start and till its very end respectively. These two attributes are also used to determine the audience's interestingness level.

Discretization. Some data mining algorithms require the inputs should be categorical or discrete rather than continuous. Besides, when the output is not necessarily a precise number and can be some value interval, we can discretize the output to improve modeling accuracy. There exists some discretization algorithm for bother supervised and unsupervised scenarios (Dougherty, 1995).

Data Scope Determination. The initial data scope is usually determined according to the understanding of the problem. Experiments can also help to determine the best time scope of the training dataset. One quarter could be a good time scope for training advertising models. But to be safe, other time scopes, including one month, two quarters, three quarters, and one year are also tested.

Modeling and Evaluation

In this phase, we need to select and apply the potential good and usable modeling algorithms and calibrate their parameters to optimal values. Typically, several algorithms can be used for the same type of data mining problem. But different algorithms show different performance and have specific requirements on the form of data. In addition to algorithm selection, tool selection is also needed. Not all the existing tools are available internally. And also different tools contain different modeling algorithms. Table 6.16 shows the characteristics of different data mining algorithms.

Table 6.16   The Characteristics of Different Data Mining Algorithms

Algorithms	Capabilities	Dataset	Interpretability	Compute complexity	Dimensional Scalability
Decision Tree	Classification, regression	Hybrid	Good	Low	Good
ANN	Classification, regression	Continuous	Weak	Higher	Weak
Rule induction	Classification	Hybrid	Good	Low	Good
SVM	Classification, regression	Continuous	Medium	Medium	Good
Naïve Bayes	Classification	Hybrid	Good	Low	Good
Rough set	Classification	Continuous	Good	Medium	Medium
Regression	Regression analysis	Continuous	Good	Low	Medium
KNN	Classification	Continuous	Medium	Low	Weak
Clustering	Clustering analysis	Continuous	Weak	Low	Weak
Association Rules	Association analysis	Discrete	Good	Higher	Weak

Before the models are applied to real business, they should be evaluated on their performance (how good they are) in terms of accuracy, reliability, robustness, and so on. Accuracy is the most common performance measurement for prediction task. In addition to technical evaluation, the models should also be evaluated from business perspective by customer and business experts. This will guarantee that the models properly achieve the business objectives and realize true business values. The evaluation result will be used for making decision whether the models should be adopted.

Algorithm and Tool Selection

Following the discussion in the previous subsection, both classification and regression algorithms could be used for prediction, but whether they can be used finally also depends on the form of the modeling data. For passer distribution prediction, the output attributes are continuous; some input attributes are discrete and some are continuous, so some regression algorithms, such as logistic regression, can be used here. For dominant passer prediction, the output attribute is discrete, so the classification algorithm can be used.

For TargetPotential prediction, the output is discretized and most of the input attributes are discrete, so a classification algorithm can also be used.

In addition to algorithm selection, data mining tools have to be selected. Three data modeling tools, Microsoft SSAS, JMP, and IDEAL are under consideration. Both JMP and IDEAL are not good at handling a very large dataset. IDEAL usually consumes a much longer time than the other two modeling tools with the same dataset. JMP usually consumes too much memory so as to be unaffordable for large datasets. And how to access the models built in JMP from other applications, or how to integrate the models into other applications, is still under investigation. Microsoft SSAS is not only able to manipulate a large dataset but is easier to use and integrate with other applications. In SSAS, three algorithms, decision tree, naïve Bayes, and association rules can be used for classification based on discrete inputs. And logistic regression can be used for training passer distribution predictive models. We tested these algorithms and found that the decision tree model realizes the highest evaluation accuracy among the three classification algorithms.

Modeling Process

Inputs Filtering. Usually not all the selected features in the previous phase are really helpful. During the modeling process, we need observe the dependency between the output attribute and the input attributes and ignore the less depended input attributes in next modeling activities. In this way we can find an optimal set of input attributes for modeling. In the SSAS model viewer, we can drag the slider on the left to view the dependencies at a different level. There are also other techniques used for this purpose, such as a statistics-based method, an entropy-based method, greedy search, simulated annealing, and evolutionary algorithms.

Parameter calibration. Modeling parameters usually influence modeling results. Different algorithms have different parameters. There are three important parameters, complexity penalty, score method, and split method in the decision tree algorithm and some other parameters for other algorithms, which should be tuned according to both experimental results and the results of the previous steps, problem understanding, data understanding, and algorithm properties. Table 6.17 shows some typical parameters of different algorithms, which could be specified and tuned during the modeling process.

Table 6.17   The Meaning of the Typical Parameters of Different Algorithms

Algorithms	Typical parameters
Decision tree	Pruning confidence: the smaller of the value, the more pruning performed and the more generalized tree obtained.
	Minimal number of cases within a node: the larger the value, the more generalized tree obtained.
	Maximal tree depth: the smaller the value, the smaller, generalized tree obtained
ANN	Number of hidden layers: the larger the value, the slower the network converges.
	Number of hidden units: the larger the value, the more complicated models can be trained.
	Learning rate: smaller learning rate will result in slower convergence, but usually can lead to better resolution than larger learning rate.
	Momentum constant: if the learning rate is small, then Momentum constant should be increased to expedite the convergence; on the contrary, if the learning rate is large, then Momentum constant should be decreased to void the instability of the network.
RIPPER	Optimization iterations: usually 2 ~ 5 is OK for the value. Over increasing iterations has little influence to the result.
SVM	Kernel function and its parameters, penalty parameter: these parameters have complicated and significant influence to the classification result, which usually need to be determined by other auxiliary methods.
KNN	Number of neighbors: For too small a value, the result is apt to be influenced by noise and outliers, but too large a value will lead to more classification errors.
K-means	Number of clusters (k): An overly small value results in few clusters, which are usually uninterpretable and with unclear semantics. An overly large value results in many similar and few distinct clusters.
Association rules	Support: small support leads to more frequent itemsets and higher time cost. Confidence: The rules with low confidence are not practical.
	Maximal number of items in rule premise: including too many items in the rule premise leads to lower representativeness.

Technical Evaluation

Theoretically, there are three methods for accuracy evaluation, leave-one-out, cross-validation, and partition. Cross-validation is used for small and medium size datasets and partition for large datasets. Leave-one-out is seldom used in practice. We use the partition method for evaluation owing to the availability of huge amount of data, that is, part of the data for training and the remainder for evaluation.

The evaluation result can be viewed by lift chart and classification (confusion) matrix in SSAS. From a classification matrix, we can see the number of records that are classified correctly and wrongly as well as the numbers of records that are misclassified from one predicted value to another. By observing the lift chart and classification matrix, we can further understand the characteristics of the modeling data and analyze possible causes of declining test accuracy to determine how to further improve it.

In order to show the effectiveness of predictive modeling and the advertising models, besides the test accuracy of the models on test dataset, some business metrics, such as average dwelling time or average sold out, should be evaluated before and after the adoption of the advertising models in the digital signage. The evaluation results should also be synched up with the customer and business experts for their review from a business perspective.

Deployment and Integration

Creation of the model is generally not the end of the project. We need to utilize the model to create business values identified at the beginning of the project. The deliverable could be some knowledge about the data and business organized and presented in a way that the customer can use it. The deliverable could also be an executable model integrated with or accessed from other applications, which can respond to user's inputs and return outputs. Usually, the deployment and integration need the cooperation of customer, business experts and the modeling experts.

Different modeling tools support different levels and ways of integration. Some can export the model into other applications, while others provide access to the model they host through APIs, PMML (Predictive Model Markup Language), or some kind of scripts. The predictive models built into SSAS can be accessed from other applications or web interface with DMX (Data Mining eXtension). DMX is kind of SQL-like script and can be embedded into other programming languages, such as C# and Java. A prototype was developed to demonstrate the access to the predictive models in SSAS from another application.

Model Update and Maintenance

The pattern captured by the predictive model may change with time, so the model may be out of date after a period of time. There comes a need to retrain the models to keep them updated. One way is to retrain the models regularly, such as weekly, biweekly, monthly, or quarterly. Another way is to retrain the models on demand. The models are retrained when the prediction accuracy declines below some threshold, or a retraining request received from the user. Accordingly, the training dataset needs to be update regularly to ensure the models are created from up to date data.

Cloud-Based Data Mining Services Infrastructure

In this section we discuss the cloud-based services, the cloud-based services developed and offered in the data mining module of IAF and finally about the recommended infrastructure for deploying the data mining services.

Introduction to Cloud-Based Service

Cloud computing is the delivery of computing as a service rather than a product, whereby shared resources, software, and information are provided to computers and other devices as a metered service over a network (typically the Internet).

Cloud computing is a marketing term for technologies that provide computation, software, data access, and storage services that do not require end-user knowledge of the physical location and configuration of the system that delivers the services. A parallel to this concept can be drawn with the electricity grid, wherein end-users consume power without needing to understand the component devices or infrastructure required to provide the service.

In a traditional IT model, adding new applications and expanding your infrastructure can lead to excessive operational expenses driven by:

- Complex, monolithic systems that are difficult to modify or expand.

- A constantly growing staff of specialists for each solution.

- Poor utilization levels of servers and storage, increasing your hardware, power and cooling, and data center real estate costs.

Such traditional problems can be eliminated with the cloud-based services. The following are the various services that can be provided in cloud:

- *Software as a Service* (*SaaS*). Cloud application services or SaaS deliver software as a service over the Internet, eliminating the need to install and run the application on the customer's own computers and simplifying maintenance and support. What makes a cloud application different from other applications is its elasticity. Cloud applications have the ability to scale out and in. This can be achieved by cloning tasks into multiple virtual machines at runtime to meet the changing work demand.

■ *Platform as a Service.* Cloud platform services, also known as Platform as a Service (PaaS), deliver a computing platform and/or solution stack as a service, often consuming cloud infrastructure and sustaining cloud applications. It facilitates deployment of applications without the cost and complexity of buying and managing the underlying hardware and software layers. Cloud computing is becoming a major change in our industry, and one of the most important parts of this change is the shift of cloud platforms. Platforms let developers write certain applications that can run in the cloud or even use services provided by the cloud. There are different names being used for platforms that can include the on-demand platform, or Cloud 9. Regardless of the nomenclature, they all have great potential in developing, and when development teams create applications for the cloud, each must build its own cloud platform.

■ *Infrastructure as a Service.* Cloud infrastructure services, also known as Infrastructure as a Service (IaaS), deliver computer infrastructure, typically a platform virtualization environment as a service along with raw (block) storage and networking. Rather than purchasing servers, software, data-center space or network equipment, clients instead buy those resources as a fully outsourced service. Suppliers typically bill such services on a utility computing basis; the amount of resources consumed (and therefore the cost) will typically reflect the level of activity.

■ *Systems management as a Service.* Systems management as a service helps you monitor, assess and update assets across your organization.

■ *Desktop as a Service.* DaaS keeps the sensitive data safe, helps your organization stay compliant, and provides employees with the flexibility to work where, when, and how they want.

Cloud-Based Data Mining Services

In this section we discuss the various cloud-based services provided by the data mining module. The services exposed by the data mining module make the customer/owner not have to worry about the infrastructure and technical expertise required to maintain and run the data mining module.

1. *Storage Cloud:* this service implements the traditional Infrastructure as Service (IaaS) architecture. The basic idea is to provide data space to the customers/owners of the digital signage to store the VA data and PoP data that have been collected at the digital signage. The digital player sends the PoP data collected to the CMS, the CMS then sends each digital player's PoP data to the data mining Server. The data mining module also exposes a service that periodically collects the VA data corresponding to each of the digital players from the analytic server and stores it in the database. This service eliminates the need for the customer/owner of the digital signage to worry about the data space required to store the data.

2. *Data Management Cloud:* this service exposed by the data mining module correlates the VA dat a and PoP data stored in the database of the data mining module and creates a new dataset, which is then preprocessed to make the data suitable for the data mining process.

3. *Compute Cloud*: this is the most important service exposed by the data mining module. This service consists of the following three subservices. This service implements the SaaS architecture.

   ■ *Create New Model Service:* the objective of this service is to provide a capability to the customer/owner to create new mining models in the data mining module on the data that has been collected from the digital player and analytical server.

   ■ *Retrain Existing Model Service:* the objective of this service is to provide a capability to the customer/owner to retrain the existing mining models in the data mining module.

   ■ *Query Model Content Service:* the objective of this service is to provide a capability to the customer/owner to query the models present in the data mining module and to receive the rules corresponding to each of the digital players.

Chapter 7

The Intelligent Advertising Framework (IAF)

Problems worthy of attack prove their worth by fighting back.

—Paul Erdös

Intelligent Advertising Framework (IAF) is based on the concept of using anonymous video analytics (AVA) data and data mining concepts to achieve targeted advertising, which can then be used to measure and improve the advertising return on investment (ROI) of a digital sign. Future customers belonging to the same demographic as previous customers will be targeted based on the viewing behavior of the previous customers. By analyzing AVA viewership data collected from previous viewers in front of a display, IAF can discover their viewing patterns and use this information to train advertising models that can be deployed to the digital sign. These advertising models can then be used to choose specific advertisements from the inventory of available content to intelligently target future customers. By correlating AVA viewership information with point-of-sale (POS) data, our framework can also be used to establish a link between the response time to an advertisement by a certain demographic group and the effect on the sale of the advertised product. This chapter is a case study of how Computer Vision, Data Mining and Machine learning algorithms can be combined together to create an Intelligent system. The later part of this chapter has specific implementation details.

IAF Architecture

Figure 7.1 illustrates the end-to-end architecture for the IAF. There are four main components in this framework. They are digital signage, a data mining module (DMM), a content management system (CMS) and the digital player (DP).

- ◼ *Digital Signage:* The digital sign displays the advertisements, captures the viewership data, and sends the information to the database where the data is cleaned/filtered and then accessed by the data mining module.

- ◼ *Data Mining Module (DMM):* In the data mining module the advertising models are generated on the data collected and trained using data mining algorithms like Naïve Bayes, decision trees, and association rules. Once the models are generated they are then consumed by the content management system.

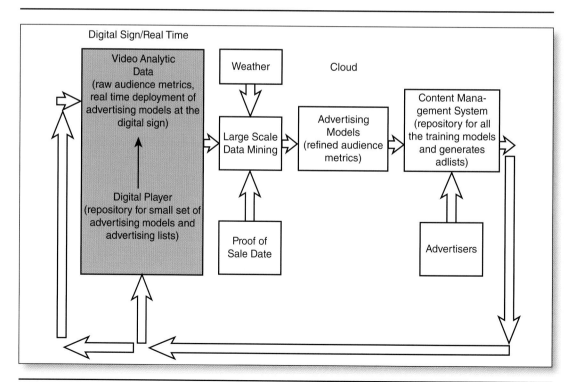

Figure 7.1 IAF Architecture

■ *Content Management System (CMS):* Using the advertising models from the data mining module and the advertisements information, the CMS generates a customized advertising list.

■ *Digital Player (DP):* The digital player generates the advertising lists in real time. This module acts as a specialized condensed repository for the information, which is mainly stored in the CMS.

Following are some of the important aspects of IAF architecture: data ownership, targeted advertising, and real time triggering.

Data Ownership

Data ownership refers to both the possession of and responsibility for information. Ownership implies power as well as control. The control of information includes not just the ability to access, create, modify, package, derive benefit from, sell or remove data, but also the right to assign these access privileges to others.

In a typical digital signage ecosystem, a number of important players are involved: the advertiser or content provider, the venue operator such as a mall or store owner, the content management system provider, the digital signage network operator, and the video analytics service provider. Due to the large number of parties involved, data sharing and data ownership become important considerations for IAF. Each module of the IAF architecture (Figure 7.2) is dependent on the other module for data transfer. Each module uses the data differently than the other modules. Thus the question about data ownership arises. Multiple owners can also be dangerous in a number of ways. Since the data is handled by multiple sources there is a good chance of the data being corrupted or that certain parties might inhibit other parties from getting access to the data.

The IAF architecture proposes a tentative solution for data ownership. It is based on the paradigm that was defined by Loshin (2002). He has identified a list of parties who could potentially claim the data. They are:

■ *Creator*—The party that creates or generates data

■ *Consumer*—The party that uses the data owns the data

■ *Compiler*—This is the entity that selects and compiles information from different information sources

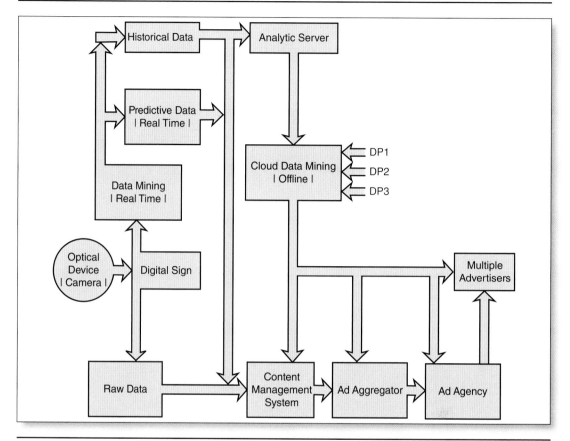

Figure 7.2   IAF Data Ownership Flow

■ *Enterprise*—All data that enters the enterprise or is created within the enterprise is completely owned by the enterprise

■ *Funder*—The user that commissions the data creation claims ownership

■ *Decoder*—In environments where information is "locked" inside particular encoded formats, the party that can unlock the information becomes an owner of that information

■ *Packager*—The party that collects information for a particular use and adds value through formatting the information for a particular market or set of consumers

■ *Reader as owner*—The value of any data that can be read is subsumed by the reader and, therefore, the reader gains value through adding that information to an information repository

■ *Subject as owner*—The subject of the data claims ownership of that data, mostly in reaction to another party claiming ownership of the same data

■ *Purchaser/Licenser as Owner*—The individual or organization that buys or licenses data may stake a claim to ownership

We will use these roles as a guideline in defining the owners for the IAF system.

■ *Digital Sign:* This will be the creator since the VA data gets generated at the digital sign.

■ *Data Mining Module:* This module will be the consumer, since it will be using the VA data created at the digital sign to generate the advertising models using data mining principles.

■ *Predictive Data:* This module is the decoder, since in the real-time scenario, the data gets locked here and gets encoded to generate the playlist to target the current viewers.

■ *Analytic Server:* The raw data sent by the digital sign gets converted in the analytic server to useful data, thus it is a good candidate for the packager role.

■ *Cloud-based Data Mining:* Fits the role of a compiler, since it compiles all the information for the various digital players; information such as the playlist.

■ *CMS:* It will be the consumer, since it uses the information generated by the different modules to generate the ad list.

■ *Ad Aggregator:* This will be the compiler; it is a repository for all the advertising information.

- ◼ *Ad Agency*: All the advertisements are collected by the ad agency, so it reads all these ads and can thus claim ownership of the advertising data. It is a perfect example of the reader as owner.

- ◼ *Multiple Advertisers:* An advertiser whose ad got played on the digital sign could claim the ownership of the VA data, mostly in response to other advertiser claim for ownership. Thus the advertisers fit the role of subject as owner.

Targeted Advertising

The main idea behind the concept of targeted advertising is to show the audience certain ads that have in the past been viewed for a reasonable amount of time by the audience belonging to the same demographics. Targeted advertising will be discussed in detailed in the later sections.

Real Time Triggering

One of the most important functions of the IAF is targeting the viewers in real time. The real time processing takes place at the digital player end. Each digital player receives advertising models from the CMS. The advertising model has a parameter called the confidence value. It helps us decide if we need to play the ads in online or offline mode. So when the VA data gets analyzed in the real time mode, then the rules from the advertising model are chosen and the confidence value attached to this rule is compared with the threshold value. If the value falls short of the threshold, then the default playlist gets played, but if the value is same or greater than the threshold, then the ad list gets modified and the ads targeting the current viewers are played. After the current ad, either the player can go back to playing the default playlist or could play targeted ads. Figure 7.3 shows the detailed flow for the real time triggering in a digital player.

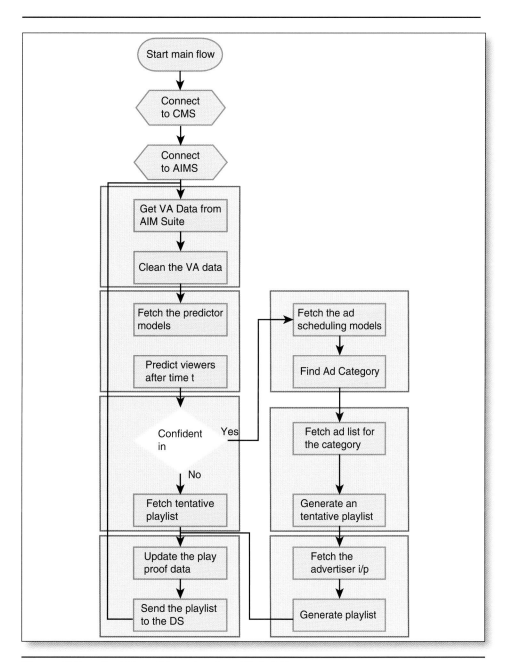

Figure 7.3   Real Time Triggering in a Digital Player

Main Components in IAF

This section covers the main components of IAF, such as the data mining module, content management system, digital player, and AVA component in detail.

Data Mining Module

The basic task of the data mining module of the IAF is to achieve the targeted advertising by making use of the data mining technology. Data mining is the process of extracting hidden information or knowledge or relationships from the data. Data mining commonly involves four classes of tasks; they are

- *Association Rule Learning*—Searches for relationships between variables. For example a supermarket might gather data on customer purchasing habits. Using association rule learning, the supermarket can determine which products are frequently bought together and use this information for marketing purposes. This is sometimes referred to as market basket analysis.

- *Clustering*—Clustering is the task of discovering groups and structures in the data such that data in each group or structure have the same behavior or are someway related to each other.

- *Classification*—Classification is the task of identifying the class or category of a data based upon the previous learning. For example, an e-mail program might attempt to classify an e-mail as legitimate or spam. Common algorithms include decision tree learning, nearest neighbor, naïve Bayesian classification, neural networks, and support vector machines.

- *Regression Analysis*—In regression analysis the main focus is on finding out a relation between a dependent variable and one or more independent variables. More specifically, regression analysis helps one understand how the typical value of the dependent variable changes when any one of the independent variables is changed, while the other independent variables are held fixed.

The data mining module tries to apply one or more of these data mining techniques to find out the hidden relationships such as relation between the audience types and advertisements, relation between audience types, and so on. In the data mining module we have built two types of mining models.

A model is a set of rules, where each rule gives a correlation between a target variable and set of input variables. Each rule is associated with a confidence value that will be used in deciding whether that particular rule is confident enough for prediction purpose. The following are the two mining models in IAF.

Ad Category Model

The ad category model is built on the viewership data and the proof of play (POP) data. It contains a set of rules that correlate the most appropriate advertisement category or advertisement with particular demographic audience type and context (time, location, weather). In the ad category model, we have two sub models:

1. *Ad Category Real Time Model*: This model contains a set of rules used for real time triggering. The rules in this model are used for predicting an advertisement category or advertisement for a particular demographic audience type who have been recognized in front of the display in real time.

Example:

If Digital-Sign-Id = Chandler Mall and Time-Slot = Morning and Day-of-Week = Friday and Gender = Female and Age = Young and Weather = Clear and Ad-Category = Outdoors and Targeted-Ads = bicycle, then Potential-Target = Very-Strong (at 80 percent confidence).

2. *Ad Category Offline Model*: This model contains a set of rules used for scheduling an advertising playlist for a particular digital sign for a particular time of the day.

Example:

If Digital-Sign-Id = Chandler Mall and Time-Slot = Morning and Time = 9:00-9:30 and Day-of-Week = Friday and Weather = Clear and Ad-Category = Category-1 and Targeted ads = Ad-1, then Potential-Target = likely (at 70 percent confidence)

Passer Pattern Model

This model contains a set of rules that help us in discovering audience behavior or predicting future audience based on previous audience. In the passer pattern model we have two sub models:

1. *Passer Pattern Discovery:* This model contains a set of rules that predicts the dominant audience type for a particular digital sign and for a particular time of the day.

Example:

If Digital-Sign-Id = Chandler Mall and Time-Slot = Morning and Time = 10:00~10:30 and Day-of-Week = Friday and Weather = Clear, then (dominant) passer type = senior female (at 70 percent confidence)

2. *Passer Prediction:* This model contains a set of rules that predicts the audience type for a particular digital sign based on the audience already in front of that digital sign.

Example:

If Digital-Sign-Id = Chandler Mall and Time-Slot = Morning and Day-of-Week = Friday and Weather = Clear and Current-Dominant-Passer-Type = Senior-Female then Next (dominant) Passer -Type = Senior-Male.

Functionality

The functionality of the DMM is mainly divided into three important processes:

1. *Create New Model Process:* The main objective of this process is to create new mining models in the data mining module. Figure 7.4 shows the detailed process flow for creating new mining models. Following are the important components of this process.

■ *Data Connector:* This component fetches the AVA data and weather data from the database.

■ *Data Preprocessor:* This component preprocesses the fetched data from the database in such a way to improve the efficiency of the

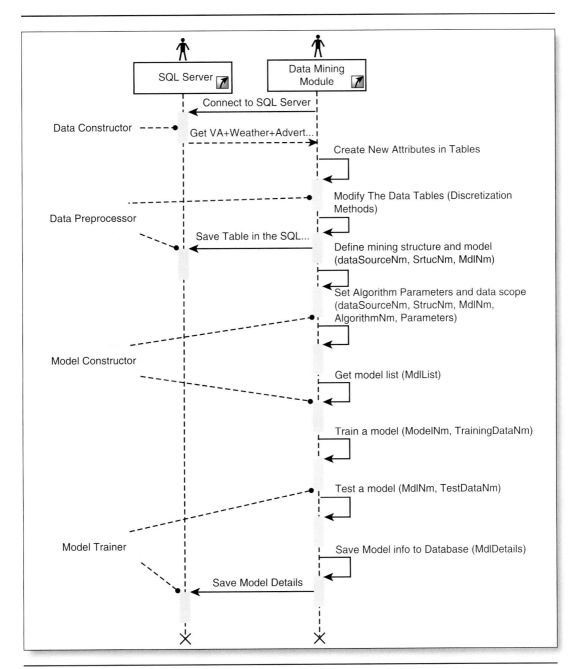

Figure 7.4   Create New Model Process Flow

mining model. Preprocessing techniques such as discretization and normalization are applied.

■ *Model Constructor:* This component defines a new mining structure and mining model. It also customizes the model with data filters, training parameters, and so on.

■ *Model Trainer:* This component trains a particular model with the selected trained data set, tests a particular model with the selected test data set, evaluates the performance of the mining models, and saves the model information to the database.

2. *Query Model Content Process:* This particular process is initiated when the CMS request for mining model content. Figure 7.5 shows the detailed process flow for the query model content process. This component of DMM accepts the requests from the CMS, processes the requests and sends the results back to CMS. The possible requests that CMS can make are requests for ad category real-time model content, ad category offline model content, passer pattern discovery model content, and passer prediction model content.

3. *Retrain Existing Model Process:* In this process all the models that have been built in the create new model process will be retrained with the new set of training data and testing data. During this process the training conditions are reconfigured accordingly for the new training data set. Figure 7.6 shows the detailed process flow diagram for the retrain existing model process. Following are some important components of the process:

■ *Data Connector:* This component fetches the new AVA data and weather data from the database.

■ *Model Constructor:* This component deletes the model structure and model information of the existing models. It also reconfigures the training conditions for each of the existing models to suit the new data set.

■ *Model Trainer:* This component trains a particular model with the selected trained data set, tests a particular model with the selected test data set, evaluates the performance of the mining models, and saves the model information to the database.

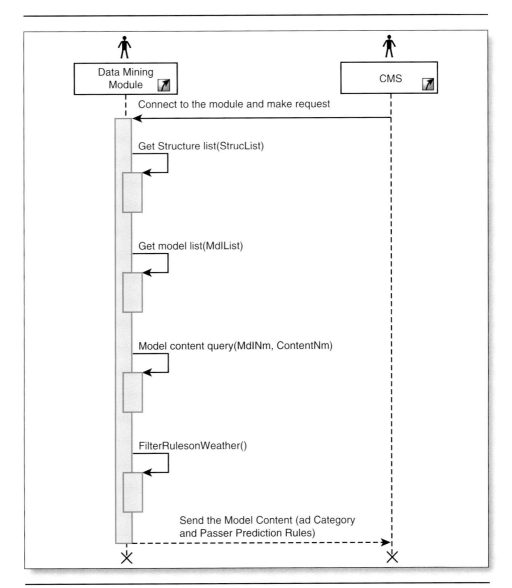

Figure 7.5   Query Model Content Process Flow

Data Mining Module Data Flow

Figure 7.7 shows the complete data flow of the data mining module. The diagram clearly shows the data movement between different processes of the data mining module and database, and between the CMS and the data mining module. Please refer to the above section for the explanation of various components in the data flow diagram.

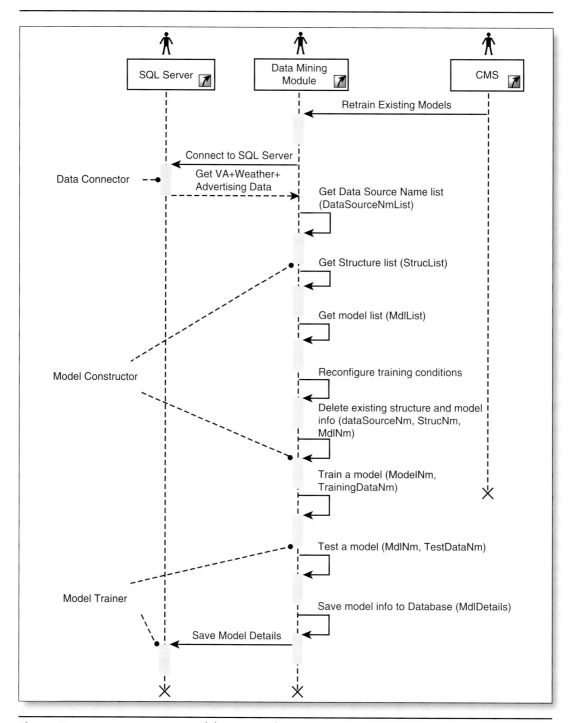

Figure 7.6 Retrain Existing Models Process Flow

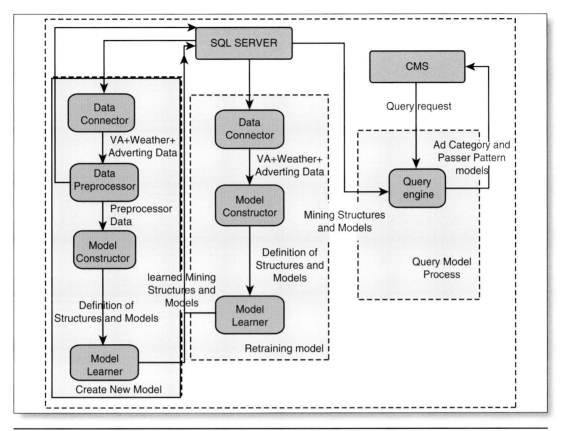

Figure 7.7   Data Mining Model Data Flow

Data Mining Module Class

Figure 7.8 shows the class diagram of the data mining module. The following are some of the important components of the class diagram:

■ *DataMiningModule:* This class is the base class for the DMM. It provides all the basic functionalities such as to make connections to the database server, create new models, test models, train models, query model content, query model prediction, and retrain existing models.

■ *SQL ServerDB Interface:* This class is responsible for the communication between the DMM and database server.

■ *DMMAdCategory:* This class is exposed as web service to CMS. It provides functionalities such as to send ad category model content

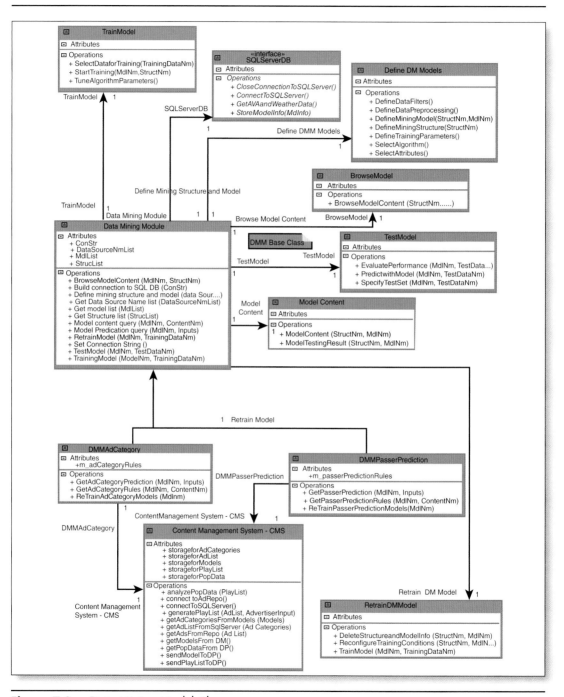

Figure 7.8   Data Mining Model Class

to CMS, send ad category model prediction results to CMS and to retrain the ad category models in DMM.

■ *DMMPasserPrediction:* This class is exposed as web service to CMS. It provides functionalities such as to send passer prediction model content to CMS, to send passer prediction model prediction results to CMS, and to retrain the passer prediction models in DMM.

■ *DefineDMModels:* This class provides the functionality to create new mining models in DMM. In specific it provides functionalities such as to define the mining model, define the mining structure, select mining algorithms, define data filters, define data preprocessing, and select training parameters.

■ *ModelContent:* This class provides the functionality to query the model content and model testing results.

■ *TestModel:* This class provides functionality to test a model in the DMM. It provides functionalities such as to specify the test data set, predict with a particular model on the test data set, and to evaluate the performance of the model.

■ *TrainModel:* This class provides functionality to train a model in DMM. It provides functionalities such as to specify the training data set for a particular model, to tune the algorithm parameters of a particular model, and to start the training process.

■ *RetrainDMModel:* This class provides functionality to retrain existing models in the DMM. It provides functionalities such as to delete the model structure and model information, to reconfigure the training conditions, and to train the model finally.

■ *BrowseModelContent:* This class provides functionality to visualize the model content.

Content Management System

The basic task of the CMS is to fetch the ad category and passer pattern models from the data mining module and then generate an ad list and playlist based on the rules in the models and also the advertisers input.

Functionality

The functionality of the CMS is mainly divided into four important processes:

1. *Player-Specific Model Extractor:* This process is initiated by sending a request to the DMM for the latest ad category and passer pattern models. After receiving the models from the DMM, the player-specific model extractor segregates the rules in the models for each of the digital player based on the digital player unique ID in each of the rules; these segregated rules are then stored in the CMS database. Figure 7.9 shows the detailed process flow for the player-specific model extractor process.

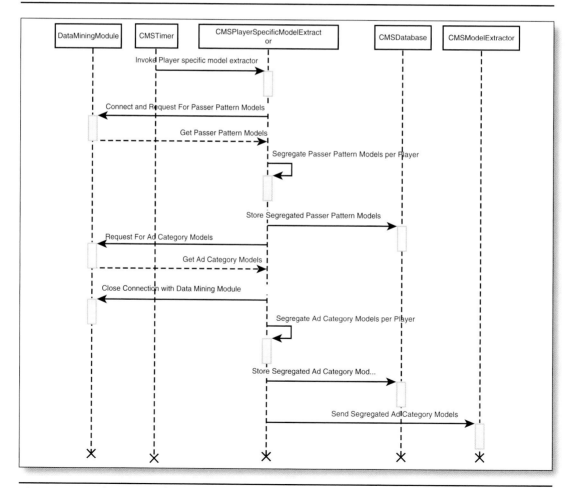

Figure 7.9   Player-Specific Model Extractor Process Flow

2. *Model Extractor:* The model extractor receives the segregated models from the player-specific model extractor process and then extracts the ad categories from them. These ad categories are then arranged by time of the day and then sent to the ad list generator process. Figure 7.10 shows the detailed process flow for the model extractor process.

3. *Ad List Generator:* This process receives the ad categories for each digital player that has been extracted in the model extractor process and then fetches the ad information such as the ad name, ad duration, and so on corresponding to each ad category from the advertisements database. With this ad information the process generates the ad list for each digital player. The final ad list corresponding to each digital

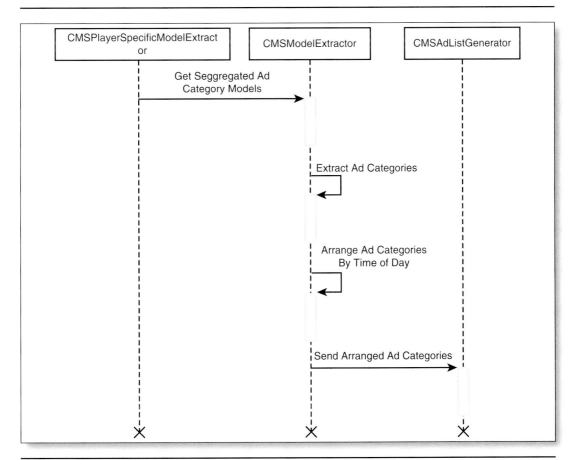

Figure 7.10 Model Extractor Process Flow

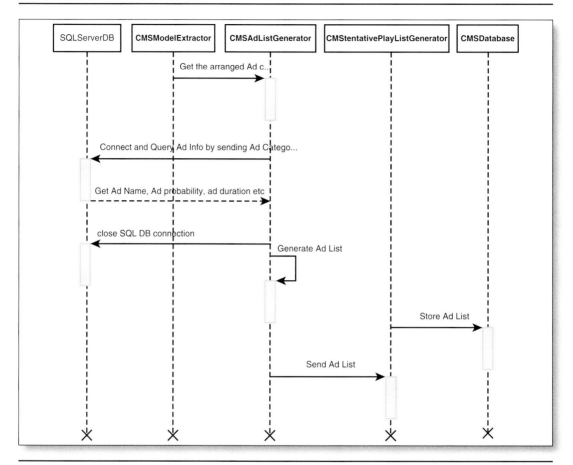

Figure 7.11 Ad List Generator Process Flow

player is then stored in the CMS database. Figure 7.11 shows the detailed process flow for the ad list generator.

4. *Tentative Playlist Generator and Advertiser Input Scheduler:* Figure 7.12 describes the flow of tentative playlist generator and advertiser input scheduler. The tentative playlist generator receives the ad list from the ad list generator and generates a tentative playlist based on play probability. The advertiser input scheduler fetches advertisers' preferences and generates a default playlist. The scheduler stores the default playlist in the CMS database for further usage.

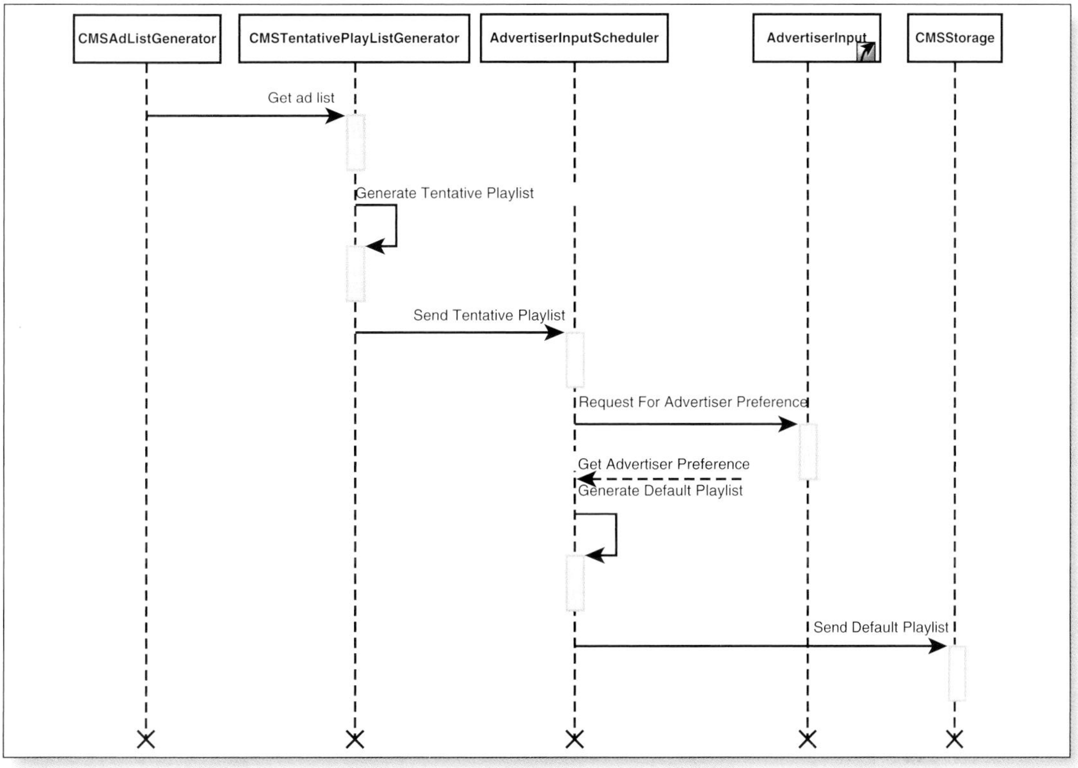

Figure 7.12 Tentative Playlist Generator and Advertiser Input Scheduler Process Flow

CMS Data Flow

Figure 7.13 shows the complete data flow of the CMS. The diagram clearly shows the data movement between different processes of the CMS. The following are some of the important components of the data flow.

■ *Player-Specific Model Extractor:* This connects to the data mining module and fetches passer pattern and ad category models. These models are segregated per player and sent to the DP.

■ *Model Extractor:* The model extractor extracts the ad categories from ad category models and sends them to the ad list generator.

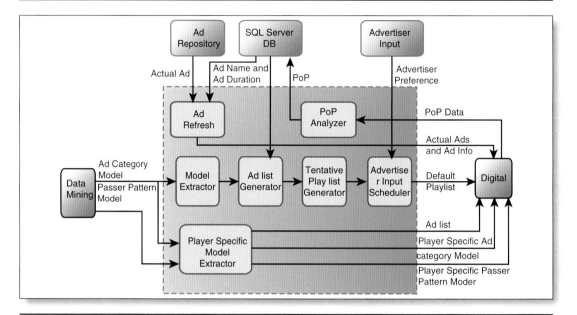

Figure 7.13 CMS Data flow

■ *Ad List Generator:* This module queries a SQL Server database based on ad categories and generates an ad list. An ad list is sent to the tentative playlist generator and DP.

■ *Tentative Playlist Generator:* This module analyzes the ad list based on the play probability and generates a tentative playlist. It is sent to the advertiser input scheduler.

■ *Input Scheduler:* This module fetches advertiser input and incorporates advertiser preferences in the tentative playlist to generate a default playlist. The default playlist will be sent to the DP.

■ *Ad Refresh:* This module checks for new ads in the ad repository and sends these actual ads (video files) to the DP. If new ads are present, then it fetches ad information from the SQL Server database and sends it to the DP.

■ *PoP Analyzer:* Proof of play data fetched from the DP is sent to SQL Server

CMS Class

Figure 7.14 shows the complete class diagram of the CMS. The following are some of the important components:

- *CCMSTimer:* This class implements the timer functionality that invokes the player-specific model extractor for communication with the data mining module and Proof of Play (PoP) interface.

- *CCMSPlayerSpecificModelExtractor:* This class connects to data mining module through the data mining module interface. It retrieves ad category models and passer pattern models, segregates them per player, and stores them in the CMS database. It sends segregated ad category models to the model extractor.

- *CCMSModelExtractor:* This class extracts the ad categories from segregated ad category models. Extracted ad categories are arranged by time of day and sent to the ad list generator.

- *CCMSAdListGenerator:* This class queries SQL Server for ad information based on the ad categories through the SQL Server database interface. The ad list is generated from ad information and stored to the CMS database for further usage in the DP.

- *CCMSTentativePlayListGenerator:* A tentative playlist is generated from the ad list based on the play probability, and it is sent to the advertiser input scheduler.

- *CCMSAdvertiserInputScheduler:* This class generates a default playlist by incorporating advertiser preferences in the tentative playlist.

Interface classes in CMS are as follows:

- *CDMModuleInterface:* This interface class connects with the data mining module and gets the passer pattern and ad category models.

- *CSQLServerDBInterface:* This class queries SQL Server for ad information based on the ad categories and updates the PoP data to SQL Server.

- *CPoPInterface:* The PoP interface class requests proof-of-play data from the DP and converts it into a SQL Server–compatible format. Formatted data is sent to a SQL Server database by using the SQL Server database interface.

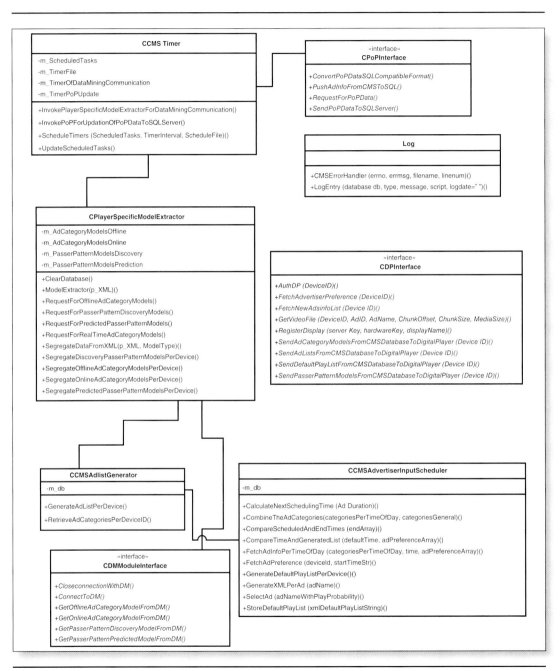

Figure 7.14 Content Management System Class

- *CAdvertiserInputInterface:* This class fetches the advertiser preference and sends it to advertiser input scheduler for generating the default playlist.

- *CAdRefreshInterface:* This interface class connects with the ad repository and checks for the new ads. New ads and their information from SQL Server are sent to the DP through the DP interface.

- *CDPInterface:* This class is responsible for communication between the CMS and the DP. The CMS sends ad category models, passer pattern models, the ad list, the default playlist, actual ads, and CMS information. It fetches PoP data from the DP.

Digital Player

The basic task of the digital player is to fetch the player-specific ad category model, passer pattern model, and ad list from the CMS and store them in the DP database. The DP extracts the ad path for each ad in the ad list and then fetches all the ads from the ad repository and stores them in the DP database. The digital player then generates a default playlist from the ad list generated in the CMS, and finally it plays the advertisements in the playlist according to the schedule.

Functionality

The following are some of the important components of the digital player:

- *VA Data Analyzer:* This component fetches the current VA data (current audience data in front of the DP) from the AIM suite and then extracts the passer pattern rules for that particular timeslot from the DP database. It then uses the current VA data as input, and, with the help of the passer pattern rules, it predicts the future VA data. This predicted future VA data is then sent to the model analyzer for further processing. Figure 7.15 describes the detailed process flow for the VA data analyzer component.

- *Model Analyzer:* The model analyzer receives the predicted VA data from the VA data analyzer. It then fetches the ad category model from the DP database and extracts the most prominent ad category/ad, based on the predicted VA data. The model analyzer then multiplies the confidence value associated with the predicted VA data and predicted ad category/ad data to get a final confidence value. Based on this final confidence value, the model analyzer decides whether

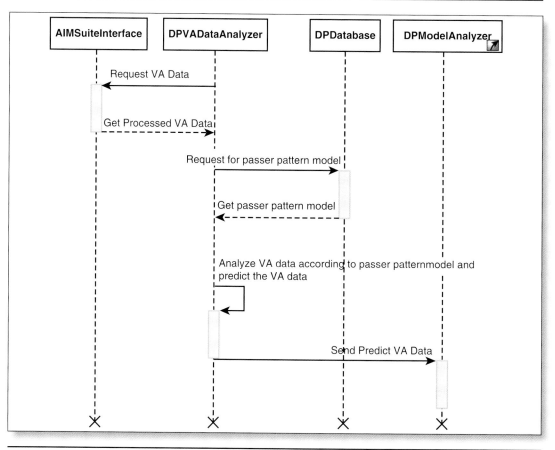

Figure 7.15 VA Data Analyzer Process Flow

the DP should operate in online mode or offline mode. Figure 7.16 shows the detailed process flow for the model analyzer.

■ *Tentative Playlist Generator:* If the DP is operating in the online mode, this component receives the ad category/ad from the model analyzer. It then fetches the ad list from the DP database and generates a tentative playlist based on ad list. The tentative playlist is then sent to the DP online. Figure 7.17 shows the detailed process flow for the tentative playlist generator.

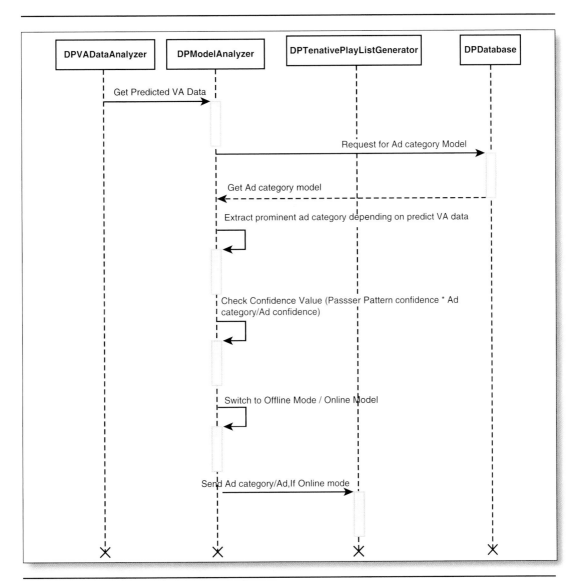

Figure 7.16 Model Analyzer Process Flow

Following are the two operating modes in which the digital player functions:

1. *DP Online Mode:* The digital player operates in this mode if the final confidence value that has been calculated in the model analyzer process is greater than the fixed threshold value. The tentative playlist

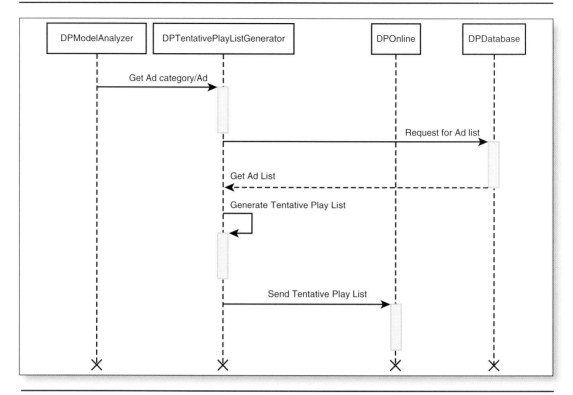

Figure 7.17 Tentative Playlist Generator Process Flow

is obtained from the tentative playlist generator component, and advertisements are selected from the tentative playlist based upon the probability values associated with each ad. The selected ad is then associated with an actual ad and scheduled. The scheduled ad name and its time are stored in the DP database as PoP data and finally sent to the display for playing. Figure 7.18 shows the detailed process flow for DP online mode.

2. *DP Offline Mode:* The digital player operates in this mode if the final confidence value that has been calculated in the model analyzer process is less than the fixed threshold value. The default playlist is then retrieved from the DP database and an advertisement is selected, depending on the scheduling time. The selected ad is then associated with an actual ad and scheduled. The scheduled ad name and its time are stored in

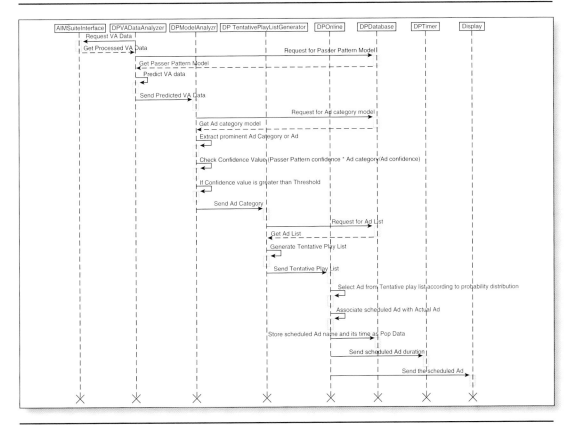

Figure 7.18 DP Online Mode Process Flow

the DP database as PoP data and finally the ad is sent to the display for playing. Figure 7.19 shows the detailed process flow for the DP offline mode.

Digital Player Data Flow

Figure 7.20 shows the detailed data flow for the digital player. Please refer to the earlier sections for most of the important components of the data flow diagram.

Digital Player Class

Figure 7.21 shows the detailed class diagram of the digital player module. Following are some of the important classes of the digital player:

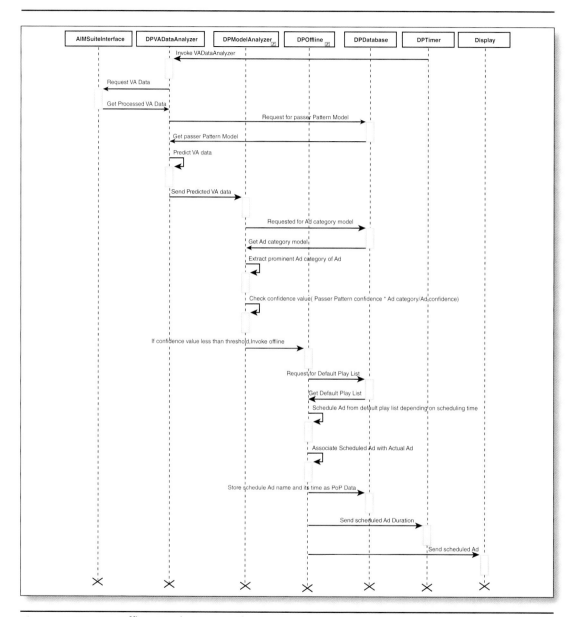

Figure 7.19 DP Offline Mode Process Flow

■ *CDPTimer:* This class incorporates timer functionality. It invokes the VA data analyzer for fetching processed VA data from the AIMS interface and CMS interface for models, ad list, and default playlist updates. It also invokes the CMS interface for fetching actual ads and

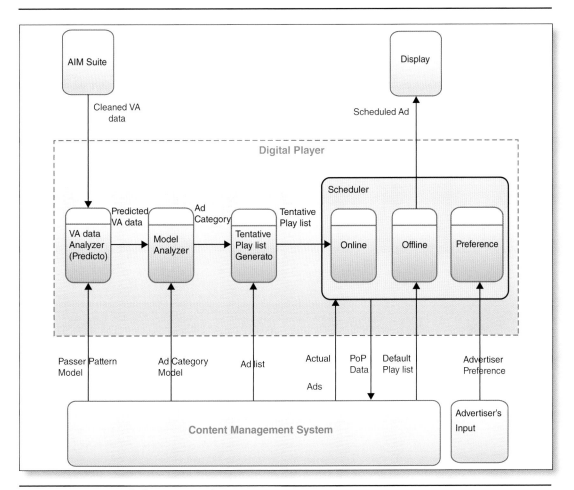

Figure 7.20 Digital Player Data Flow

their information. The DP timer checks for advertiser preference and if it exists, schedules the ad. It also invokes the AIM Suite interface for fetching real-time VA data.

■ *CDPVADataAnalyzer:* This class connects to the AIMS through the AIMS interface class and collects processed VA data. It predicts the passer pattern type for the next timeslot using passer pattern models. It sends predicted VA data to the model analyzer.

■ *CDPModelAnalyzer:* This class receives predicted VA data from the VA data analyzer and retrieves ad category models from the DP database.

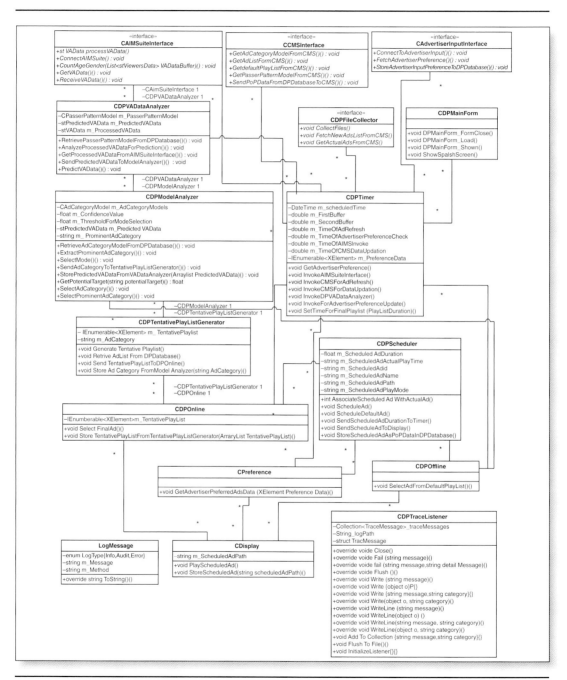

Figure 7.21 Digital Player Class

The prominent ad category/ad is extracted according to predicted VA data. The confidence value of the passer pattern model and ad category model are multiplied. If the multiplied confidence value is greater than the threshold then the extracted prominent ad category/ad is sent to the tentative playlist generator; otherwise the DP continues in offline mode.

- *CDPTentativePlayListGenerator:* This class receives the ad category/ad from the model analyzer. It generates a tentative playlist using the ad list from the DP database and ad category/ad. This list is sent to the DP online.

- *CDPScheduler:* This class associates the selected ad with an actual ad and schedules it. This ad is sent to display and its duration to timer. It also stores the ad name and its time in the DP database as PoP data.

- *CDPOnline:* This class is derived from the DP scheduler class. It selects an ad from the tentative playlist based on probability distribution.

- *CDPOffline:* This class is derived from the DP scheduler class. It retrieves the default playlist from the DP database and selects an ad depending on the scheduling time.

- *CPreference:* This class is derived from the DP scheduler class. It fetches advertiser preference and ad information from the DP database to select an ad.

- *CDisplay:* This class plays the scheduled ad on display.

Interface classes in the DP are as follows:

- *CAIMSuiteInterface:* This class connects to AIMS and fetches real-time data and processes it. Processed VA data is sent to the VA data analyzer whenever it asks.

- *CCMSInterface:* This class connects to the CMS and fetches models, ad list, default playlist, actual ads with their information, and stores it into the DP database. On the request from CMS, it sends PoP data.

- *CAdvertiserInputInterface:* This class fetches the advertiser preference to schedule an ad at a particular time. This preference is stored in the DP database.

Targeted Advertising

In this section we will give a brief overview about the Targeted Advertising Process and IAF working modes.

Targeted Advertising Process

The targeted advertising process is realized based on anonymous video analytics (AVA). AVA is a passive and automated audience measurement technology based on computer vision theory. It helps digital signage operators to measure marketing ROI by capturing audience data such as total number of viewers, average attention span, and even the gender and age of viewers as they pass by a screen. More advanced data correlations are also possible, such as matching anonymous viewership data with point-of-sale data. AVA plus data correlation provides advertisers a more effective and accurate way to measure the effectiveness of their ads than traditional sampling and extrapolation method.

The detailed targeted advertising process includes the following phases: viewing event creation, training data integration, advertising model training, primary playlist creation, and playlist finalization.

Viewing Event Creation

Based on the following two steps, an AVA component can detect a viewer and record the start time, end time, and duration of his or her viewing behavior. Combined with the recognized demographic features, a viewing event is created that states when, where, and which type of viewer watched the digital sign and for how long:

1. *Human face detection.* With a standard, low-cost optical sensor embedded in the digital display panel, a video feed of the audience in front of the screen is processed in real time by the AVA component. The AVA system passively analyzes the video feed and matches subsections of each video frame to the general pattern of a frontal human face in real time. The assumption is that any individual looking towards the digital screen will also be front-facing from the perspective of the camera. The face pattern can be learned in an offline process by feeding a large number of anonymous face images to a machine learning algorithm. The algorithm is able to learn the relationship between the type of pixel arrangements (or pixel intensity variations) and human faces.

2. *Demographics recognition.* Furthermore, by feeding face images labeled with demographics, such as gender and age, to the above machine learning algorithm, then it can be extended to recognize pixel combinations that correspond to gender, age, and other key demographics. At this moment, a mathematical pattern is learned to categorize the facial images into general demographic groups.

Training Data Integration

By correlating the viewing events with ad playing events that state when, where, and which ad was displayed and for how long, the AVA system can create various viewing relationship reports and statistics, such as total number of viewers, average attention span, and so on. These reports and statistics tell how effective the displayed ads are and what kind of audience is being attracted. In this way, it provides digital signage operators with quantitative viewership information and enables them to analyze the ROI.

It should be emphasized that the AVA component is privacy-friendly. It only detects the presence of a mathematical human face as well as its demographic features, but it does not identify who the face belongs to. Moreover, only viewing events are recorded, which are completely anonymous. And no images or video footage are stored, so there is no way to link back to any specific individual from the viewing events. The audience's privacy is well protected.

Advertising Model Learning

Based on the correlation of the viewership information with ad playing information such as ad name and ad category, the DMM is responsible for learning meaningful viewing patterns (or advertising models), like when, where, under what weather, and to what extent what group of audience is interested in what type of ads. It consists of following subcomponents:

■ *Data Connector:* Connects and gets access to the training data repository. The data is made of original AVA data, playlist data, weather data, and ad data.

■ *Data Preprocessor:* Realizes necessary data preprocessing actions, like deriving new attributes from original attributes for modeling purposes.

- *Model Constructor:* Defines data mining models with a specified algorithm, training data scope and training parameters.

- *Model Learner:* Learns advertising models according to the model definition; also tests the learned models against the testing data in terms of accuracy.

- *Query Engine:* Both prediction result and model content (such as rules) can be queried against an advertising model. This enables extraction and deployment elsewhere of the model content to achieve better efficiency for real-time applications.

Primary Playlist Creation

After the advertising models are generated, they get transferred to the CMS. The CMS then extracts the ad categories from the models and creates an ad category list. The ad information (such as actual ad location) corresponding to the ad categories are then fetched from the ad information table. Based on the ad category list, the CMS creates initial ad lists, which are modified in the advertiser input scheduler based on the advertisers' inputs. Each advertiser is assigned a certain priority, which rearranges the initial ad lists in the advertiser input scheduler. Figure 7.13 shows the data flow diagram of CMS.

Playlist Finalization

Finally the shuffled ad lists get transferred to the digital player. It generates the default playlist by extracting the path from the ad list and then getting the ads from the ad repository. The digital player operates in either online or offline mode. In online mode, digital player selects an ad based on the probability distribution calculated using advertising models. In the offline mode, the digital player selects an ad from the default playlist based on the scheduling time. It switches between these two modes depending on the confidence level of the advertising models. That means when the confidence goes beyond some predefined threshold, the digital player works in online mode; otherwise, it works in offline mode.

IAF Working Modes

Three targeting modes, seeing-based targeting, prediction-based targeting, and context-based targeting are used in IAF. Seeing-based targeting is the most accurate targeting mode and is used first whenever possible. Prediction-based targeting is used when seeing-based targeting cannot meet a real time requirement. Context-based targeting is the last choice, which is always usable even if the first two targeting modes are not applicable.

All of these three targeting modes are based on the advertising models trained by the DMM. If due to some reason, the advertising models are not accurate enough or not applicable and cannot be used in the targeting process, then IAF will switch to the offline working mode. It only uses the known knowledge and external inputs (including that from advertisers) to create the playlist and will not leverage the recommendation from the advertising models. It will switch back when some advertising models are applicable again.

Data Mining for Targeted Advertising

Targeted advertising is a type of advertising whereby advertisements are placed so as to reach consumers based on various traits such as demographics, purchase history, or observed behavior. On one hand, targeted advertising helps to identify potential customers, create a real-time relationship with these customers, improves their experience, and provides them cross-sell services to boost incremental revenue. On the other hand, it helps to reduce waste and improve advertisers' return on investment (ROI) by just placing advertisement to the potential purchasers rather than the whole population.

Targeted advertising has been adopted in many industries, including banking, insurance, and telecom marketing. But targeted advertising is still a new concept for the digital signage industry. How to realize targeted advertising in digital signage is an interesting question. That requires the digital signs have the capability to dynamically select and play advertisements according to the traits of the audiences in front of them, rather than select and play in a predefined or random order. A future audience belonging to the same demographic as a previous audience will be targeted based on the viewing behavior of the previous audience. This section introduces how to use data mining technology to discover the viewing patterns of the audience and realize targeted advertising.

Multiple Advertising Model Training

For the purpose of capturing the patterns contained in new incoming data, two different ways are used to retrain the advertising models, regular retraining and on-demand retraining. Regular retraining is triggered regularly, such as weekly or monthly. On-demand retraining is triggered when the performance of the models is lower than a predefined threshold or a retraining request is received from users or operators. Besides, to fully make use of the advantages of different data mining algorithms, multiple data mining algorithms, including decision tree, association rule, naïve Bayes, and logistic regression are used to train advertising models in parallel. All the trained advertising models are sent to digital signs. The digital sign can then use the best advertising model with respect to test accuracy or combine multiple advertising models to select the ad to play.

Audience Targeting Methods

Three targeting approaches are described below.

Seeing-Based Targeting

Seeing-based targeting means targeting the audience once the digital sign "sees" the audience. For example, three young females and one senior male are seen passing by the digital sign, and then the advertising models are queried with this input and the most appropriate ad is selected to play. This is the most accurate targeting method given the demographic information of the audience has been captured and used.

Prediction-Based Targeting

Prediction-based targeting first predicts the passers coming in the future period of time and then targets them. For example, it is predicted that three young females and one senior male will pass by the digital sign within the next 20 seconds, and then the most appropriate ad is to be selected per the advertising models and prepared to play. This is quite useful in the scenario that follows. In some cases, such as when the time cost of the whole targeting process is longer than the audience's dwelling time, the seeing-based targeting doesn't work: by the time the digital player gets the selected ad prepared and displayed on the screen, the audience has already looked away and will never look back,.

Context-Based Targeting

Context-based targeting targets the ads just depending on the context, such as targeting date/time, device location, or weather information. For example, on a clear Wednesday morning between 9 a.m. and 11 a.m. during November and December, an ad for senior males will be selected to play on digital sign A per the advertising models. This is useful when passer type prediction is not reliable or no passer patterns can be discovered from the training data.

Weighted Audience Counting

To realize prediction-based targeting, a passer prediction model is needed to predict the passer type in the next time slot. To train this model, weighted audience counting is used to create the training dataset. The count of each passer type is weighted according to the time points when that type of passer passes by the digital sign. For each passer type, we use the following process to calculate its weighted count:

3. Slice timeslot T into 10 equal intervals, numbered as $t0, t1, \ldots, t9$.

4. Label all that type of passer coming within timeslot T with a position $P = 0, 1, \ldots, 9$ according to which interval in which they come.

5. The weighted count of this passer type is calculated by

$$C = \sum_{P=10}^{9} n * \left(1 - \frac{P}{10}\right)$$

where n is the number of the passer labeled as position P.

Table 7.1   An Example of a Passing Audience

t0	t1	t2	t3	t4	t5	t6	t7	t8	t9
	2FA				1FA			3FA	

Table 7.1 shows an example about passing Female Adult (FA) within timeslot T. Then the weighted count for Female Adult in T is

$$C = 2 * \left(1 - \frac{1}{10}\right) + 1 * \left(1 - \frac{5}{10}\right) + 3 * \left(1 - \frac{8}{10}\right) = 2.9.$$

Do the above process for all the passer types in timeslot T and a table like Table 7.2 can be obtained. Repeat the above procedure for all the timeslots. Then a training dataset is created, which includes many rows of weighted counts.

Table 7.2   An Example of Weighted Audience Counting

Female				Male			
Child	**Young**	**Adult**	**Senior**	**Child**	**Young**	**Adult**	**Senior**
0.7		2.9			2.5	3.2	

Passer Prediction Models

Two types of passer prediction models are created, the passer distribution prediction model and the dominant passer prediction model.

Passer Distribution Prediction Model

Based upon the above dataset, specify the eight passer types as predict variables, and train a prediction model. The trained model tells the predicted passer distribution in next timeslot.

Dominant Passer Prediction Model

Based upon the above dataset, select the type of the passer with a maximum count as the dominant passer type, specify the dominant passer type as a predict variable, and train a prediction model. The trained model tells the predicted dominant passer type in the next timeslot. For example, the dominant passer type in Table 7.2 is Male Adult, whose weighted count is the maximum (3.2).

Advertising Rule Example

Corresponding to the three targeting approaches, the below illustrates three types of advertising rules.

Seeing-Based Targeting Rules

If deviceID = 561 and timeslot = morning and day = Friday and gender = female and age = young and weather = clear and IsWeekend=0 and MediaId = 10 and MediaCategory = outdoor, then TargetPotential = 0.9 (at 80 percent confidence).

Prediction-Based Targeting Rules

Here describes two kinds of prediction-based targeting rules.

Passer Distribution Prediction Rule. If deviceID = 561 and timeslot = morning and time = 11:00~12:00 and day = Friday and IsWeekend =0 and weather = clear then

$$NFC = a1*CFC + b1*CFY + c1*CFA + d1*CFS + e1*CMC + f1*CMY + g1*CMA + h1*CMS + i1$$

$$NFY = a2*CFC + b2*CFY + c2*CFA + d2*CFS + e2*CMC + f2*CMY + g2*CMA + h2*CMS + i2$$

$$NFA = a3*CFC + b3*CFY + c3*CFA + d3*CFS + e3*CMC + f3*CMY + g3*CMA + h3*CMS + i3$$

$$NFS = a4*CFC + b4*CFY + c4*CFA + d4*CFS + e4*CMC + f4*CMY + g4*CMA + h4*CMS + i4$$

$$NMC = a5*CFC + b5*CFY + c5*CFA + d5*CFS + e5*CMC + f5*CMY + g5*CMA + h5*CMS + i5$$

$$NMY = a6*CFC + b6*CFY + c6*CFA + d6*CFS + e6*CMC + f6*CMY + g6*CMA + h6*CMS + i6$$

$$NMA = a7*CFC + b7*CFY + c7*CFA + d7*CFS + e7*CMC + f7*CMY + g7*CMA + h7*CMS + i7$$

$$NMS = a8*CFC + b8*CFY + c8*CFA + d8*CFS + e8*CMC + f8*CMY + g8*CMA + h8*CMS + i8$$

where NFC, NFY, NFA, NFS, NMC, NMY, NMA, and NMS respectively mean Next Female Child, Next Female Young, Next Female Adult, Next Female Senior, Next Male Child, Next Male Young, Next Male Adult, and Next Male Senior representing the weighted counts of each audience type in the Next timeslot; CFC, CFY, CFA, CFS, CMC, CMY, CMA, and CMS respectively mean Current Female Child, Current Female Young, Current Female Adult, Current Female Senior, Current Male Child, Current Male Young, Current Male Adult, and Current Male Senior representing the weighted counts of each audience type in the Current timeslot. And a1, …, a8, b1, …, b8, …, i1, …, i8 are the regression coefficients trained by regression algorithms.

Dominant Passer Prediction Rule. If deviceID = 561 and timeslot = morning and time = 11:00~12:00 and day = Friday and IsWeekend =0 and weather = clear and current dominant passer = senior female then next dominant passer = senior male.

Context-Based Targeting Rules

If deviceID = 561 and timeslot = morning and time = 9:00–9:30 and day = Friday and weather = clear and IsWeekend=0 and MediaId=10 and MediaCategory = Media Category 1, then TargetPotential = 0.5 (at 70 percent confidence).

Ad Selection Based on Advertising Models

Based on the advertising models and rules, we can select the most appropriate ads for play.

Ad Selection for Seeing-Based Targeting

Use the available inputs to query the seeing based targeting rules and summarize the Weighted Target Potential WTP = f(# of Passer, Target Potential, Confidence) for the same ads, then get a list of ads with Weighted Target Potential.

Table 7.3   An Example of Targeting Rules

Passer type	# of Passer	Media Category	Medial ID	Target Potential	Confidence
FY	3	Outdoor	112	0.9	0.8
FY	3	Shoes	116	0.7	0.9
MS	1	Shoes	116	0.5	0.7

Assume that three young females and one senior male are seen passing by the digital sign, and the ads within applicable rules are as those in Table 7.3 Based on this table, the weighted target potential can be computed as (# of Passer * Target Potential * Confidence), then summarized in Table 7.4

Table 7.4   Weighted Target Potential

Media Category	Medial ID	Weighted Target Potential
Outdoor	112	2.16
Shoes	116	2.24

Rank the ad list based on weighted Target Potential, and select top m ads as the recommended ads. Correlating with other factors, such as advertiser's input to finalize the final ads to play.

Ad Selection for Prediction-Based Targeting

Regarding passer distribution prediction, we have to calculate the weighted counts of all the passer types in the current timeslot, CFC, CFY, CFA, CFS, CMC, CMY, CMA, CMS, and feed them and other available inputs to the passer distribution prediction model. Then the weighted counts in the next timeslot, NFC, NFY, NFA, NFS, NMC, NMY, NMA, NMS can be determined, assuming the weighted counts look like those in Table 7.5.

Table 7.5 Values of all the Passer type

NFC	NFY	NYA	NFS	NMC	NMY	NMA	NMS
		2.9			2.2		1.6

Using the same process as above, the final playing ads can be determined.

Regarding dominant passer prediction, after calculating the weighted counts of all the passer types in the current timeslot, CFC, CFY, CFA, CFS, CMC, CMY, CMA, CMS, we just need to select and feed the Current Dominant Passer type and other available inputs to the dominant passer prediction model, and get the Next Dominant Passer type. Since only one (the dominant) passer type is considered, # of passer is not used for the calculation.

Ad Selection for Context-Based Targeting

Use context information (time, location, weather) as input to query context based targeting rule and get a list of ads with Target Potential and Confidence. Rank the list and determine the final playing ads taking into account advertiser's inputs.

Training data collection and preparation

This section will illustrate how to collect the viewer event data, player event data, and weather data as well as how to correlate all this data and create training data tables. To aid in this process, we set up a test network of five digital signs at five different locations (Beijing, Pune, Bangalore, two locations in Chandler, Arizona). They were set up using the same architecture as mentioned in the previous sections. We ran fake ads on this sign and used it collect data. We collected this over a period of two quarters.

Viewer event collection

Figure 7.22 depicts the viewer event data flow. Where Intel AIM Suite resides in digital sings and works as the Anonymous Video Analytics component, it captures human faces and recognizes whose demographic information, that is, gender (Male and Female) and age buckets (Child, Young Adult, Adult and Senior). And on this basis creates viewer events. Table 7.6 shows an exemplar viewer event, it means a Male Young Adult watched the digital sign numbered 562 for 6336 milliseconds from 14:24:44.300 to 14:24:50.637 on February 8, 2012.

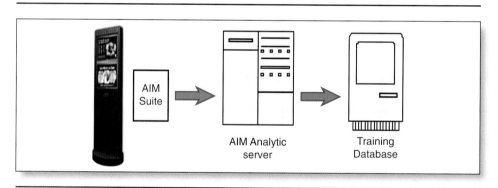

Figure 7.22 Viewer Event Data Flow

Table 7.6   Viewer Event Example

ViewerEventId	Device_ Id	Date	Start_Time	End_Time	Viewing_ Time	Gender	Age
175	562	2012/2/8	14:24:44.300	14:24:50.637	6336	male	Young_adult

The viewer events are regularly uploaded to AIM Analytic server, saying every 5 minutes. And data preprocessing, such as noise filtering is performed there. Users can do some statistical analysis and create reports with AIM

Analytic server. For purpose of learning advertising models, the viewer events are downloaded into a SQL server database. This can be implemented though web APIs accessing to AIM Analytic server as below. Where username, password, application code (which is got after the installation of Intel AIM Suite) and data range for a particular digital sign should be specified within the link. The event data is downloaded to a training database on a daily basis. https://www.cognovision.com/analytics/rpc_get_aimview_log.php?username=UserName&password=PassWord&ac=Application Code&start_year=2012&start_month=1&start_day=27&end_year=2012&end_month=2&end_day=15&v=2&show_fields=1

Player Event Collection

Figure 7.23 shows the player event flow. Where the digital player plays the ads stored in the digital sign and creates player events. Table 7.7 shows an example of player event. It means that digital sign numbered 562 played a media #28 for 15 seconds from 14:24:40 to 14:24:55 on February 8, 2012. The value "Offline" of Player Mode indicates this player event performs without using advertising models. Whose value "Online" indicates the playing media is recommended by advertising models.

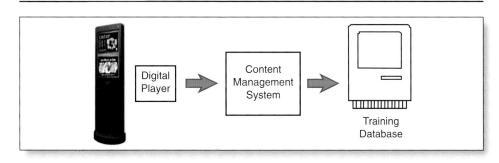

Figure 7.23 Player Event Flow

Table 7.7   Player Event Example

PlayerEventId	Device_Id	Media_Id	PlayingDuration	Start_Time	End_Time	PlayerMode
514	562	28	15	2012/2/8 14:24:40	2012/2/8 14:24:55	Offline

The player events are uploaded to a CMS (Content Management System) regularly. The upload frequency is configurable as every *x* hours. The CMS then regularly transfers the player events to training database by calling web services. Below is an example of the definition of the web services.

The CMS also maintains the device and advertisement information. Here a device refers to the digital sign. We deployed five digital signs for an internal pilot. Table 7.8 shows the information of all the devices. Where ActivationCode, UserName, and Password are used for extract the viewer events from the AIM Analytic server. UTC_TimeDiff indicates the time difference between the UTC time and the local time, which is used for time synchronization.

Table 7.8 Device Information Table

Device_ Id	Device_ Name	Device_ Country	Device_ City	Device_ ZipCode	Signage_ Type	Installation_ Date	Activation Code	User Name	Pass word	UTC_ Time Diff
561	A	India	Bangalore	NULL	NULL	2011/1/1				-330
562	B	China	Beijing	100190	NULL	2011/1/1				-480
563	C	India	Pune	NULL	NULL	2011/1/1				-330
564	D	USA	Chandler	NULL	NULL	2011/1/1				420
565	E	USA	Chandler	NULL	NULL	2011/1/1				420

Table 7.9 shows an example of the advertisement maintained by CMS. Where Media_Path indicates where the actual media file is stored, Media_Source indicates where the advertisement is from, Media_type indicates the type of the media file, and PulledByCMS indicates if the file has been downloaded by the digital player.

Table 7.9 An Example of Advertisement

Media_ Id	Media_ Name	Media_ Path	Primary_ Media Category	Secondary_ Media Category	Media_ Expiry Date	Language	Media_ Source	Media_ SizeMB	Media_ type	Pulled By CMS	Media Duratio InSecs
28	Smart Phone	NULL	Electronics	NULL	NULL	NULL	NULL	NULL	NULL	NULL	NULL

Both the device information and advertisement information are transferred from CMS to the training database. This data helps to create accurate advertising models. But this data doesn't need to be transferred regularly, and one-time transfer plus incremental update would be a good solution.

Weather Data Collection

Weather data is also collected to provide the context to advertising models, which are correlated with the viewer and player events. Table 7.10 shows an example of the collected weather data, which describes the weather, the maximum and minimum temperature in the location of digital sign # 562 at the daytime of the day.

Table 7.10 Weather Data Example

WeatherInfoID	Date	Time_Slot	Weather	MaxTemp	MinTemp	DeviceID
21	2012/2/8	Day	Scattered T-Storms	78	66	562

The weather information is available in some public weather services, such as that provided by www.weather.com. Here is an example link to obtain the above weather data. The Location Code and KEY should be instantiated when using the link. With this link, the above weather data can be extracted and loaded into database on daily basis.
http://xoap.weather.com/weather/local/LocationCode?cc=*&dayf=1&link=xoap&prod=xoap&par=1287801927&key=KEY.

Training Data Correlation

Having all the above data in the training database, we can correlate them and create the training datasets. According to the modeling task, we basically need to create three training tables: an ad category modeling table, a Passer Prediction modeling table, and a Passer pattern modeling table.

The ad category modeling table is created based upon viewer events, player events, device information, ad information and weather data. Table 7.11 shows a record in the ad category modeling table, where TimeSlot, DayOfWeek, IsWeekEnd, and Time derive attributes according the date, start time, and end time of the viewer event. FromMediaBeginning and TillMediaEnd indicate if the audience watched the media from its very beginning and until its very end respectively. PotentialTarget indicates the potential of the audience's interest in the particular media content, whose values are defined according to the values of Viewing_Time and TillMediaEnd as shown in Table 7.12. And Potential Weight is the numerical counterpart of the categorical values of PotentialTarget, which will be used during the ad selection process.

Table 7.11   Ad Category Modeling Data Table

Fields	Value
ID	235
ViewerEventId	175
PlayerEventId	514
Device_Id	562
TimeSlot	Afternoon
Date	2012/2/8
DayOfWeek	Wednesday
IsWeekEnd	NO
Time	14:00:00~14:30:00
Start_Time	14:24:44.300
End_Time	14:24:50.637
Gender	MALE
Age	Young_ADULT
Media_Id	28
PrimaryMediaCategory	Electronics
SecondaryMediaCategory	None
MaxTem	78
MinTem	66
Weather	Scattered T-Storms
Country	China
City	Beijing
ZipCode	100190
FromMediaBeginning	No
TillMediaEnd	No
PotentialTarget	Very Strong

Table 7.12   Definition of Values of PotentialTarget

PotentialTarget	Viewing_Time	TillMediaEnd	Potential Weight
Very weak	<=1 sec		0
Weak	1~3 sec	No	0.3
Likely	1~3 sec	Yes	0.5

| Strong | 3~6 sec | 0.7 |
| Very strong | >6 sec | 0.9 |

Both the Passer Prediction modeling data table and the Passer pattern modeling data table are created based upon only viewer events, device information, and weather data, as shown in Table 7.13 and Table 7.14. Passer Prediction is to predict the dominant passer type in the next time slot (saying 30 seconds) based on the dominant passer type in the current time slot as well as the context (time, location, weather, and so on). The dominant passer type is the passer type having the maximum number of audience in a particular time slot. The calculation of dominant passer type is illustrated in Chapter 4. What should be noticed is that although we only have eight basic passer types (Male Child, Male Young Adult, Male Adult, Male Senior, Female Child, Female Young Adult, Female Adult, and Female Senior), the dominant passer type could be some mixed types, such as MaleYoungAdult-FemaleAdult when both the two types have maximum number of audience in the time slot. The Passer Pattern data table is used to discover passers' patterns in different context and doesn't include NextDominant as a field, given we will not predict the dominant passer type in the next time slot with this table. And also the Time filed usually has longer duration (for example: one hour) than that in the Passer Prediction data table. We don't expect to capture meaningful patterns in a very short time duration, such as in seconds or several minutes.

Table 7.13 Passer Prediction Modeling Table

ID	**218**	**219**
Date	2012/2/8	2012/2/8
Time	14:00:00 ~14:00:30	14:00:30 ~14:01:00
TimeSlot	Afternoon	Afternoon
Device_Id	562	562
Signage_type	NULL	NULL
DayOfWeek	Wednesday	Wednesday
IsWeekEnd	NO	NO
MaxTem	78	78
MinTem	66	66
Weather	Scattered T-Storms	Scattered T-Storms
Country	China	China

City	Beijing	Beijing
ZipCode	100190	100190
CurrentDominant	MaleYoungAdult	FemaleYoungAdult
NextDominant	FemaleYoungAdult	FemaleSenior

Table 7.14 Passer Pattern Modeling Table

ID	**218**	**219**
Date	2012/2/8	2012/2/8
Time	14:00:00 ~15:00:00	15:00:00 ~16:00:00
TimeSlot	Afternoon	Afternoon
Device_Id	562	562
Signage_type	NULL	NULL
DayOfWeek	Wednesday	Wednesday
IsWeekEnd	NO	NO
MaxTem	78	78
MinTem	66	66
Weather	Scattered T-Storms	Scattered T-Storms
Country	China	China
City	Beijing	Beijing
ZipCode	100190	100190
CurrentDominant	MaleAdult	FemaleSenior

Advertising Models Creation

This section illustrates how we learn the advertising models based on the above three modeling data tables.

Algorithm Selection and Orchestration

According to the modeling tasks, we have three predicted variables, PotentialTarget, NextDominant, and CurrentDominant in the above three tables. Since all these variables have categorical values, we can use classification algorithms to train predictive models. Moreover, Microsoft SSAS† (SQL Server Analysis Service) is a popular tool used for OLAP (on-line analytical processing) and data mining, which is efficient and easy to use and the trained models are easy to be integrated with other applications. We select three classification algorithms, Decision Tree, Naïve Bayes and Association Rules in SSAS for predictive modeling.

We train the predictive models with these three algorithms in parallel and test the models with a separate dataset. The information about the trained models and the test accuracy is recorded into a data table, as shown in Table 7.15. Since we have four different types of rules (passer prediction, passer pattern, ad category real time and ad category offline) to be trained, each training process creates 12 models with the three algorithms. Test accuracy and training parameters are also recorded in the table. The models with maximum test accuracy for each type of rules are set as active, which will be sent to the digital player and work as advertising models.

Table 7.15 Model Information Table

Model_Id	Model_Name	Created_Date	Algorithm	Accuracy	Active	Training Parameters
1252	PasserPrediction-DT	2011/11/15 15:25:24	Decision_Tree	0.5638	1	Complexity_penalty=0.6 Minimum_Support=10.0 Score_method=4 Split_Method=3
1253	PasserPrediction-AR	2011/11/15 15:25:25	Association_Rules	0.5328	0	Maximum_ItemSet_Size =3 Minimum_ItemSet_Size=1 Minimum_Probability=0.4 Minimum_Support=0
1254	PasserPrediction-NB	2011/11/15 15:25:25	Naive_Bayes	0.5237	0	Maximum_states=100 Minimum_dependency_probability=0.0000000001
1255	PasserPatten-DT	2011/11/15 15:25:33	Decision_Tree	0.5324	1	Complexity_penalty=0.6 Minimum_Support=10.0 Score_method=4 Split_Method=3
1256	PasserPatten-AR	2011/11/15 15:25:33	Association_Rules	0.4738	0	Maximum_ItemSet_Size =3 Minimum_ItemSet_Size=1 Minimum_Probability=0.4 Minimum_Support=0
1257	PasserPatten-NB	2011/11/15 15:25:33	Naive_Bayes	0.5121	0	Maximum_states=100 Minimum_dependency_probability=0.0000000001
1258	AdCategoryRealtime-DT	2011/11/15 15:25:42	Decision_Tree	0.5453	0	Complexity_penalty=0.6 Minimum_Support=10.0 Score_method=4 Split_Method=3

1259	AdCategoryRealtime-AR	2011/11/15 15:25:42	Association_Rules	0.5687	0	Maximum_ItemSet_Size =3 Minimum_ItemSet_Size=1 Minimum_Probability=0.4 Minimum_Support=0
1260	AdCategoryRealtime-NB	2011/11/15 15:25:42	Naive_Bayes	0.5980	1	Maximum_states=100 Minimum_dependency_probability=0.0000000001
1261	AdCategoryOffline-DT	2011/11/15 15:25:50	Decision_Tree	0.5629	1	Complexity_penalty=0.6 Minimum_Support=10.0 Score_method=4 Split_Method=3
1262	AdCategoryOffline-AR	2011/11/15 15:25:50	Association_Rules	0.5543	0	Maximum_ItemSet_Size =3 Minimum_ItemSet_Size=1 Minimum_Probability=0.4 Minimum_Support=0
1263	AdCategoryOffline-NB	2011/11/15 15:25:50	Naive_Bayes	0.4632	0	Maximum_states=100 Minimum_dependency_probability=0.0000000001

Training and Retraining process

The training process can be triggered by calling Microsoft SSAS service using DMX statements. Such a DMX statement is shown below. This statement can be embedded into programs so is able to be invoked by other application. Where [Ad Category Modelling Data Table UTC] is a model name, [IntelligentAdvertisingFramework] is a database name, and [AdCategoryModellingDataTable] is the name of a table in the database:

```
INSERT INTO [Ad Category Modelling Data Table UTC] ([ID],
device_ID, [Date], TimeSlot, DayOfWeek, IsWeekEnd, Time,
Gender, Age, Media_nam, PrimaryMediaCategory,MaxTem,
MinTem, weather, Country, city, ZipCode, PotentialTarget)
OPENQUERY([IntelligentAdvertisingFramework],'SELECT [ID],
device_ID, [Date], TimeSlot, DayOfWeek, IsWeekEnd, Time,
Gender, Age, Media_nam, PrimaryMediaCategory,MaxTem, MinTem,
weather, Country, city, ZipCode, PotentialTarget From
[AdCategoryModellingDataTable]')
```

To shape the training and retraining process, we defined several configuration files. One configuration file is as shown below, which defines the names of other eight configuration files (AdCategoryRealtime.xml, AdCategoryOffline. xml, PasserPrediction.xml, PasserPatten.xml, AdCategoryRealtime-Retraining. xml, AdCategoryOffline-Retraining.xml, PasserPrediction-Retraining.xml, and PasserPatten-Retraining.xml) as well as the retraining parameters. Within the eight configuration files, four are used for the training process and four for the retraining process. For regular retraining, the parameters define the time and frequency of the retraining. For on-demand retraining, one parameter specifies the exact date and time of the retraining, and another parameter specifies the threshold-to-trigger retraining, that is, when the test accuracy of the models is below the threshold, whose retraining is triggered.

```xml
<?xml version="1.0" ?>
<Configuration>
<TrainingStructureFiles>
  <structure type="AdCategoryOffline" name=
  "AdCategoryOffline.XML" />
  <structure type="AdCategoryRealtime"
  name="AdCategoryRealtime.XML" />
  <structure type="PasserPatten" name="PasserPatten.XML" />
  <structure type="PasserPrediction" name=
  "PasserPrediction.XML" />
</TrainingStructureFiles>
<RetrainingStructureFiles>
  <structuretype="AdCategoryOffline-Retrain"name=
  "AdCategoryOffline-Retraining.XML" />
  <structuretype="AdCategoryRealtime-Retrain"name="AdCatego
  ryRealtimeRetraining.XML" />
  <structure type="PasserPatten-Retrain" name=
  "PasserPatten-Retraining.XML" />
  <structure type="PasserPrediction-Retrain" name=
  "PasserPrediction-Retraining.XML" />
</RetrainingStructureFiles>
<RetrainingParameters>
  <Parameter name="RegularRetrainingStartDateTime"
  value="2011-11-01 00:00:00" />
  <Parameter name="RegularRetrainingFrequency"
  value="Weekly" />
  <Parameter name="OnDemandRetrainingDatetime"
  value="2011-11-01 00:00:00" />
  <Parameter name="OnDemandRetrainingAccuracyThreshold"
  value="50%" />
</RetrainingParameters>
</Configuration>
```

Within the eight configuration files, AdCategoryRealtime.xml, AdCategoryOffline.xml, PasserPrediction.xml, and PasserPatten.xml are used for training process definition. AdCategoryRealtime-Retraining.xml, AdCategoryOffline-Retraining.xml, PasserPrediction-Retraining.xml, and PasserPatten-Retraining.xml are used for retraining process definition. Each of the four defines the training or retraining process of one particular type of rules. The content of AdCategoryRealtime.xml, shown below defines all the training algorithms and parameters for creation of ad category real time rules. Where the <sources> tag defines the data source table and the training and testing data scope, here it means using the latest three days of data for testing and 30 days of data before the test data for training. The <Structurecolumns> tag defines the selected variables for the modeling process, which can be used by different algorithms and models. The three tags, <DTModel>, <ARModel>, and <NBModel> respectively define the Decision Tree, Association Rule, and Naïve Bayes models. The <Modelcolumns> tag defines the used variables as well as their roles in a particular model. The <ModelFilter> tag defines the filter of the training data. The <Parameters> tag defines the training parameter of a particular model.

```xml
<?xml version="1.0" ?>
<structure type="AdCategoryRealtime">
<sources><sourcetype="DataTable"value="[IntelligentAdverti-
 singFramework].[dbo].[AdCategoryModelingData]" />
  <source type="TrainingDataScope" value="30" />
  <source type="TestingDataScope" value="3" />
</sources>
<Structurecolumns>
  <column name="ID" type="int" continuity="KEY" />
  <column name="Device_ID" type="int" continuity="
  DISCRETE" />
   <DTModelcolumn name="Date" type=" date"
    continuity="Continuous" />
  <column name="TimeSlot" type="text" continuity="DISCRETE"
   />
  <column name="DayOfWeek" type="text"
   continuity="DISCRETE" />
  <column name="IsWeekEnd" type="text" continuity="
  DISCRETE" />
     <column name="Time" type="text" continuity="DISCRETE"
       />
  <column name="Gender" type="text" continuity="DISCRETE"
   />
   <column name=" Age" type="text" continuity=" DISCRETE"
    />
   <column name="media_name" type="text" continuity="
   DISCRETE" />
   <column name=" PrimaryMediaCategory" type="text"
```

```
      continuity=" DISCRETE" />
    <column name=" MaxTem " type="int"
     continuity="Continuous" />
    <column name=" MinTem " type="int"
     continuity="Continuous" />
    <column name="weather" type="text" continuity="DISCRETE"
     />
    <column name="Country" type="text" continuity="DISCRETE"
     />
    <column name=" city" type="text" continuity="DISCRETE"
     />
    <column name="ZipCode" type="text" continuity="DISCRETE"
     />
    <column name=" PotentialTarget" type="text"
     continuity="DISCRETE" />
</Structurecolumns>
<Models>
<DTModel>
<Modelcolumns>
  <DTModelcolumn name="ID" type=" KEY" />
  <DTModelcolumn name="Device_ID" type=" input" />
  <DTModelcolumn name="Date" type=" ignore" />
    <DTModelcolumn name="TimeSlot" type=" input" />
<DTModelcolumn name="DayOfWeek" type=" input" />
  <DTModelcolumn name="IsWeekEnd" type=" input" />
  <DTModelcolumn name="Time" type=" input" />
  <DTModelcolumn name="Gender" type=" input" />
  <DTModelcolumn name=" Age" type=" input" />
  <DTModelcolumn name="media_name" type=" input" />
  <DTModelcolumn name=" PrimaryMediaCategory" type=" input"
   />
  <DTModelcolumn name=" MaxTem " type=" input" />
  <DTModelcolumn name=" MinTem " type=" input " />
<DTModelcolumn name="weather" type=" input" />
<DTModelcolumn name="Country" type=" input" />
<DTModelcolumn name=" city" type=" input" />
<DTModelcolumn name="ZipCode" type="ignore" />
<DTModelcolumn name=" PotentialTarget" type=" predict_only
 " />
</Modelcolumns>
<ModelFilter>   <Filter SQLquery="Date >='2012-02-01'" />
 </ModelFilter>
<Parameters>
  <Parameter name="Complexity_penalty" value="0.6" />
  <Parameter name="Minimum_Support" value="10.0" />
  <Parameter name="Score_method" value="4" />
```

```
      <Parameter name="Split_Method" value="3" />
</Parameters>
</DTModel>
<ARModel>
<Modelcolumns>
  <ARModelcolumn name="ID" type=" KEY" />
  <ARModelcolumn name="Device_ID" type=" input" />
  <ARModelcolumn name="Date" type=" ignore" />
    <ARModelcolumn name="TimeSlot" type=" input" />
<ARModelcolumn name="DayOfWeek" type=" input" />
  <ARModelcolumn name="IsWeekEnd" type=" input" />
  <ARModelcolumn name="Time" type=" input" />
  <ARModelcolumn name="Gender" type=" input" />
   <ARModelcolumn name=" Age" type=" input" />
   <ARModelcolumn name="media_name" type=" input" />
   <ARModelcolumn name=" PrimaryMediaCategory" type="
    input" />
   <ARModelcolumn name=" MaxTem " type=" ignore" />
    <ARModelcolumn name=" MinTem " type=" ignore" />
<ARModelcolumn name="weather" type=" input" />
<ARModelcolumn name="Country" type=" input" />
<ARModelcolumn name=" city" type=" input" />
<ARModelcolumn name="ZipCode" type="ignore" />
<ARModelcolumn name=" PotentialTarget" type=" predict_only
 " />
</Modelcolumns>
<ModelFilter>  <Filter SQLquery="Date >='2012-02-01'" />
 </ModelFilter>
<Parameters>
  <Parameter name="Maximum_ItemSet_Size" value="3" />
  <Parameter name="Minimum_ItemSet_Size" value="1" />
  <Parameter name="Minimum_Probability" value="0.4" />
  <Parameter name="Minimum_Support" value="0" />
</Parameters>
</ARModel>
<NBModel>
<Modelcolumns>
  <NBModelcolumn name="ID" type=" KEY" />
  <NBModelcolumn name="Device_ID" type=" input" />
  <NBModelcolumn name="Date" type=" ignore" />
    <NBModelcolumn name="TimeSlot" type=" input" />
<NBModelcolumn name="DayOfWeek" type=" input" />
 <NBModelcolumn name="IsWeekEnd" type=" input" />
 <NBModelcolumn name="Time" type=" input" />
 <NBModelcolumn name="Gender" type=" input" />
  <NBModelcolumn name=" Age" type=" input" />
```

```
    <NBModelcolumn name="media_name" type=" input" />
    <NBModelcolumn name=" PrimaryMediaCategory" type=" input"
    />
    <NBModelcolumn name=" MaxTem " type=" ignore" />
     <NBModelcolumn name=" MinTem " type=" ignore" />
<NBModelcolumn name="weather" type=" input" />
<NBModelcolumn name="Country" type=" input" />
<NBModelcolumn name=" city" type=" input" />
<NBModelcolumn name="ZipCode" type="ignore" />
<NBModelcolumn name=" PotentialTarget" type=" predict_only
 " />
</Modelcolumns>
<ModelFilter>    <Filter SQLquery="Date >='2012-02-01'" />
 </ModelFilter>
<Parameters>
  <Parameter name="Maximum_states" value="100" />
  <Parameter name="Minimum_dependency_probability"
    value="0.0000000001" />
</Parameters>
</NBModel>
</Models>
</structure>
```

Sample Advertising Models

After the training process finishes, we can get a set of models for each type of rules. Figure 7.24 shows the trained decision tree of ad category real time model. Each path starting from the root node and ending at another node (including

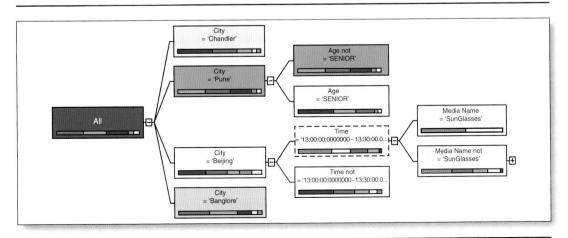

Figure 7.24 Decision Tree of Ad Category Real Time Model

the inner nodes and leaf nodes) composes a decision rule. All these rules can be extracted from the model. Including the paths that end at inner nodes can help to deal with the situation of missing input values. A subset of rules extracted from this model as shown in Table 7.16, where the confidence indicates the percentage of cases in which the rule holds or is correct.

Table 7.16   Sample Rules Extracted from Ad Category Offline Model

Antecedent	Consequent	Confidence
City = 'Beijing'	Potential Target = Weak	0.16
City = 'Beijing'	Potential Target = Very Strong	0.31
City = 'Beijing'	Potential Target = Likely	0.13
City = 'Beijing'	Potential Target = Strong	0.25
City = 'Beijing'	Potential Target = Very Weak	0.15
City = 'Beijing' and Time = '13:00:00~13:30:00'	Potential Target = Weak	0.14
City = 'Beijing' and Time = '13:00:00~13:30:00'	Potential Target = Very Strong	0.03
City = 'Beijing' and Time = '13:00:00~13:30:00'	Potential Target = Likely	0.23
City = 'Beijing' and Time = '13:00:00~13:30:00'	Potential Target = Strong	0.21
City = 'Beijing' and Time = '13:00:00~13:30:00'	Potential Target = Very Weak	0.39
City = 'Beijing' and Time = '13:00:00~13:30:00' and Media Name = 'SunGlasses'	Potential Target = Likely	0.46
City = 'Beijing' and Time = '13:00:00~13:30:00' and Media Name = 'SunGlasses'	Potential Target = Very Weak	0.54
City = 'Beijing' and Time = '13:00:00~13:30:00' and Media Name not = 'SunGlasses'	Potential Target = Weak	0.18
City = 'Beijing' and Time = '13:00:00~13:30:00' and Media Name not = 'SunGlasses'	Potential Target = Very Strong	0.03
City = 'Beijing' and Time = '13:00:00~13:30:00' and Media Name not = 'SunGlasses'	Potential Target = Likely	0.17

City = 'Beijing' and Time = '13:00:00~13:30:00' and Media Name not = 'SunGlasses'	Potential Target = Strong	0.25
City = 'Beijing' and Time = '13:00:00~13:30:00' and Media Name not = 'SunGlasses'	Potential Target = Very Weak	0.36
City = 'Beijing' and Time = '13:00:00~13:30:00' and Media Name = 'MobilePhone'	Potential Target = Weak	0.05
City = 'Beijing' and Time = '13:00:00~13:30:00' and Media Name = 'MobilePhone'	Potential Target = Very Weak	0.95
City = 'Beijing' and Time = '13:00:00~13:30:00' and Media Name not = 'SunGlasses' and Media Name not = 'MobilePhone'	Potential Target = Weak	0.20
City = 'Beijing' and Time = '13:00:00~13:30:00' and Media Name not = 'SunGlasses' and Media Name not = 'MobilePhone	Potential Target = Very Strong	0.04
City = 'Beijing' and Time = '13:00:00~13:30:00' and Media Name not = 'SunGlasses' and Media Name not = 'MobilePhone'	Potential Target = Likely	0.20
City = 'Beijing' and Time = '13:00:00~13:30:00' and Media Name not = 'SunGlasses' and Media Name not = 'MobilePhone'	Potential Target = Strong	0.29
City = 'Beijing' and Time = '13:00:00~13:30:00' and Media Name not = 'SunGlasses' and Media Name not = 'MobilePhone'	Potential Target = Very Weak	0.27

From the decision tree in Figure 7.24, we can see that location is the most differentiable input, time plays an important role for the digital signage in Beijing, and age is an important input for Pune. But gender doesn't show the effect for the predictive modeling. One main reason is that it is a very small percentage of female audience in the training data set, the male audience is dominant in the training process and training result. Another reason is that the fake ads we used didn't show different attraction to different genders. Next, we will use some real content, such as GPTW (Great Place To Work) events for display. These events are collected in Chandler, Bangalore, and Beijing.

Advertising Rule Deployment and Selection

Figure 7.25 shows the flow of the advertising rules from SSAS database to the digital player. Once CMS calls the rule extraction web services provided by DMM (Data Mining Module), DMM extracts the advertising rules from SSAS database using DMX and return the rules to CMS. And CMS will transfer the rules to the digital player on a daily basis.

A DMX statement for rule extraction from decision tree model is as follows. Where [AdCategoryModelling-DT] is the name of the trained decision tree model:

```
SELECT FLATTENED NODE_DESCRIPTION, (select Attribute_name,
attribute_value, [Probability] from node_distribution where
[support]>0) as t from [AdCategoryModelling-DT].CONTENT
WHERE  node_support>0
```

After the rules are transferred to and deployed in the digital player, they are ready to be used for targeted advertising. But in many cases there could be multiple rules that are satisfied by the given inputs. The calculation of the playing probabilities of the ads recommended by these rules is described in Chapter 4. But before the calculation, we need to filter out some dependent rules and use only independent rules for the calculation. Here we give a definition of rule dependency.

Definition: Rule A is dependent on Rule B if satisfying either of the below conditions:

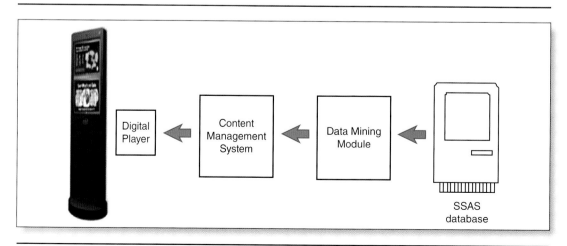

Figure 7.25 Flow of Advertising Rules

1) The antecedent of Rule A is explicitly contained by the Antecedent of Rule B.

2) The antecedent of Rule A is able to be derived from the Antecedent of Rule B.

For example, assume we have below inputs, City = 'Beijing' and Time = '13:00:00~13:30:00' and Media Name = 'SunGlasses'. Then all the satisfied rules by the inputs in Table 7.16 are shown in Table 7.17. But the antecedent of Rules #1~5 is explicitly contained by the antecedent of Rules #6~10, which is explicitly contained by the antecedent of Rules #11~12. So according to the above definition, Rules #1~5 are dependent on Rules #6~10, which are dependent on Rules #11~12. So given the above inputs, although all the 12 rules are satisfied, only Rules #11~12 should be used and others should be filtered out.

Table 7.17 The First Example of Satisfied Rules

Rule	Antecedent	Consequent
1	City = 'Beijing'	Potential Target = Weak
2	City = 'Beijing'	Potential Target = Very Strong
3	City = 'Beijing'	Potential Target = Likely
4	City = 'Beijing'	Potential Target = Strong
5	City = 'Beijing'	Potential Target = Very Weak
6	City = 'Beijing' and Time = '13:00:00~13:30:00'	Potential Target = Weak
7	City = 'Beijing' and Time = '13:00:00~13:30:00'	Potential Target = Very Strong
8	City = 'Beijing' and Time = '13:00:00~13:30:00'	Potential Target = Likely
9	City = 'Beijing' and Time ='13:00:00~13:30:00'	Potential Target = Strong
10	City = 'Beijing' and Time ='13:00:00~13:30:00'	Potential Target = Very Weak
11	City = 'Beijing' and Time ='13:00:00~13:30:00' and Media Name = 'SunGlasses'	Potential Target = Likely
12	City = 'Beijing' and Time ='13:00:00~13:30:00' and Media Name = 'SunGlasses'	Potential Target = Very Weak

Let's look at another example. Assume given the below inputs, City = 'Beijing' and Time = '13:00:00~13:30:00' and Media Name = 'MobilePhone'. Then some satisfied rules are shown in Table 7.18.

Table 7.18 The Second Example of Satisfied Rules

Rule #	Antecedent	Consequent
1	City = 'Beijing' and Time = '13:00:00~13:30:00' and Media Name not = 'SunGlasses'	Potential Target = Weak
2	City = 'Beijing' and Time = '13:00:00~13:30:00' and Media Name not = 'SunGlasses'	Potential Target = Very Strong
3	City = 'Beijing' and Time = '13:00:00~13:30:00' and Media Name not = 'SunGlasses'	Potential Target = Likely
4	City = 'Beijing' and Time = '13:00:00~13:30:00' and Media Name not = 'SunGlasses'	Potential Target = Strong
5	City = 'Beijing' and Time = '13:00:00~13:30:00' and Media Name not = 'SunGlasses'	Potential Target = Very Weak
6	City = 'Beijing' and Time = '13:00:00~13:30:00' and Media Name = 'MobilePhone'	Potential Target = Weak
7	City = 'Beijing' and Time = '13:00:00~13:30:00' and Media Name = 'MobilePhone'	Potential Target = Very Weak

Although the antecedent of Rules #1~5 (only need considering "Media Name not = 'SunGlasses'") are not explicitly contained by the antecedent of Rules # 6~7, "Media Name not = 'SunGlasses'" can be derived from "Media Name = 'MobilePhone'". So Rules #1~5 are dependent on Rules #6~7, and should be filtered out of the calculation.

Some other such examples are shown in Table 7.19. In the table, we can figure out Rule #1 is dependent on Rule #2, Rule #3 is dependent on Rule #4, Rule #5 is dependent on Rule #6, and Rule #7 is dependent on Rule #8. These dependent rules should be filtered out of the calculation of ad selection.

Table 7.19 Other Examples of Rule Dependency

Rule #	Antecedent	Consequent
1	City = 'Beijing' and IsWeekEnd = 'No'	Potential Target = Weak
2	City = 'Beijing' and DayOfWeek = 'Friday'	Potential Target = Very Strong
3	City = 'Beijing' and TimeSlot = 'Afternoon'	Potential Target = Likely

4	City = 'Beijing' and time = '13:00:00~13:30:00'	Potential Target = Strong
5	City = 'Beijing' and Country = 'China' and City ='Beijing'	Potential Target = Very Weak
6	City = 'Beijing' and Device_ID =562	Potential Target = Likely
7	City = 'Beijing' and SinageType = 'Dynamic'	Potential Target = Strong
8	City = 'Beijing' and Device_ID =562	Potential Target = Very Weak

Chapter **8**

Privacy in Intelligent Systems

Luck is the residue of design.
— Branch Rickey, former owner of the Brooklyn Dodgers baseball team

Computers are not only becoming faster, they are also becoming increasingly intelligent, promising efficient functioning of individuals and organizations (referred to in this chapter as "users"). More and more intelligent computing systems are gathering behavioral data from day-to-day activities and retrieving information to create behavioral models with the goal to assist users perform tasks more efficiently than ever before. Some familiar examples of such systems include books, music, and movies suggestions on online stores (such as Amazon, Netflix, and Pandora) based on past purchases; credit card and loan suggestions made by banks based on a user's credit history; and tailored advertisements displayed in browsers based on a user's email interaction history.

One outcome of this trend is a widespread use of personal information. The behavioral information about a person that in the recent past used to be a matter of interest to only a few acquaintances is now a subject of analysis by a myriad of intelligent systems spread all over the world. On the one hand, this growing interest is not necessarily a concern if the information is being used exactly in the way the user consents for it to be used. On the other hand, numerous cases have been reported in which the actual use of the information goes beyond the consented use. The central issue here is drawing the boundary line around the consented use based on the concepts of privacy.

Information Privacy

The concept of privacy has historically been vague and open to interpretations as evidenced by a number of court cases surrounding the definition of privacy and numerous revisions involving what should and should not be included in the definition. Building upon these developments, Samarjiva (1991) defines privacy as "the capability to explicitly or implicitly negotiate boundary conditions of social relations." This definition covers privacy across multiple parties involved in a wide range of activities.

In the context of computing technology, any type of relation is formed by performing three actions on user data: gathering of data, processing of data to retrieve information, and dissemination of information. A technology that claims to be respecting privacy must control data and information flow such that the user's consent boundaries are not crossed. In fact Gellman (1991) proposes that privacy in this context can be understood as "data protection," primarily because data protection allows the system to contain the information within the boundaries negotiated with the user. The type of information of critical importance is Personally Identifiable Information (PII).

Personally Identifiable Information

National Institute of Standard and Technology (NIST) defines PII as:

> …Any information about an individual maintained by an agency, including (1) any information that can be used to distinguish or trace an individual's identity, such as name, social security number, date and place of birth, mother's maiden name, or biometric records; and (2) any other information that is linked or linkable to an individual, such as medical, educational, financial, and employment information (NIST 2010).

Examples of PII include name (full name, maiden name, mother's maiden name, and so on), personal identification number (social security numbers, driver's license number, and so forth), address (street or email address), asset information (IP address, MAC address, host specific identifiable information), telephone numbers, personal characteristics (photographic image of face or other distinguishing characteristic, x-rays, fingerprints, biometric image data), and information about personally owned property (vehicle registration number, license plate number, title number, and so on).

Most intelligent systems capture one or more of these pieces of information. For example, systems based on computer vision used for traffic surveillance, mapping, and gaming consoles employ regular optical cameras or infrared cameras to capture a scene. The captured data may contain images of faces or license plates. Similarly, targeted advertisement systems often capture a user's browsing behavior (which includes IP address and email address), purchase history, and more recently, information about the members in the user's social network. Capturing of PII is a necessity for the effective functioning of most intelligent systems for a system aiming to autonomously help a user must "know" the user first. PII, however, is a double-edged sword, helping a user on the one side and raising several privacy concerns on the other side.

Privacy Concerns

Bellotti et al. (1993) identified two classes of privacy concerns relating to communications and computing technology: (1) concerns covering technical aspects of a system, and (2) concerns covering multimedia and communication aspect of a system. The first concern primarily deals with what computer scientists and engineers study under the topics of algorithm design, data security, encryption, and network security. It is a system-oriented aspect. The second concern can be understood as user-oriented. It involves design of input and output interfaces and user interaction with the system. The study of such concerns is not restricted to the fields of computer science and engineering, but goes beyond to psychology, sociology, and other anthropocentric disciplines.

This classification can guide the design of traditional rigid computing systems, where rigid computing systems refer to the systems that always produce the same outputs for a given sequence of user inputs. In such systems, designers and engineers often need only concern themselves with the technical aspects because the system depends primarily on the user inputs and not on the user itself; the user is assumed to be a constant. The system designers of intelligent systems, however, may find it difficult to resolve privacy issues using this classification. When the user is no longer a constant entity, the interaction between these two classes of privacy concerns gets increasingly complex, and designers can no longer concern themselves only with technical aspects. Figure 8.1 shows the flow of interaction between computing systems and users for traditional and intelligent systems.

To illustrate this issue, I take an example of the Intel AIM Suite and Intelligent Advertisement Framework (IAF), which are discussed elsewhere in

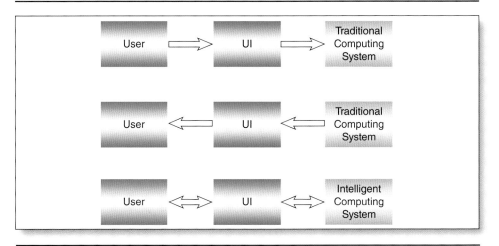

Figure 8.1 User and System Interaction Flow for Traditional Computing Systems (Top and Center) versus Intelligent Computing Systems (Bottom)

this book. The Intel AIM Suite performs audience measurement and provides anonymous attention and demographics data to IAF. The IAF in turn updates in real time the advertisements played on the digital signage to target the detected audience more effectively. When the audience becomes aware of a reactive digital signage, their behavior changes and so do the attention and demographic data. Furthermore, if the digital signage supports user interaction, then the technical aspects of the display influence user behavior. The underlying issue here is that the flow of influence is no longer unidirectional (from the system to the user or the user of the system).

This opens a whole new universe of topics that a system engineer needs to understand. In order to limit the scope of topics outside computing technology, this chapter follows a holistic, system-oriented approach to privacy. Using the pointers provided by the various aspects of a computing system (intelligent or otherwise), engineers can identify specific privacy issues and address them.

This system-oriented approach is based on the dataflow in intelligent computing systems (see Figure 8.2). The system captures data from the environment, performs various analyses on the data, and creates information output to send back to the environment. Based on this dataflow, the three basic modules of an intelligent computing system are: (1) the data capture or input module, (2) the data analysis or processing module, and (3) the

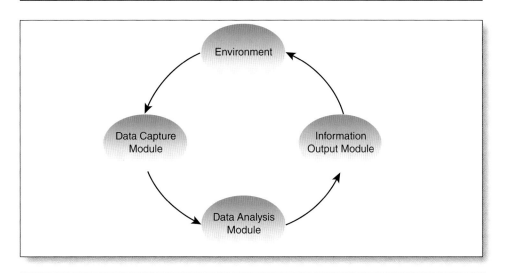

Figure 8.2   Flow of Data for Intelligent Computing Systems

information output module. For a simple drawing application, a traditional computing system, the data collection module takes mouse input from the user; the data analysis module performs geometric operations; and the information output module draws a particular shape. For a targeted Internet advertisement system, an example of an intelligent system, the data collection module captures user browsing and clicking behavior; the data analysis module creates mathematical models of user behavior; and the information output module displays customized UI and content for the particular user. The following subsections present privacy concerns associated with each of these three modules. The discussions will be focused on intelligent systems, for traditional systems are only a subset of intelligent systems. It should also be noted that a single module may have privacy concerns related to both technical and communication classes.

Data Capture Module

The data capture module in an intelligent system usually consists of software UI, hardware interaction devices, and automatic sensors. The purpose of this module is to capture data for the purposes of understanding user behavior. It can also act as an interface between the user and the system. This module can perform some pre-processing operations on the captured data (such as filtering, noise-removal, encryption, or compression), but no behavioral information is extracted. For example, Intel AIM Suite uses USB or IP cameras to capture RGB images of the scene. The images are sent from the sensor to the computer running the system via a secured link. They are then converted to a different color space and smoothed. At this stage, there is no image analysis performed to extract user information. Since there is no PII explicitly extracted at this stage, privacy issues are not obvious but present.

Ineffective Design of Input Interfaces

Data capture modules often need to facilitate interaction with users to gather data. Poor design of this interaction may lead to several privacy concerns. For example, a system capturing image data (such as, for example, in audience measurement, surveillance, or customer assistance) of people's faces in public places may continuously display the images as they are captured. On the surface this does not seem to raise any privacy issues, but this is prone to unauthorized access to the captured data (for example, by taking a snapshot of the images being displayed). Some possible approaches to address such issues are discussed later in this chapter. Similarly, when capturing textual information, visual display of PII as it is being input by the user is a poor design choice. Most web browsers support obfuscation of such sensitive information, but the onus is upon the designers to respect the sensitivity of the data and handle it appropriately.

Inadvertent Capture of Extraneous Data

Less is more when it comes to the capture of PII. Intelligent systems often facilitate input of data in various forms and granularity making it prone to privacy issues. For example, for a system processing images in real time, such as Intel AIM Suite, the relevant data is an image or a current snapshot of the scene. A video input for such systems, which has more information than an image, should be considered extraneous, and therefore, the system should not facilitate video capture in its input module. Similarly, in a system collecting users' location information (such as maps or social networking applications), designers must identify the granularity of the required information. A postal code is extraneous information when just the name of the city suffices.

Unsecured Sensor Data Transmission

This could well be called the classic privacy issue and must not be left unaddressed. In intelligent systems, the data transmission at the input module level often occurs between a sensor and a processing facility (a single computer or cloud computers). Examples of such transmission includes camera sensor data transfer over USB, motion or accelerometer sensor data transfer using Bluetooth or NFC, and location sensor information using a TCP/IP connection. Most of these media support secured transmission.

Data Analysis Module

The data analysis or processing module lies at the heart of an intelligent computing system. This module receives data from the capture module and is responsible for extracting user behavior information. Depending on the nature of the system, this module may or may not retrieve PII. For example, surveillance systems, personal recommender systems, and some targeted advertisement systems require PII, whereas audience measurement systems, social media monitoring systems, and some recommender systems (such as Amazon, Pandora, and Netflix) do not require PII. Depending on the PII requirements of intelligent systems, different kinds of privacy concerns can be raised.

Unsecured PII Transmission

Intelligent systems often have components spread across the Internet and privacy-sensitive data is transmitted from one component to another. For example, an audience measurement system, such as Intel AIM Suite, gathers audience impression data on a client computer and transmits the data to a central server for data mining and analytics generation. Similarly, in recommender systems user-specific browsing information is transmitted to a central server. Such processes can be identified in numerous intelligent systems in which a central web-based knowledgebase is created from user behavior information retrieved separately on distributed client computers. When the data being transmitted contains PII then this raises a classic privacy concern and network security becomes of vital importance.

Unsecured PII Storage

Systems requiring PII store large amounts of privacy-sensitive data. When the system has a client-server architecture the storage is often distributed across both the client and the server locations. This raises potential concerns related to the storage of PII. While web server data security has well been recognized as one of major privacy concerns, secured storage of PII on the client side is equally important. Client computers are usually not only functionally distributed, but are also physically distributed across distant locations. PII storage on client computers has an added challenge of diverse location distribution.

Incomplete Processing of PII

Is PII completely removed from the processing pipeline? For example, if an audience measurement system is not using PII then all the links associating an image of a person to a particular behavior should be removed.

Output Module Privacy

The output module forms an interface between the user and the intelligent system. Once an intelligent system completes processing data, the output is generated either in the form of information (as audio, video, text, or some form of tactile response) or a set of decisions. The system can also transmit the output to other systems. In this section we discuss only the systems that present the information in some media format; the other type of systems can be studied as a sequence of intelligent systems.

Development of Privacy Safe Systems

The development of a system can be divided into three major stages: design stage, implementation stage, and deployment stage. In this section, we discuss various approaches designers can take during each of these three stages to develop privacy safe systems.

Design Stage

Addressing privacy concerns during the system design phase is the least expensive way to develop privacy safe systems.

Identifying Relevant PII

Once a system is conceptualized, specify what the inputs and outputs of the system are. Find out which of those data are PII. Take, for example, a digital signage audience measurement system. Intel AIM Suite does not store PII data and an algorithm was designed to make sure of this.

Minimizing PII Requirements

Once PII have been identified based on the initial design of the system, rethink the system requirements to minimize the PII essential for the functioning of the system. Start removing PII one by one until you have created the smallest possible set of PII that are essential for the functioning of the system.

Optimizing Use of PII

Once the smallest set of PII has been created, find out if it is possible to substitute those PII by some type of anonymous information. For example, with a depth camera, just capture depth and no RGB information. Make sure that the usage of PII is optimized and all the nonessential usage is removed. Superfluous use of sensitive information will raise the probability of privacy threats.

Implementation Stage

Anonymizing Data

All the data flow across different components of the system should be anonymized. For example, one approach to implement this is to replace all PII by a system-related unique ID. This makes sure that if the security of some component of the system is compromised then the threat is not spread across the entire system.

Similarly, input modules should also anonymize the captured data. One approach, as implemented in Intel AIM Suite, would be to disable or hide the display of visual input information by default and only temporarily enabling it upon the explicit request of the operator (see Figure 8.3).

Similarly, for input modules requiring textual input, privacy can be preserved by obfuscating or hiding the PII from within the interface (see Figure 8.4).

Figure 8.3   Intel AIM Suite Hides Input Images by Default

Secured Data Transmission

Transmission of data over the network should be secured. Various network and data security principles can be used to implement this.

Secured Data Storage

All the PII being stored in a database must be encrypted. Intelligent systems not only store current application data, but also store training data. All stored data should facilitate restricted access.

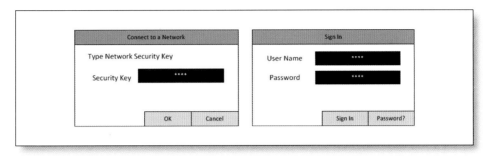

Figure 8.4   Hidden Password Input Fields in Some Common Interfaces

Deployment Stage

Edward T. Hall identified four different types of spaces that people perceive when interacting socially: intimate, personal, social, public. What information people are willing to share depends on the space in which they are interacting. This concept of spaces can also be extended to deployment of intelligent computing systems. Designers can address privacy issues by identifying the space in which the system is being deployed.

Intimate Space Deployment

For the current privacy purposes, we define intimate space as the space in close proximity of a user in which only the user interacts with the intelligent system. The information output in this space does not require a high degree of privacy preservation. However, the intelligent system must allow users to control the amount and the way the information is being output. For example, user's PII may be displayed, but the user should have the option to disable the display.

Personal Space Deployment

We define personal space as the space in which a user and her good friends and family members interact with the intelligent system. For designing output modules in this space only the relevant PII should be displayed.

Social Space Deployment

We define social space as the space in which a user and her acquaintances interact with the intelligent system. Examples of this space include an office environment, a classroom, and a social gathering.

Public Space Deployment

We define public space as the space in which anyone can interact with the intelligent system. Examples of this space include offices concierge desks, hospitals, train stations, and airports.

Summary

Information privacy has become a widespread topic of discussion across various computing disciplines. Numerous theoretical constructs have been proposed to formalize this discussion, but analysis of privacy from a system design perspective has been largely missing. In this chapter, we propose an analysis of privacy that is based on the generic architecture of intelligent systems. An intelligent system can be into divided into three functional modules: the data collection module, the data analysis module, and the information output module.

Using this analysis, we identify various high level privacy concerns involved in the design of intelligent systems. We further address these concerns at the three development stages of intelligent computing systems: the design stage, the implementation stage, and the deployment stage. The system-design–oriented approach presented in this chapter provides a concrete understanding of the issues surrounding privacy, and system designers can directly use this understanding to develop privacy-safe intelligent systems.

Chapter **9**

Healthcare Applications and Analytics

There are no facts, only interpretations.

—Friedrich Nietzsche

The healthcare sector and medicine in particular is one of the oldest forms of analysis. There are so many health care applications that involve data analysis that it can by itself evolve into a very specialized field. In this chapter we hope to introduce some of the topics which make healthcare applications so interesting to study. We will also look into health care analytics related to real-time analysis of a reconstructed image.

Growing Healthcare Demands

With the aging population, the cost of healthcare will continue to rise. Figure 9.1 shows the expected population increase in the older population relative the population as a whole. Figure 9.2 shows the expected effect on the Gross Domestic Product (GDP) for the US in the coming years. So the concern and emphasis of research in healthcare is real. There is a big push too within private industry and the government to address this healthcare crisis. Data mining and various analysis techniques are starting to be considered crucial to successfully addressing the efficiencies required to keep costs under control and yield the best ROI.

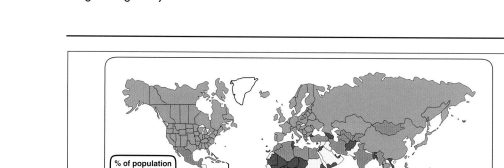

Figure 9.1   World Population Map with Respect to Age

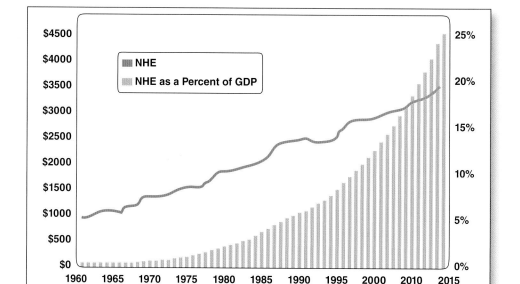

Figure 9.2   US Department of Commerce- Healthcare Cost

Healthcare is using analytics in many areas. Business intelligence analytics is used to attempt to determine where the procurement spending is happening in an attempt to reduce costs. This is not necessarily as interesting in this discussion because this is not unlike any other type of business intelligence analysis performed on any business. However, some of the more challenging aspects of the business intelligence come when combining reimbursement patterns with procurement. This can yield very interesting results. The up side of business intelligence in healthcare is that it requires very little direct patient data in the analysis.

Individual hospital efficiencies concerned with discharge rate and readmissions are starting to become very important because of recent legislation that will start to consider efficiency of care. This legislation will measure these types of indicators to determine reimbursement—providing incentives for efficiency. It will be natural for healthcare providers to start taking every possible datum available to determine why the person is readmitted. This will drive the need for both large datasets and continuous updating of data. The data the provider is likely to track will include prescription/medicine, therapeutic and diagnostic equipment usage, and diagnosis.

Knowledge discovery and data mining (KDD) of the medical records promises will help to identify novel patterns of clinical data. This has been reasonably successful in mining text in radiology reports. This approach offers the ability to look through many of the reports and look for anomalies.

Standards: An Absolute Necessity for Analytics

The healthcare industry has been slow to adopt many standards for data exchange and interoperability. There are many reasons for this, not the least of which is the real challenge of preserving a patient's privacy. Several standards are starting emerge for data exchange and this is allowing more applications of analytics.

One of the oldest of the data exchanges is of radiology image data. DICOM (Digital Imaging and Communications in Medicine) is the standard for storing, handling, transmitting, and printing medical images. This is one of the oldest and most widely accepted standards in healthcare, allowing all kinds of mining techniques to be applied to the images. This standard allows storing image data into a picture archiving and communication system (PACS) for later retrieval by a standard set of tools available from several vendors.

Data exchange protocols for patient data other than imaging has had a very slow adoption rate. This can in part be attributed to the lack of an automated way to acquire the data. Unlike image data, which naturally is in a digital format, patient data gathered from other modalities have relatively small data sets and have not been traditionally connected to the networks. These medical devices also stay in service anywhere from 10 to 15 years adding the extra burden of supporting an infrastructure that does not refresh in the tradition manor. The forcing function now is the drive for efficiency by requiring electronic medical records.

Real-Time Analytics: Ultrasound Object ID

One analytics application that could be quite interesting would involve real-time analysis of the reconstructed image from ultrasound. Unlike the analysis of saved images from magnetic resonance imaging (MRI) or computed tomography (CT), ultrasound images are typically created and could be analyzed in real time. Ultrasound devices also have the advantage of having small form factors and they are typically less expensive than most other imaging modalities.

Acquiring and interpreting ultrasound images can be very challenging. Acquiring useful images often takes special training by an operator and physical manipulation of the ultrasound probes to acquire the best picture. All these adjustments are made in real time during the examination. Interpreting these images, once acquired, is often time-consuming since the operator skill could vary and the radiologist must compensate for the inconsistencies during analysis. With the increase in performance of processors, machine learning and analytics could be applied to this modality to help improve outcomes and allow the expansion of the use of this device in new markets.

Ultrasound Basics

The transducer is at the heart of the ultrasound system. It generates the acoustic waves by converting magnetic, thermal, and electrical energy into mechanical energy. The most efficient technique in medical ultrasound uses the piezoelectric effect. This effect can be realized in a quartz crystal. When mechanical stress is applied across the surface of a quartz crystal, an electrical potential is produced. If electrical potential is introduced across this material, a mechanical deformation can be produced. In this manner, a piezoelectric transducer converts an oscillating electric signal into an acoustic wave and is able to convert the acoustic waves into an electrical signal.

Linear array transducers are the type typically used in ultrasounds today. However these transducers are used in a very controlled manner to optimize the focusing and steering of the arrays. The ultrasound image is formed by repeating this process. Figure 9.3 illustrates a simple example of an 8-element linear array focusing the transmitted beam. One can assume that each array element is a point source that radiates a spherically shaped wave front into the medium. Since the top element is the farthest from the desired focus point for this illustration, it is excited first. The remaining elements are excited in the appropriate time interval so that the acoustic signals from all of the transducers arrive at the focal point at the same time. Huygens' principle indicates the net acoustic signal is the sum of the signals that have arrived from each source. At the focal point the contributions from each transducer add in phase to produce a peak in the acoustic signal.

For receiving the ultrasound echo, the phased array works in reverse. The echo is incident on each array element at a different time. The received signals are electronically delayed so that the delayed signals add a phase for the echo originating at the focal point. For echoes originating elsewhere, at least some of the delayed signals will add out of phase, reducing the receive signal relative to the peak at the focus. In receive mode, the focal point can be dynamically adjusted so that it coincides with the range of returning echoes. As shown in Figure 9.4, focus 1 could be the first and strongest set of signals but the focal point can be changed electronically recognizing there are more areas that will essentially be in focus. This is called dynamic receive focusing and was first implemented by von Ramm and Turstone in 1976.

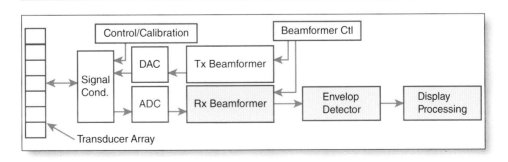

Figure 9.3   An 8-Element Linear Array Focusing the Transmitted Beam

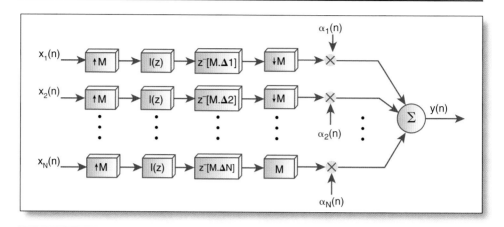

Figure 9.4 Block Diagram of the Receive Beamformer

Ultrasound Software Prototype

An ultrasound software prototype was developed to help understand the bottlenecks in processor performance for this specific class of application. Although it is not a full implementation of an ultrasound device, it acts as one of many applications Intel uses to serve as a proxy for understanding programming techniques, optimizations of code, pipeline and memory structure required for this type of application. We can use this prototype to suggest areas where video analytics could be performed in real time in an ultrasound application.

Figure 9.5 shows the block diagram of a simplified ultrasound imaging implementation. The transducer array consists of a number of transducers that

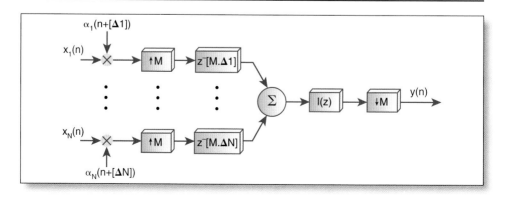

Figure 9.5 Simplified Block Diagram of the Receive Beamformer

connect to signal conditioners and the AFE (ADCs/DACs) required for the application. As suggested earlier, the beamformer is responsible for helping to focus the acoustic waves for both generation and acquisition of the acoustic waveforms. An envelope detector extracts the information carried from the receive beamformer, which is then stored and prepared for display. The parameters for this prototype are shown in Table 9.1.

Table 9.1   Parameters for Ultrasound Imaging

Parameter	Value
Number of transducers	128
Number of scanned lines per frame (steering directions)	128
Angle aperture	90 degrees
Number of samples acquired, per transducer per line	3000
Output image dimensions	640x480 (pixels)
Image resolution	8-bit grayscale
Target number of frames per second	30
Input signal resolution	12-bit fixed point
Output signal resolution	8-bit fixed point
Computational precision (all stages)	32-bit floating point

Receive Beamformer

This block implements essentially a delay and sum synthetic receive focusing with linear interpolation and dynamic apodization. Figure 9.4 shows the flow diagram for this block.

For each scan line that is acquired, each signal stream $xk(n)$ coming from the transducer elements passes through an upsampler, interpolation filter $I(z)$, a delay element, a downsampler, and is multiplied by a dynamically varying apodization coefficient. The resulting signals are then accumulated and a single stream $y(n)$ is sent to the next processing stage. The delay values are pre-computed, multiplied by M and rounded to the nearest integer value (operator$\lfloor\rfloor$) and stored in a look-up table (LUT), and are recomputed each time a new line starts to be acquired. The apodization function updates itself for each sampling period of the input streams. All its coefficients are also pre-computed and stored in a LUT.

The interpolation filter is a first-order linear interpolating filter. If this filter is decomposed into its M polyphase components, only N/M of its taps need to be computed (*N* being the total number of taps). An interperlation/decimation factor of 4 was chosen for this prototype, which means that the filter has a 7-tap, linear-phase FIR configuration.

In terms of the number of floating-point DSP operations per second, and assuming the filter instances process 2 taps per input sample, the structure of Figure 9.4 would require more than 7.3 GFlops for real-time 30 FPS B-mode imaging. If we rearrange the architecture a bit using 128 parallel filters being transformed into a single filter having the same impulse response, we can simplify the design. The block diagram is equivalent to the previous one except the loss of accuracy in the delays and applied apodizaition coefficents.

Although the channel streams are accumulated at the higher sampling, at most the same number of additions is performed since, for each *M* samples of the upsampled signals, only one is not equal to zero. This interpolating filter is now a decimating filter; an efficient polyphase implementation is also possible.

Assuming the worst-case scenario in which all delay values are the same, the number of operations for the beamforming algorithm is now 3.1 GFLOPs. This represents a 57 percent reduction in computational complexity as compared to the original approach.

Envelop Detector

The envelop detector uses a Hilbert tranformer as its central building block. The incoming signals are seen as being modulated in amplitude, where the ultrasound pulses carry (modulate) the information to be displayed. Figure 9.6 shows its block diagram. The order of *L* of the Hilber transformer is 30 for our prototype. The logarithm consumes 10 opertions per sample; the computation requirements for this block would be 437.8 MFLOPs.

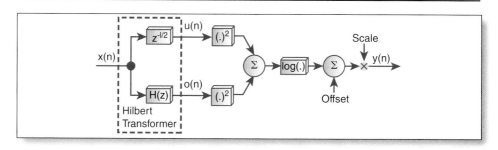

Figure 9.6   Block Diagram of the Envelope Detector

Display Processing

The main responsibility of this block is to convert the array containing all the information to be displayed from polar to Cartesian coordinates. Figure 9.7 illustrates the tranformation performed in this module in which a hypothetical scanned object (a rectangle) is "de-warped" for proper visual representation. In this case, θ represents the steering angle, d the penatration depth, and x and y are the pixel coordinates in the output image.

During initialization, the applications takes the physical parameters of the system and determines the active pixels in the output of the target frame. Using the conversion fomulas, a LUT is built that stores all the information required for the mapping between coordinate spaces. Bilinear interpolation is performed in the (d,θ) space for the increased quality of the output images.

For a 640×480 pixel image and for a 90-degree angle aperture, the number of active pixels is about 150,000. To obtain the output pixel amplitude values, the four nearest values are read from the polar-coordinate space, and bilinear interpolation is performed using the mapping information computed upon

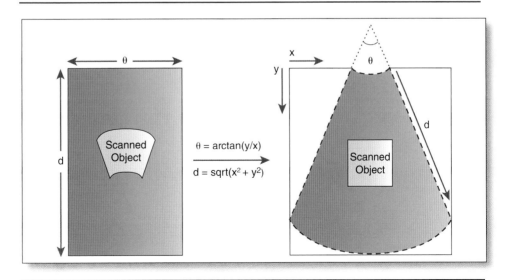

Figure 9.7   Polar-to-Cartesian Conversion of a Hypothetically Scanned Rectangular Object

initialization. Figure 9.8 illustrates this process. For each pixel, 13 operations are performed. For a 30 fps system, 58.5 MFLOPs are required.

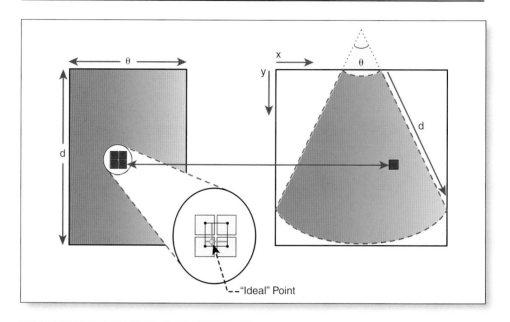

Figure 9.8   Bilinear Interpolation

Distribution of Performance

Performance analysis for our prototype is often used as an indicator for applications performance for processor generations and has an indicator for techniques used in programming. Table 9.2 shows the performance of this algorithm on a cycle basis for various Intel implementations. You will note the AVX and threading optimizations and the impact on performance.

Table 9.2   Multi Thread Performance with AVX enabled

	Original				Optimized			
	1 thread		**1 thread**		**2 threads**		**4 threads**	
	µs	%	µs	%	µs	%	µs	%
Beamf	1,722,460	98%	273,327	94%	141,211	93%	100,198	93%
Envdet	16,669	1%	14,056	5%	7,557	5%	4,889	5%

Display	16,158	1%	3,997	1%	2,605	2%	2,311	2%
Threading	203	0%	124	0%	1,044	1%	860	1%
Total	1,755,491	100%	291502.717	100%	152417.5	100%	108258.363	100%

	Original		Optimized					
	1 thread		1 thread		2 threads		4 threads	
	µs	%	µs	%	µs	%	µs	%
Beamf	185,049	98%	21,871	93%	11,097	91%	6,532	89%
Envdet	2,030	1%	1,039	4%	519	4%	268	4%
Display	1,890	1%	716	3%	496	4%	432	6%
Threading overhead	21	0%	7	0%	80	1%	146	2%
Total	188,990	100%	23,633	100%	12,192	100%	7,378	100%

Recognizing some of the increases in performance over generations, it is now possible to add machine learning and analytics to the ultrasound application. Figure 9.9 is an example flow that may be considered when looking at this type of application. Note that it may be possible to perform some of the analysis before the display processing to get more processing

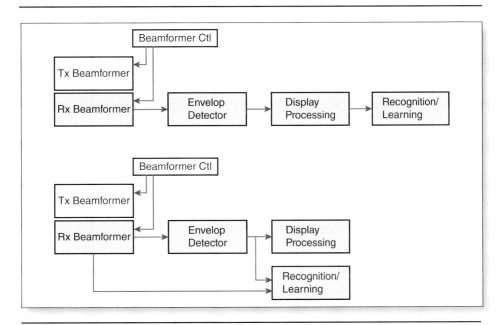

Figure 9.9 Machine learning flow in Ultra Sound application

done in parallel. As the performance increases in the smaller form factors, more of intelligence will be able to be added to this modality to increase its efficacy.

Analytics in Healthcare: Consumerization of Data

As world aging, costs, ubiquitous handheld form factors, and government mandated programs (such as US federal requirements for electronic medical records [EMR] and health information exchange [HIE]), increase steadily, the demand for improved health outcomes and "consumerization" of healthcare via analytics will increase. The amount of data created globally last year alone was over one zettabyte—the equivalent of one billion terabyte hard drives. How to effectively and efficiently analyze this data and positively impact healthcare is the immediate challenge.

The term *big data* was coined for an increasingly voluminous amount of variously sourced unstructured or semistructured data that requires new and complex analytics within a tolerable amount of time to drive intelligent business decisions and discoveries. Volume (large and relative), velocity (fast to information), variety (many sources and formats), and variability (many ways to interpret) describe big data. The techniques and technologies that make big data economical will require the decision scientist to be flexible, consider multidisciplinary approaches, and involve the use of current and new algorithms. For example, typical algorithms in preprocessing data may include Hidden Markov models, Kalman filters, or Bayesian Network modeling, but may also be combined with other tools, such as autocorrelation or time-reversal invariance, to meet validation testing or accuracy requirements. And these new combinations may have to be performed at the server rather than the client level due to the volume of, say, physiological monitoring of EMG frequencies captured many times a second from a large patient base. In all cases, the physiological boundary conditions are critical to consider while analyzing. That is, is it absolutely necessary to capture frequencies that often or will once every minute suffice? Being context-aware during big data healthcare analytics is critical for managing accurate and actionable output as well as recognizing artifacts that need to be removed.

Emerging now is the "consumerization" of healthcare using big data with always-on-always-connected devices with handheld form factors that make it easy for a consumer to manage his or her own healthcare or behaviors that impact their healthcare. Dr. Eric Topal, author of *The Creative Destruction of Medicine: How the Digital Revolution Will Create Better Health Care*, states that 90 percent of physicians have never heard of online health communities such as PatientsLikeMe and CureTogether, where large populations manage their health with peers. This disruptive activity will become more common as analytic firms such as SAS, IBM, and Oracle drive their analytic solutions into the consumer market.

Adding to the growing consumerization are the many software applications available for download in the healthcare domain for an iPad† or iPhone†; currently, healthcare apps exceed 13,000. Millions of Web sites are available for the "worried well" or those with specific chronic or acute conditions to access. Typically, these immediate resources are outside of government regulatory oversight. However, in a review of www.fda.gov, a number of regulated medical products are emerging that utilize these form factors or have regulated software that do. Examples include Andon's iHealth BP3 Automated Blood Pressure for use at home with an iPhone or iPad, Airstrip RPM that captures physiological readings on an iPhone, and MIM Software's Mobile MIM for making medical diagnoses on an iPhone or iPad based on computed tomography (CT), magnetic resonance imaging (MRI), and nuclear medicine technology such as positron emission tomography (PET). While Mobile MIM is indicated for use only when a full workstation is not available, the inference is clear: mobile health for consumers as well as clinicians is increasing. FDA guidelines for mobile apps are currently undergoing public comment, and earlier this year, the Medical Device Data Systems (MDDS) ruling was implemented which considers the regulation of electronic data systems as medical devices. It is clear that the ecosystem for healthcare targeting the connected consumer is adapting quickly.

Consumerization of de-identified HIE big data will be demanded as more clinicians, states, and regions subscribe to the upload of specific EMR data. Capturing appropriate data and applying actionable information to drive improved health outcomes as a consumer is seamlessly connected throughout their day is an opportunity for big data to have meaningful applicability. By segmenting populations via classification algorithms, personalized medicine may become a reality—and be provided directly at the consumer's fingertips.

Analytics in Healthcare: From Data to Information

Health analytics can range in complexity depending on what questions are being asked, the context of the data, and the integration of data sources. Algorithms can be applied to breast cancer cell analysis, EEG and ECG analysis, prosthesis design, optimization of transplant times, hospital expense reduction, hospital quality improvement, and emergency-room test advisement, to name only a few. Payors are utilizing analytics to assess commonalities, drug efficacy, and telemedicine. Genetic analysis for biomarkers that indicate current or future disease is becoming more mainstream and less expensive; genetic analysis is big data with predictive modeling, classification, and/or segmentation algorithms applied. Utilizing this type of information to better manage a patient's outcome or even inclusion into a disease study-group or management plan would contribute greatly to reducing healthcare costs as the population ages.

The data generated throughout the healthcare ecosystem, therefore, has many opportunities to be actively managed in order to provide information for action. This data can be "mined" to discover new relationships and to uncover inferences for deeper analyses. The term *data mining*, as with many terms in analytics, has a number of broad meanings and often overlaps with other terms. However, it is typically considered "knowledge discovery," and the uncovering of new information in large databases, including big data above. Data mining typically consists of basic statistical analyses, looking for patterns, associations, and relationships within the data to separate into distinct groups for further processing, and artifact removal (significant in the healthcare realm due to the impact of human interference to the sensor, such as, for example, an inferior signal-to-noise ratio).

Data mining is usually sourced from warehousing, or storage, of data. However, as real-time analytics with cloud capability emerges with faster processor speeds, increased multithreading, parallelism, and virtualization, data mining is evolving from a retrospective and static data analyses to a vital and potent engine of information. In the future, data mining may be considered merely a portion of a software application on a smart phone, to drive consumer health decisions, say, in nutritional content of food he or she buys. But to the data scientist, it is an integral part of gaining knowledge about the data population and is now inclusive of predictive models, neural networks, decision trees, and regression models to drive process improvement and operational excellence. Ultimately, these models, when applied in healthcare, can be used to improve patient outcomes.

Data mining and associated algorithm manipulation are becoming more pervasive in clinical analyses. For example, predictive analytics (inclusive of predictive modeling) are an advanced approach of classifying typically unsupervised data and predicting an outcome based on a pattern. Such an approach examines a *priori* knowledge of data and extracts variables to predict data points or trends in the future. Utilizing regression methods, machine learning, or a host of different statistical tools, predictive analytics have become an elegant method with which to predict the future with a defined accuracy based on the models applied. Pattern recognition, a algorithmic tool often used in neural network applications (that is, in machine learning), is defined as the act of taking in raw data and taking an action based on the category of the pattern. Using a *priori* pattern knowledge of a signal or the intrinsic pattern regularity itself, models can be created that may augment the clinician's decision to better assess the patient's trending. The oft-used term *dynamic* implies that the pattern is being reassessed with each new data point entered by the patient and counteracts intrinsic data decay of a predictive model.

A number of investigators have applied predictive modeling (also known as dynamic pattern recognition) to the decomposition of a biosignal, even though many comment about noisy data with varying space and time attributes. Helal investigated diabetes patients unobtrusively in their homes ("Smart Homes") while collecting behavioral, blood pressure, and glucose data. He applied the Hidden Markov model, achieving 98 percent recognition accuracy of activities and chewing. A review of "smart" wearables for remote health monitoring by Lymberis indicated that embedded medical decisions have relied thus far on fuzzy logic or neural network models. Lisetti performed an extensive literature survey in the study of physiological signals recognizing human emotions. A number of common statistical tools were applied in healthcare studies such as Analysis of Variance (ANOVA) and Multivariate Analysis of Variance (MANOVA). In other studies Lisetti reported, Sequential Floating Forward Search (SFFS), Fisher Projection (FP), Principal Component Analysis (PCA), and Discriminate Function Analysis (DFA) were applied. No common tool was used, however, suggesting that there is a wide range of applications and ramifications for applying predictive modeling or a common statistic to biological models. Each is typically unique and requires careful classification due to the impact of other biological signals and artifacts.

Another area of focus has been the use and theory of clinical decision support systems which are typically computerized expert systems that utilize artificial intelligence and machine learning to supplement a clinician's decisions. At its most basic level, decision support systems can be suggestions based on simple algorithms. Eren reports that there are two types of decision support systems: rules-based or expert systems (including probabilistic and cognitive models). Either can be applied in healthcare.

The foundation of any predictive analytics exercise typically includes 1) data acquisition from the sensor 2) feature generation and pre-processing, 2) feature selection, 4) classification of the design, and 5) system evaluation using a training set (see Figure 9.10).

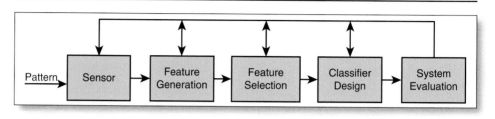

Figure 9.10 Basic Stages of Predictive Modeling (Dynamic Pattern Recognition)

Bayesian models are one statistical inference tool used in *feature generation*, a preprocessing step that considers the posterior distribution of all the uncertain quantities (missing, latent, unobserved data). The posterior distribution is the product of likelihood and a *priori* knowledge, represented mathematically as

$$P(H|E) = (P(E|H)\, P(H))\, /\, P(E)$$

where:

H = some hypothesis

E = observed evidence

P (E|H) = conditional probability of seeing E if H happens to be true (likelihood)

P (H) = the *a priori* probability of H that was inferred before new evidence became available

P (E) = marginal probability of E; the a *priori* probability of witnessing the new evidence E under all possible hypotheses

Minimizing the number of class assignment errors on new, unlabeled observations is the goal of any predictive analytics exercise, and Bayesian models are some of the most robust models. Following generation, features can now be selected that are of interest in decision making during *Feature Selection*.

Selecting the *Classifier Design* can depend on whether training data of known class labels are available or not. In the case where some information is known, a semi-supervised learning approach using a *priori* knowledge can be used to assist in the design of a classification system. Prior to selecting the classifier, it is important to consider

- The number of subpopulations or groups contributing observed data

- Separation of the subpopulations

- Sample sizes of number of observations in each sample

- Number of variables or dimensions measured on each observation

- Within-group covariance matrix

- Costs associated with misclassification

- Distribution of the data (multivariate, bivariate)

Clustering may help classify the pattern sets in a semi-supervised learning scenario, and include proximity measures (how similar or dissimilar two feature vectors are), clustering criterion (what is the criteria used to segregate the clusters), and clustering algorithms. Many clustering algorithms exist today.

System evaluation consists of verifying the performance of the classifier and assessing the error rate, where testing is often performed on the training set (for example, Resubstitution Method, Holdout method (two subsets), or Leave-One-Out Method (N-1)). Recall, precision, and overall accuracy are also key in assessing misclassification.

Predictive analytics are but one approach that can be used in healthcare and new algorithms will be developed for this sector as more decision scientists undertake the challenge of healthcare revolution. Whether dealing with big data or not, the importance of healthcare analytics is critical to overcoming the deluge of the aging population and healthcare costs. The consumer with new form factors will be the market disrupter; however, medical device companies are also exploring where analytics can be exploited—such as real-time analytics in ultrasound.

Another example of transforming data to information in healthcare can be demonstrated by machine learning. Machine learning, with its roots in artificial intelligence, provides the user with opportunities to apply algorithms on a machine to learn new information from known properties of a dataset. Machine learning can be applied online in near real time, or offline depending on the goals and needs of the application. Wernick, Yang, and Brankov (2010) define machine learning as "concerned with 1) the development of algorithms that quantify relationships within existing data, and 2) the use of these identified patterns to make predictions based on new data." Clearly, the algorithms in predictive analytics, pattern recognition, and neural networks can be applied to machine learning as well.

While the term *machine learning* is relatively new to healthcare, brain mapping and computer-aided diagnosis have been applying the concepts for many years. New to this field is the application of machine learning to neurostimulation of brain fibers to accelerate more fluid motions of para- and quadriplegics' artificial limbs, and to medical imaging in mammography. Wernick, Yang, and Brankov (2010) applied a number of algorithms in prediction of microcalcification of breast tissue in mammography:

■ An enhanced support vector machine classifier

■ A successive enhancement learning

■ A relevance vector machine classifier

■ Statistical resampling

Their algorithm construct rendered minimal cost of calculations and a 94 percent detection rate.

With the growing EMR field, researchers are now using machine learning techniques to gain new knowledge in a form that enables effective reasoning and, ultimately, better patient outcomes. For example, a hybrid intelligent system developed for diagnosis and treatment of prostate cancer by Koutsojannis, Nabil, Tsimara, and Hatzilygeroudis (2009) utilized EMR data of symptoms and test results. By applying a fuzzy expert system resulting in if-then rules, the system resulted in an accuracy, sensitivity, and specificity of .93, .97, and .99, respectively. As EMRs and HIEs proliferate, opportunities for applying machine learning increase as resultant knowledge demonstrates improved patient outcomes.

Kodratoff (1994) provides an oft-cited taxonomy for machine learning based on

■ Machine learning application goal(s)

■ The nature of available data

■ The nature of the available background knowledge (if any)

■ The type of learning to be performed

■ The type of interactions wished after learning

Using these "learning inquiries," a series of application taxonomies are presented to assist the user in selecting appropriate tools and associated algorithms, predominantly from the European ESPRIT project Machine Learning Toolbox (MLT) P2154 and its guidance tool, the Consultant. While many algorithms are appropriate for machine learning, and many tools exist, the MLT Consultant provides a general framework for assisting users in selecting tools based on application conditions.

As need for data to information translation increases and seamless connectivity is expected by consumers and/or decision makers, machine learning will become more prevalent and robust. The decision scientist should not be encumbered as to which algorithm is more appropriate, but as system complexity increases, a unique combination of algorithms may provide new insights and knowledge.

Conclusion

Healthcare use cases for analytics are numerous today and the computational power is allowing more to be suggested. Once the standards are fully implemented and deployed, many more opportunities for analytics can be realized. Sensor technology and continuous monitoring in healthcare will also become much more interesting as smart phones become commoditized and the wireless infrastructure becomes even more efficient.

Chapter 10

Optimizing Machine Learning Algorithms on GPUs

In theory, there is no difference between theory and practice. But in practice, there is.

—Yogi Berra

This chapter provides a comprehensive detail on methodologies that can be considered to optimize video analytics (VA) algorithms by exploring multicore capabilities of both CPU and graphics processing unit (GPU) in parallel. It describes the problems encountered and the possible solutions for porting the video analytic algorithm using parallel programming capabilities. The procedures used for measuring algorithm performance and silicon performance are explained. The performances of VA algorithms on different Nvidia GPUs are quantitatively evaluated and compared. The performance comparison shows that the performance of the built-in graphics processor for the 3rd Generation Intel® Core™ processor family, codenamed Ivy Bridge, is similar to that of the Nvidia's GPUs.

This chapter also describes the differences in architectures of Intel's Ivy Bridge and Nvidia's GPUs.

Overview

Video analytics applications are computationally intensive; these can perform well with a CPU/GPU combination. It is important to identify performance bottlenecks or hotspots of the code. These can be identified by using different available performance profiling tools like the Vtune™ analyzer, Intel Performance Tuning Utility (Intel PTU), and so on. Optimizing hotspot functions will reduce the overall execution time of the program.

The GPU is designed for graphics processing. It contains many small processing elements to process data and deal with computationally intensive applications. The massive processing capability of GPU attracts programmers to start exploring general purpose computing with the GPU. As GPU architecture gives best performance for algorithms that exhibit high data parallelism and high arithmetic intensity, so the performance attained compared to the central processing unit (CPU) are dependent on the particular application.

The general-purpose CPU is capable of running various applications and has now provided multiple cores to process data as well as task in parallel. A recent innovation is the use of runtime libraries, (for example Intel offers the Intel Threading Building Blocks (Intel TBB) for parallel execution of CPU application and to make proper use of CPU cores.

In this technical write-up, analysis of various GPU architectures, their comparative analysis, and optimization of VA applications using Intel TBB and OpenCL (CPU-GPU combination) has been detailed. The Intel Audience Impression Metrics Suite (Intel AIM Suite) is considered as a case study, to demonstrate various optimization techniques and for performance bench-marking. Intel AIMSuite is a video analytics based on the OpenCV framework. It is used to provide demographic information in an anonymous setting. It can provide age, gender, and viewing time information. More information on Intel AIMSuite is available at http://intel.cognovision.com/intel-aim-suite.

GPU Architecture

A GPU is designed such that more transistors are devoted to data processing rather than data caching and flow control, as shown in Figure 10.1. In a GPU application, a large data set is mapped to small independent data elements and processed in parallel. Thus compute-intensive arithmetic operations on large data can be performed in a very short time. GPUs also have a larger memory bus width than CPUs, which results faster memory access.

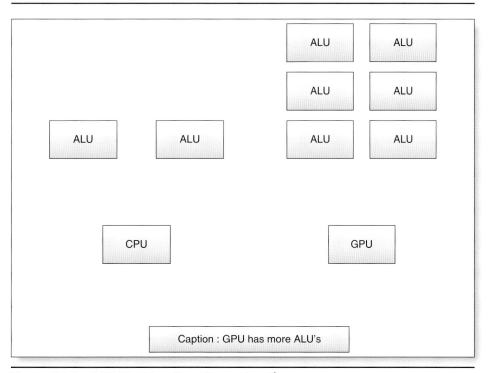

Caption : GPU has more ALU's

Figure 10.1 GPU Has More Data Processing Elements

Intel Ivy Bridge Architecture

Ivy Bridge is the codename for Intel's 22 nm die shrink of the Sandy Bridge microarchitecture. Intel introduced a completely redesigned GPU core onto the CPU package. The advantage is that an integrated GPU's power consumption is less than that of a dedicated GPU.

The 3rd Generation Intel Core processor family, codenamed Ivy Bridge includes several improvements, including integrated graphics. These are explained below.

CPU Features

Basic features of Ivy Bridge are based on Intel Core i7 microprocessors. The Intel Core i7 CPUs have four CPU cores with Intel Hyper-Threading Technology support, 8 MB level-3 cache, and incorporate Intel Turbo Boost Technology. The processor selected for this case study has a clock frequency of 2.2 GHz.

GPU Features

The Ivy Bridge GPU has an array of 16 execution units (EUs) at 400 MHz clock frequency. It has around 16 bit wide single-precision floating point (SP FP) capability. It is an in-order SIMD machine. It provides hardware multithreading support that allows several thread contexts to be active

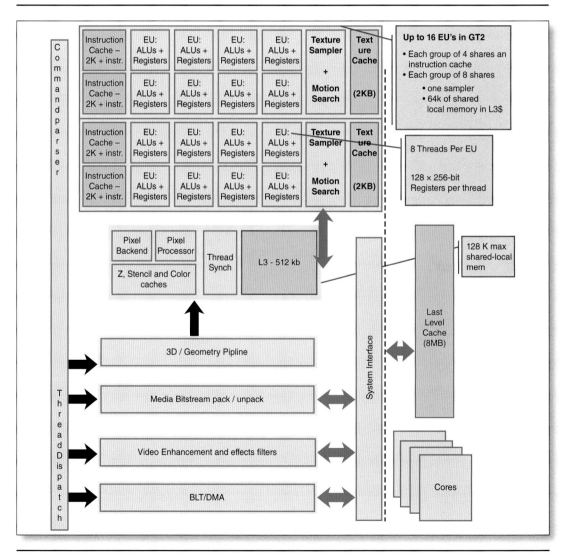

Figure 10.2 Ivy Bridge GPU Architecture

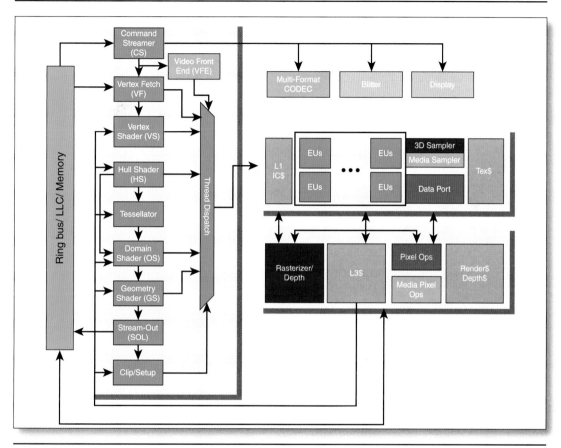

Figure 10.3 Ivy Bridge Microarchitecture

simultaneously. The card includes various on-chip memories such as 64KB shared local memory, which is shared between 8 EUs. Intel HD Graphics [Intel 3rd generation processor] GT2 also has special functional unit like texture sampler unit to perform highly specialized operations.

Figure 10.2 shows architectural features of an Ivy Bridge GPU. Figure 10.3 shows the Ivy Bridge microarchitecture.

GPUs provide support for gather/scatter instructions from memory, something that is not efficiently implemented on CPUs. Gather/scatter operations are important to increase SIMD utilization for applications requiring access to noncontiguous regions of memory to be operated upon, in a SIMD fashion. Furthermore, the availability of a texture sampling unit helps to speedup throughput of computing applications that spend a substantial amount of time in these operations. Ivy Bridge L3 supports good throughput for scatter/gather architecture:

- 2 cache lines/cycle peak throughput—up to 32 DW/cycle
    - One CL/cycle for every 8 EUs. Make sure threads use both sets of EUs to get full bandwidth!

- All accesses collapsed into a single line (so only the number of distinct lines matters).

The Ivy Bridge GPU provides support for OpenCL 1.1, DirectX 11, and OpenGL 3.1.

In Sandy Bridge there were two GPU configurations: GT1 and GT2. Sandy Bridge's GT1 had 6 EUs (shaders/cores/execution units) while GT2 had 12 EUs; both configurations had one texture sampler. Ivy Bridge was designed to scale up and down more easily. GT2 has 16 EUs and 2 texture samplers. Intel is increasing the number of EUs in Ivy Bridge; however, these EUs has much better performance than their predecessors, effectively in Ivy Bridge the bulk of the (up to 60-percent) increase in GPU performance is observed.

Intel also added a graphics-specific L3 cache within Ivy Bridge. Despite being able to share the CPU's L3 cache, a smaller cache located within the graphics core allows frequently accessed data to be accessed without firing up the ring bus.

There are other performance enhancements within the shader core. Scatter and gather operations now execute 32x faster than Sandy Bridge, which has implications for both GPU compute and general 3D gaming performance.

Despite the focus on performance, Intel reduced the GPU clock in Ivy Bridge. It now runs at up to 95 percent of the Sandy Bridge GPU clock, at a lower voltage, while offering much higher performance.

Nvidia GPU Architecture

The following section reviews Nvidia GPU architecture.

GeForce† GTX 400/500 Fermi Architecture

The GeForce GTX 400/500 family of GPUs is based on NVIDIA's Fermi architecture.

Fermi's third generation streaming multiprocessor (SM) introduces several architectural innovations that improve both the performance and accuracy of complex graphics and compute workloads, as shown in Figure 10.4. Each of Fermi's SMs contains 32 CUDA processors—a fourfold increase over prior SM designs. By employing a flexible scalar architecture, CUDA cores achieve full performance on a variety of workloads such as textures, shadow maps, and complex shaders. The result is consistently high performance. Each CUDA processor has a

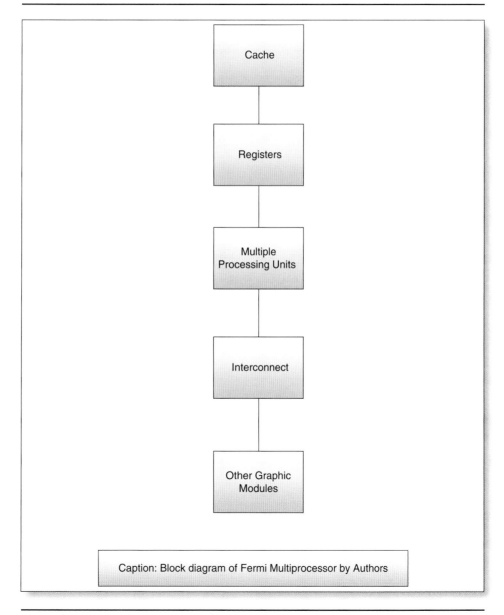

Caption: Block diagram of Fermi Multiprocessor by Authors

Figure 10.4 Fermi Streaming Multiprocessor Internals

fully pipelined integer arithmetic logic unit (ALU) and floating point unit (FPU). Fermi's third generation SM also improves execution efficiency through improved scheduling. The SM schedules work in groups of 32 threads called *warps*. Each SM features two warp schedulers and two instruction dispatch units, allowing two warps to be issued and executed concurrently—twice over the prior generation. Because warps execute independently, Fermi's scheduler does not need to check for dependencies from within the instruction stream. Using this elegant model of dual-issue, Fermi achieves great performance efficiency with minimal hardware.

Cache Architecture

Fermi is the first GPU architecture with fully cached memory access, shown in Figure 10.5. In Fermi, unified cache architecture is present that extends the benefit of caching to all graphics and compute programs.

Fermi programs have access to a texture cache, an L1 cache, and an L2 cache. The L1 and L2 caches improve performance for programs with random

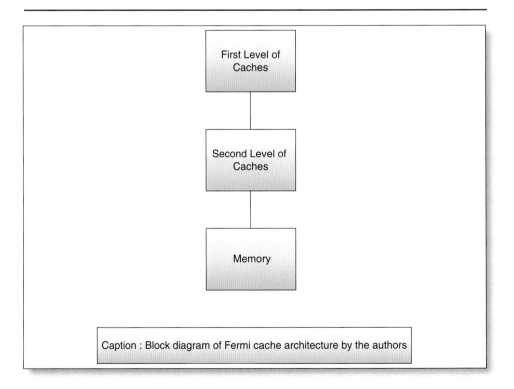

Caption : Block diagram of Fermi cache architecture by the authors

Figure 10.5 Fermi Cache Architecture

memory access patterns. The texture cache enables fast and efficient texture filtering. In addition, programs also have access to a fast, dedicated, shared memory that greatly improves GPGPU applications.

We now describe how the salient hardware features on the two architectures differ from each other, and their implications for throughput computing applications.

Comparison of Ivy Bridge and Nvidia GPU Architectures

The processing element for GPU trades off fast single-thread performance and clock speed for high throughput. Each processing element contains ALU, fetch units. Performance is directly proportional to number of processing elements exist in the GPU. Memory sizes are also an important factor to compare various GPU architectures. The above two and several other parameters are shown in Table 10.1 to make a comparison between two architectures.

Table 10.1   Ivy Bridge and Nvidia GPU Comparison

GPU Parameters	GeForce GTX 570	GeForce GTS 450	Quadro NVS 295	Ivy Bridge
Work Group Size	1024	1024	512	512
Work Item Size	1024 × 1024 x 64	1024 × 1024 x 64	512 × 512 × 64	512 × 512 × 512
Compute Units(CU)	15 (SM)	4 (SM)	1	16
Global Memory	1216 MB (Cache: 0 KB)	961 MB (Cache: 0 KB)	231 MB (Cache: 0 KB)	2104 MB
Local Memory	48 KB	48 KB	16 KB	64 KB
2D Image Size	4096 × 32768	4096 × 32768	4096 × 32768	16384 x 16384
3D Image Size	2048 × 2048 × 16	2048 × 2048 × 16	2048 × 2048 × 16	2048 × 2048 × 16
Constant Buffer	64 KB	64 KB	64 KB	64 KB
Shader Cores	480 (CUDA cores)	192	8	128
Clock frequency	1464 MHz	1764 MHz	1300 MHz	400 MHz
Warp size	32	32	32	8
Threads/Block	1024	1024	512	–
Cache line size	128 bytes	128 bytes	–	64 bytes
Cache size	240 KB	64 KB	–	2048 KB

Optimizing VA Algorithms for Ivy Bridge

Intel AIM Suite contains VA algorithms for face detection and face tracking. It is used as a case study to optimize VA algorithms using different CPU and GPU combinations.

Understanding Intel® AIM Suite

The flow of Intel AIM Suite is shown in Figure 10.6. The first step is to retrieve each frame from video. The retrieved frame is converted to grayscale. Gaussian down-sample and Gaussian blur is used for smoothing effect. The frame is subsampled to ensure performance. Motion in the frame is analyzed using previous input image. New faces are detected using Haar classifier (more information in Chapter 3). Already detected faces are tracked by using a search window on predicted space and matching the histogram.

Right Candidates for GPU

The required algorithm features on a GPU are:

1. High data parallelism

2. Low input data reutilization

3. Algorithms with big data streams

4. High arithmetic complexity per stream element

To partition the workload of CPU and GPU, first analyze algorithms that are suitable for the GPU as per the above criteria, because all general-purpose algorithms are not suitable for GPUs. We can extract these features through the evaluation of different routines and decide which algorithms are suitable for the CPU and which are for the GPU.

Algorithms that are good candidates for the GPU are analyzed from the Intel AIM Suite application and they were developed on a software platform called OpenCL that runs on the GPU.

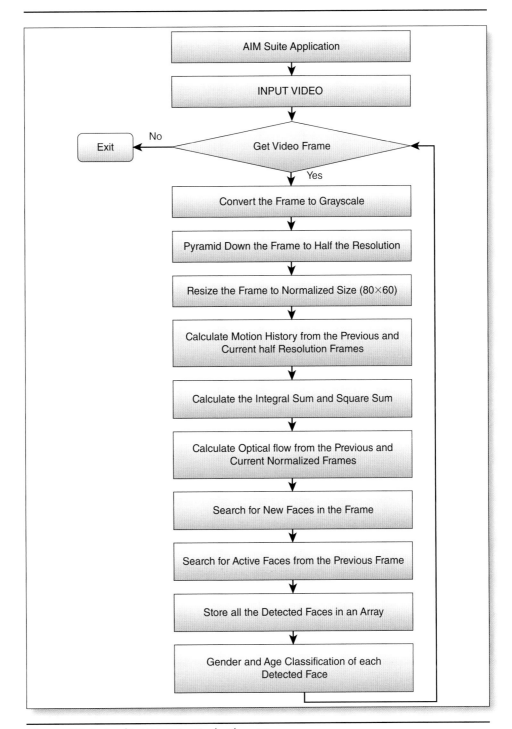

Figure 10.6 Intel® AIM Suite Code Flow Diagram

GPU Optimization

The following section focuses on GPU optimization.

Optimization Using HMPP

The HMPP tool generates OpenCL code that can be ported on to the GPU for further processing. This tool takes care of data transfer between CPU and GPU. For executing code on the CPU or GPU device using HMPP, one has to generate codelets for Hotspot functions.

Hotspot Identification

Hotspot analysis could not be done using any profiling tools because the Intel AIM Suite has a lot of nested libraries included in it. The profiling tool was unable to find out hotspot functions. So hotspots were found out manually. We used operating system timers to find out the time taken for each function in the processframe function of the AIMCore library (library with the Intel AIMSuite program). The maximum time taken functions were identified as hotspot functions.

Hotspot Function Extraction

HMPP codelet creation on OpenCV library function was inconvenient, as HMPP doesn't support either library function calls or CPP code. Creating codelets in original Intel AIM Suite code would have caused difficulties in debugging the code and in accuracy checking of the functions. Also creation of codelets in the OpenCV library would have changed the OpenCV library itself. So, because of these reasons the hotspot functions were extracted outside in a separate workspace.

Extracted Workspace Creation

The separate workspace was created for the following functions:

- Resize
- Haar Classifier
- GetOpticalFlow

■ PyramidDown

■ CalcOpticalFlow

The workspace was created by extracting functionalities from the OpenCV and AIMCore libraries. Output is validated as per the original functionality of OpenCV and the workspace is used for further development.

Migration of HMPP to OpenCL

In Intel AIM Suite code functions were getting called number of times for single video with different input data of different sizes. So for each frame, loading time would be additional overhead. Using the HMPP compiler loading the data on to GPU would have deteriorated the performance achieved, whereas with OpenCL, the small data sizes provided less overhead.

Executing code in Release mode with VS2008 compiler optimization, it takes half of the time compared to debug mode. The HMPP compiler doesn't allow VS2008 to set its compiler optimization in either Debug or Release mode. Hence CPU code performance could not be achieved while using the HMPP compiler for the GPU.

HMPP doesn't support CPP whereas OpenCL does.

Due to these limitations of HMPP, the optimization platform was migrated from HMPP to OpenCL. The hotspots were ported to GPU using the OpenCL compiler.

OpenCL

OpenCL (Open Computing Language) is the open standard for general-purpose parallel programming of heterogeneous systems. OpenCL provides a uniform programming environment for software developers to write efficient, portable code using a diverse mix of multi-core CPUs, GPUs, and other parallel processors such as DSPs. OpenCL architectural details, terminologies, and optimization techniques are explained in following sections.

OpenCL Threading Model

The GPU device (in any architecture) is built around a scalable array of multiprocessors, also called execution units. An execution unit (EU) corresponds to an OpenCL compute unit. An EU executes a thread for each OpenCL work item and a thread block for each OpenCL workgroup (for example in Ivy Bridge, 8 threads/EU is allowed). A kernel is executed over an OpenCL NDRange by a grid of thread blocks, as illustrated in Figure 10.7.

Each of the thread blocks that execute a kernel is therefore uniquely identified by its workgroup ID and each thread by its global ID, or by a combination of its local ID and workgroup ID. When an OpenCL program on the host invokes a kernel, the workgroups are distributed as thread blocks to the execution units with available execution capacity. The threads of a thread block execute concurrently on one execution unit. As thread blocks terminate, new blocks are launched on the empty execution units. An execution unit is designed to execute hundreds of threads concurrently. To manage such a large amount of threads, it employs a unique architecture called

■ SIMD (Single-Instruction, Multiple-Data): used in Ivy Bridge architectures

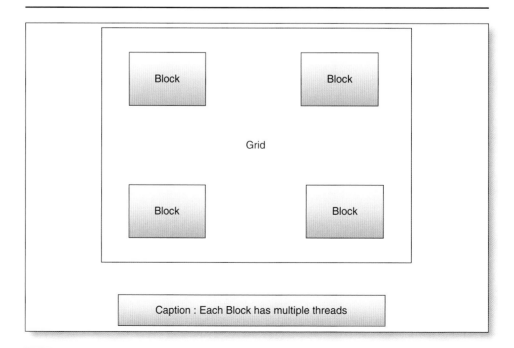

Figure 10.7 Group of Threads Corresponds to Workgroups of OpenCL

■ SIMT (Single-Instruction, Multiple-Thread): used in Nvidia architectures

To maximize utilization of its functional units, it leverages thread-level parallelism by using hardware multithreading. The execution context (program counters, registers, and so on) for each thread group processed by an execution unit is maintained on-chip during the entire lifetime of the group execution. Switching from one execution context to another therefore has no cost, and at every instruction issue time, the scheduler selects a thread group that has threads ready to execute (active threads) and issues the next instruction to those threads. In particular, each execution unit has a set of 32-bit registers that are partitioned among the cores (thread groups), and a parallel data cache or shared memory that is partitioned among the thread blocks and used to implement OpenCL local memory. There is also a maximum limit on number of resident thread blocks per execution unit. These limits as well the amount of registers and shared memory available on the execution unit are a function of the compute capability of the device. If there are not enough registers or shared memory available per execution unit to process at least one block, the kernel will fail to launch.

SIMD: SIMD (Single Instruction, Multiple Data) refers to a parallel processor that runs the exact same program, that is "single instruction" on each of its simultaneously executing parallel units. However, all those operations can perform in large batches using vectors.

SIMT: SIMT is basically SIMD at its top level. It issues an instruction, and many units execute that same instruction. There is an ability to partition those units into separate collections, each of which runs its own instruction stream. The execution unit creates, manages, schedules, and executes threads in groups of 32 parallel threads (in the case of Nvidia Fermi) called warps or in groups of 8 (in the case of Intel's Ivy Bridge). Individual threads composing a group start together at the same program address, but they have their own instruction address counter and register state, and are therefore free to branch and execute independently. When an execution unit is given one or more thread blocks to execute, it partitions them into warps that get scheduled by a warp scheduler for execution (in the case of Nvidia, CUDA) or in general scheduler partitions threads into groups according to execution capacity and then each group of threads executes one common instruction at a time. If threads of a group diverge via a data-dependent conditional branch, the warp serially executes each branch path taken, disabling threads that are not on that path, and when all paths complete, the threads converge back to the same execution path. Branch divergence occurs only within a warp; substantial performance improvements can be realized by taking care that the code seldom requires threads in a group to diverge. In practice, this is analogous to the role of cache lines in traditional code: cache line size can be safely ignored when designing for correctness but must be considered in the code structure when designing for peak performance.

OpenCL Memory Model

Work items executing a kernel have access to four distinct memory regions, as shown in Figure 10.8, global memory, constant memory, local memory, and private memory.

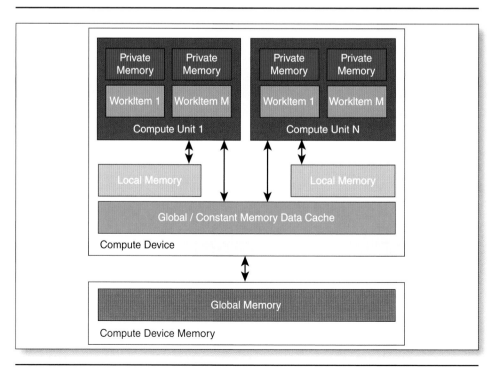

Figure 10.8 OpenCL Memory Hierarchy

Global Memory

This memory region permits read/write access to all work items in all workgroups. Work items can read from or write to any element of a memory object. Read and write operations to global memory may be cached depending on the capabilities of the device. Global memory resides in device memory and device memory is accessed via 32-, 64-, or 128-byte memory transactions.

Global memory generally is the largest capacity memory subsystem on the compute device. For most devices, global memory will be measured in gigabytes of capacity. While large and visible to all threads on a GPU, global memory should also be considered the slowest memory subsystem that also has some restrictions on use. These restrictions vary according to device, which complicates code design. Global memory should be considered as streaming memory. This means that the best performance will be achieved when streaming contiguous memory addresses or memory access patterns that can exploit the full bandwidth of the memory subsystem. Such memory operations are said to be coalesced.

Constant Memory

Constant memory is a region of global memory that remains constant during the execution of a kernel. The host allocates and initializes memory objects placed into constant memory. The constant memory space is cached. As a result, a read from constant memory costs one memory read from device constant cache.

Constant memory is exactly that, a read-only section of memory.

Local Memory

Local memory is a memory region local to a workgroup. This memory region can be used to allocate variables that are shared by all work items in that workgroup. It may be implemented as dedicated regions of memory on the OpenCL device. The local memory space resides in device memory, so local memory accesses have same high latency and low bandwidth as global memory accesses.

OpenCL local memory that is on-chip is much faster than global memory.

Local memory is used to enable coalesced accesses, to share data between work items in a workgroup, and to reduce accesses to lower bandwidth global memory.

Private Memory

Private memory is a region of memory private to a work item. Variables defined in one work item's private memory are not visible to another work item. In OpenCL the variables are of private type when no memory qualifier is specified explicitly.

So this is memory used within a work item that is similar to registers in a GPU or CPU core. Private memory is fast and can be used without need for synchronization primitives. It is allocated and partitioned at compile time by the compiler for the given kernel and card. In case of overuse of private memory, it will fall out of the private memory section and go to either cache memory (in the case of GPUs having cache memory) or to global memory (for GPUs not having cache).

GPUs that do not have cache memory will spill to global memory causing significant performance drops.

Work Items and Workgroups

A *work item* is an instance of kernel. Each work item has a unique global ID and executes the same code, but execution pathway and data operated upon can vary per work item. A work item is distinguished from others within the collection by its global ID and local ID. One of a collection of parallel executions of a kernel would be invoked on a device by a command. A work item is executed by one or more processing elements as part of a workgroup executing on a compute unit. Work items are the smallest execution entity. Every time a Kernel is launched, lots of *work items* (a number specified by the programmer) are launched, each one executing the same code. Each work item has an ID, which is accessible from the kernel, and which is used to distinguish the data to be processed by each work item.

A *workgroup* is a collection of related work items that execute on a single compute unit (see Figures 10.9 and 10.10). Work items in the group execute the same kernel, share local memory and workgroup barriers. Workgroups are assigned a unique workgroup ID with the same dimensionality as the index space used for the work items. Work items are assigned a unique local ID within a workgroup so that a single work item can be uniquely identified by its global ID or by a combination of its local ID and workgroup ID. The work items in a given workgroup execute concurrently on the processing elements of a single compute unit. Workgroups exist to

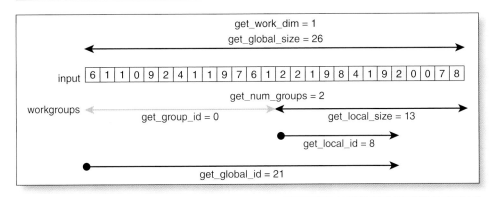

Figure 10.9 Workgroups and Work Items

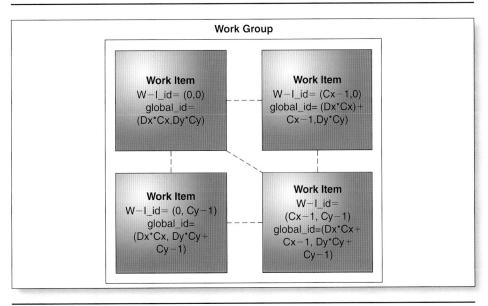

Figure 10.10 Work Items in Workgroup

allow communication and cooperation between work items. They reflect how work items are organized (it is an *N*-dimensional grid of workgroups, with *N* = 1, 2, or 3).

OpenCL does not explicitly limit the number of workgroups that can be submitted with a clEnqueueNDRangeKernel command. The OpenCL SDK automatically partitions a large number of workgroups into smaller pieces that the hardware can process.

OpenCL limits the number of work items in each group. The number can be obtained using clDeviceInfo with the CL_DEVICE_MAX_WORK_GROUP_SIZE to determine the maximum number of work items in a workgroups supported by the hardware. The local NDRange can contain up to three dimensions, here labeled as X, Y, and Z. The X dimension is returned by get_local_id (0), Y is returned by get_local_id (1), and Z is returned by get_local_id (2). The maximum number of work items that can be specified in each dimension of the workgroup to the OpenCL device can be obtained using device information API clGetDeviceInfo with CL_DEVICE_MAX_WORK_ITEM_SIZES.

Profiling of OpenCL Functions

This section describes profiling of OpenCL functions that are enqueued as commands to a command queue. Event objects can be used to capture profiling information that measure execution time of a command.

To measure the performance of GPU (OpenCL) functions we have to enable the profiling option while creating the command queue using the clCreateCommandQueue API of OpenCL. We need to set the CL_QUEUE_PROFILING_ENABLE flag of the command queue.

Table 10.2 shows the different flags used for profiling the OpenCL functions.

Table 10.2   GetEventProfilingInfo Parameter Queries

cl_profiling_info	Information returned in *param_value*
CL_PROFILING_COMMAND_QUEUED	A 64-bit value that describes the current device time counter in nanoseconds when the command identified by event is enqueued in a command queue by the host.

CL_PROFILING_COMMAND_SUBMIT	A 64-bit value that describes the current device time counter in nanoseconds when the command identified by event that has been enqueued is submitted by the host to the device associated with the command queue.
CL_PROFILING_COMMAND_START	A 64-bit value that describes the current device time counter in nanoseconds when the command identified by event starts execution on the device.
CL_PROFILING_COMMAND_END	A 64-bit value that describes the current device time counter in nanoseconds when the command identified by event has finished execution on the device.

The clGetEventProfilingInfo API is used to get the profiling information of the command queue associated with the event object.

The following code snippet gives the method of obtaining the execution time of OpenCL function:

```
ret  =  clGetEventProfilingInfo(eventGlobal, CL_PROFILING_
COMMAND_START, sizeof(cl_ulong), &start, NULL);

if(ret != CL_SUCCESS)

        {

    printf("clGetEventProfilingInfo(COMMAND_START)
failed\n");

}

ret  =  clGetEventProfilingInfo(eventGlobal, CL_PROFILING_
COMMAND_END,

sizeof(cl_ulong), &end, NULL);

if(ret != CL_SUCCESS)

        {

    printf("clGetEventProfilingInfo(COMMAND_END) failed\n" );
```

We have full control over the point at which we can start the profiling of the execution of command as explained Table 10.2.

Kernel Execution Time

Actual execution time of the kernel is obtained by stating the profiling using the CL_PROFILING_COMMAND_START and CL_PROFILING_

COMMAND_END flags. This time is exclusive of the calling overhead of the OpenCL function.

OpenCL Function Overhead Time

The overhead of the OpenCL function call can be obtained by subtracting the time obtained using CL_PROFILING_COMMAND_START flag from the time obtained by using CL_PROFILING_COMMAND_SUBMIT.

Optimization Techniques

The following are some optimization techniques that can be used.

Distributed Accumulator

In a multiply and accumulation (MAC) operation, current output is dependent on previous output. The OpenCL parallel programming model doesn't support this architecture. A distributed accumulator will remove data dependency from the MAC operation.

Vector data type (float4, float8, float16) is used for SIMD operation. Float4 vector data type is considered in Figure 10.11:

■ Phase1: Sum the each row using the float 4 vectors

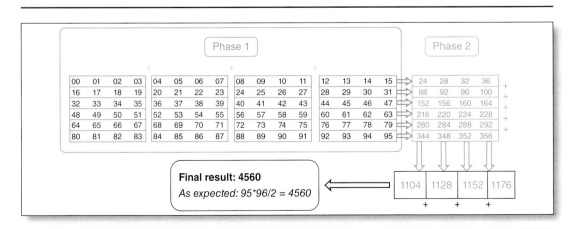

Figure 10.11 Distributed Accumulator
SOURCE: Douglas Andrade 2010

Example: $00 + 04 + 08 + 12 = 24$

- Phase2: Sum the vector results of the sum of the rows

  Example: $24 + 88 + 152 + 216 + 280 + 344 = 1104$

- Final Result: The final result is the sum of the 4 components of the last vector.

  Example: $1104 + 1128 + 1152 + 1176 = 4560$

Task Parallelism

Task parallelism is task level division between CPU and GPU. Compute devices such as CPUs can also execute task-parallel compute kernels. Task parallelism

- Executes as a single work item

- Uses a compute kernel written in OpenCL

- Employs a native C/C++ function

Figure 10.12 shows task parallelism, where arrows indicate dependencies between tasks. For example, Kernel 1 and Kernel 2 will be executed in parallel and Kernel 3 will not execute until Kernel 1 and Kernel 2 have finished.

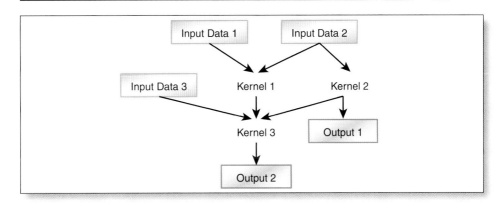

Figure 10.12 Task Parallelism between CPU and GPU

Kernel Architecture: Single versus Multiple Kernel

For the parallel workloads, at points in the algorithm where parallelism is broken because some threads need to synchronize in order to share data with each other, there are two cases:

■ Either these threads belong to the same block, in which case they should use barrier() and share data through shared memory within the same kernel invocation, or

■ They belong to different blocks, in which case they must share data through global memory using two separate kernel invocations, one for writing to and one for reading from global memory.

The second case is much less optimal since it adds the overhead of extra kernel invocations and global memory traffic. Its occurrence should therefore be minimized by mapping the algorithm to the OpenCL programming model in such a way that the computations that require inter-thread communication are performed within a single thread block as much as possible.

The following example illustrates the single and multiple kernel execution of the same loop and their performance differences. It also illustrates the use of OpenCL barrier that is used for synchronization purpose when single kernel is used.

In the following example, A and B are two buffers and we have 256 such buffers; we have to calculate their differences and calculate their additions in final_buffer.

This is the original loop in the CPU:

```
for (int i = 0; i < Outer_Loop; i++) {
    for (int j = 0; j < Inner_Loop; j++){
        TempBuff += (float)Difference_buffer((*(A + j)) -
(*(B + j)));
    }
    *(Final_buffer+ i) = TempBuff;
}
```

This is the GPU code (single kernel):

```
#define offset1 32
#define offset2 8

__kernel void Final_buffer(__global float8 *A,__global
float8 *B,
                                          __global float
*Final_buffer)
{
    int i, j;
```

```
    float8 f8TempBuff;
    int i = get_global_id(0);
    int j = get_global_id(1);
    Difference_buffer [(i*offset1)+j] = (A[j] -
B[(i*offset1)+j]);
          barrier (CLK_GLOBAL_MEM_FENCE);
i = get_global_id (0);
j = get_global_id (1);
j = j>>2;
Add_buffer[(i*offset2)+j] = Difference_buffer
  [(i*offset1) + (j*4)] +
Difference_buffer[(i*offset1)+(j*4)+1] +
Difference_buffer[(i*offset1)+(j*4)+2] +
Difference_buffer[(i*offset1)+(j*4)+3];
barrier (CLK_GLOBAL_MEM_FENCE);
i = get_global_id (0);
j = get_global_id (1);
j = j>>5;
//final float8 buffer
f8TempBuff = Add_buffer [(i*offset2) +0] +
                    Add_buffer [(i*offset2) +1] +
                    Add_buffer [(i*offset2) +2] +
                    Add_buffer [(i*offset2) +3] +
                  Add_buffer [(i*offset2) +4] +
                    Add_buffer [(i*offset2) +5] +
                    Add_buffer [(i*offset2) +6] +
                    Add_buffer [(i*offset2) +7];

Barrier (CLK_GLOBAL_MEM_FENCE);
//scalar addition
Final_buffer[i] = f8TempBuff.s0+ f8TempBuff.s1+ f8TempBuff.
s2+
                        f8TempBuff.s3+f8TempBuff.s4+
f8TempBuff.s5+
                        F8TempBuff.s6+ f8TempBuff.s7;
}
```

For multiple kernels, in the case of the Kernel 1, all the differences are calculated and stored in the Difference buffer. The float 8 is considered to do the operations in the optimized way.

The buffer size is 256 in this case, and that means a maximum of 256 differences will be there in the first Difference buffer. Here float 8 is used so the Difference buffer will contain the maximum 32 float8 values:

```
// optimized size after using float8
      #define OFFSET 32
__kernel void Difference_Calc (__global float8* A, __global
float8* B, __global float8* Difference_buffer)
{
    int i = get_global_id(0);
    int j = get_global_id(1);
    float8 f8TempBuff = (A[j] - B [(i*OFFSET) +j]);
    Difference_buffer [(i*OFFSET) +j] = f8TempBuff;
}
```

The second kernel is made to add the differences in the Difference buffer. Here the loop is unrolling by 4 times so the temporary Add buffer will contain the maximum 8 float8 type values:

```
            // optimized size after using float8
    #define OFFSET1 32
  #define OFFSET2 8

__kernel void Add_Calc (__global float8* Difference_buffer,
__global float8* Add_buffer)
{
    int i = get_global_id (0);
    int j= get_global_id(1);
    Add_buffer[(i*OFFSET2)+j]=   Difference_
buffer[(i*OFFSET1)+(j*4)]+

                Difference_buffer[(i*OFFSET1)+ (j*4)+1]+
                Difference_buffer [(i*OFFSET1+ (j*4) +2] +
                Difference_buffer [(i*OFFSET1) + (j*4) +3];
}
```

The third kernel is made to add the final float8 values in the Add buffer. After addition of all the 8 values finally we will get one float8 value and then these 8 values are added by using the scalar operation:

```
        #define OFFSET2 8
__kernel void Final_Calc (__global float* Final_buffer, __
global float8* Add_buffer)
{
    int i = get_global_id(0);
    float8 f8TempBuff;
    f8TempBuff = Add_buffer [(i*OFFSET2) +0] +
                Add_buffer [(i*OFFSET2) +1] +
```

```
                        Add_buffer [(i*OFFSET2) +2] +
                        Add_buffer [(i*OFFSET2) +3] +
                        Add_buffer [(i*OFFSET2) +4] +
                        Add_buffer [(i*OFFSET2) +5] +
                        Add_buffer [(i*OFFSET2) +6] +
                        Add_buffer [(i*OFFSET2) +7];
    Final_buffer[i] = f8TempBuff.s0+ f8TempBuff.s1+
f8TempBuff.s2+
                              f8TempBuff.s3+f8TempBuff.s4+
f8TempBuff.s5+
                              F8TempBuff.s6+ f8TempBuff.s7;
}
```

In this case single kernel is around 20 percent to 25 percent faster than multiple kernels.

Efficient Data Transfers between CPUs and GPUs

Here are some key points to keep in mind to transfer data efficiently between CPUs and GPUs.

Instead of several small transfers, use single large transfer. Applications should minimize data transfer between the host and the device. Because of the overhead associated with each transfer, batching many small transfers into a single large transfer always performs better than making each transfer separately, which means move more code from the host to the device, even if kernels are running with low parallelism in this case. Intermediate data structures may be created in device memory, and destroyed without being copied/mapped to host memory.

Use a host pointer. Higher performance for data transfers between host and device is achieved for memory objects allocated in page-locked (also known as pinned) host memory (as opposed to regular page able host memory allocated by malloc()), which has several benefits: like for some devices, page-locked host memory can be mapped into the device's address space. In this case, there is no need to allocate any device memory and to explicitly copy data between device and host memory. Data transfers are implicitly performed each time the kernel accesses the mapped memory. OpenCL applications do not have direct control over whether memory objects are allocated in page-locked memory or not, but they can create objects using the CL_MEM_USE_HOST_PTR flag and such objects are likely to be allocated in page-locked memory by the driver for best performance.

Use MapBuffer. The OpenCL API ClEnqueueMapBuffer is used to map a region of the GPU buffer object into the host address space and it returns a pointer to this mapped region. This map buffer is useful to map small regions of buffers to CPU.

Porting Video Analytics Algorithms to a GPU

Follow these steps when porting video analytics algorithms to a GPU.

1. Identify Hotspots

This step involves analyzing the code base that needs to be optimized using tools to find the hotspots or manually profiling the functions. The main aim of the step is to find the computationally intensive parts of the whole code which is utilizing more CPU cycles. Vtune and Intel PTU are some of the tools that can be used to identify the hotspots.

2. Analyzing the Hotspots

Once the portions of code that are computationally intensive are found, the functions that can be executed in parallel using the task-parallel or data-parallel model are identified. The functions that are to be executed in parallel using Task-parallel model should be independent of each other.

Porting the Hotspots

Bear these points in mind when porting the hotspots:

- The code should be modified if required to achieve data parallelism.

- The organization of input data and data structures should be analyzed. The precision and limitations of data types on GPU should be considered before writing the kernels.

- The input data structures should be modified in the CPU before transferring data to the GPU buffers, to minimize data transfers.

- The input data required for execution of code on GPU needs to be transferred into the GPU buffers.

■ Create kernels for execution of the code on to the GPU.

■ The local workgroup and work size of the kernels should be decided for optimal performance.

■ In the case of multiple kernels, the synchronizing should be maintained between the kernels as and when required.

■ Read back the output data from GPU to CPU when required for further processing.

Accuracy Check

The accuracy of the algorithm is verified in two stages:

1. *Module level accuracy.* The output of the module that is being ported using OpenCL is dumped into files and verified by comparing the output with that of the module in the base code. This helps in verifying the functioning of each module.

2. *System level accuracy.* Once all the modules are integrated the output of the system should be compared with that of the base code using a comparator that will benchmark the system level accuracy.

Once all the modules are integrated the output of the Intel AIM Suite that is stored in the form of CVL files will be compared with the CVL files of the base Intel AIM Suite code using a comparator that will benchmark the system level accuracy. Accuracy calculation is explained in detailed in the section "Accuracy Model."

Haar Classifier Optimization Using OpenCL as an Example

The Haar classifier framework is capable of processing images extremely rapidly and achieves high detection rates. There are three key functionalities involved:

1. Image representation in an *integral image*, which allows the features used by our detector to be computed very quickly. The integral image can be computed from an image using a few operations per pixel.

2. A simple and efficient classifier, which is built using the AdaBoost learning algorithm (Freund and Schapire 1995) to select a small

number of critical visual features from a very large set of potential features.

3. The method for combining classifiers in a *cascade*. This involves combining successively more complex classifiers in a cascade structure, which dramatically increases the speed of the detector by focusing attention on promising regions of the image.

Within any image sub-window the total number of Haar-like features is very large, far larger than the number of pixels. In order to ensure fast classification, the learning process must exclude a large majority of the available features and focus on a small set of critical features. The feature selection is achieved through a simple modification of the AdaBoost procedure.

The overall form of the detection process is that of a degenerate decision tree, what we call a *cascade* (see Figure 10.13).

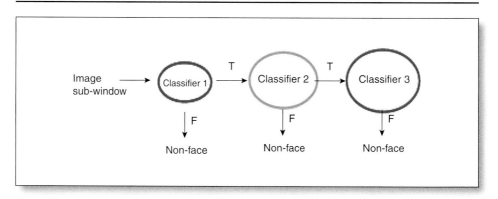

Figure 10.13 Haar Cascade Structure

A positive result from the first classifier triggers the evaluation of a second classifier, which has also been adjusted to achieve very high detection rates. A positive result from the second classifier triggers a third classifier, and so on. A negative outcome at any point leads to the immediate rejection of the sub-window.

Selection of a Haar Classifier as a GPU Candidate

In Intel AIM Suite, each frame in the video is processed and searched for human faces. This functionality is done in the process frame function.

In the Haar classifier framework, the classification for face is done at different sub-windows ranging from 20x20 to maximum face size in the image. The frame has to be processed in an overlapped windowed manner. The evaluation of each sub-window can be done in parallel onto the GPU using OpenCL.

Haar classifier is a perfect candidate for GPU because it has

1. High data parallelism

2. Low input data reutilization

3. Algorithms with big data streams

4. High arithmetic intensity per stream element

Flat Memory Structure

In Haar Classifier the cascade contains stage classifiers and each stage classifier contains a set of classifiers. Each classifier has two or three feature rectangles.

The structures are organized as shown below:

```
typedef int sumtype;
typedef double sqsumtype;

typedef struct CvHaarFeature
{
    int  tilted;
    struct
    {
        CvRect r;
        float weight;
    } rect[CV_HAAR_FEATURE_MAX];
}CvHaarFeature;

typedef struct CvHaarClassifier
{
    int count;
    CvHaarFeature* haar_feature;
    float* threshold;
    int* left;
```

```
        int* right;
        float* alpha;
}CvHaarClassifier;

typedef struct CvHaarStageClassifier
{
    int   count;
    float threshold;
    CvHaarClassifier* classifier;
    int next;
    int child;
    int parent;
}CvHaarStageClassifier;
typedef struct CvHaarClassifierCascade
{
    int   flags;
    int   count;
    CvSize orig_window_size;
    CvSize real_window_size;
    double scale;
    CvHaarStageClassifier* stage_classifier;
    CvHidHaarClassifierCascade* hid_cascade;
}CvHaarClassifierCascade;

typedef struct CvHidHaarFeature{
    struct {
        sumtype *p0, *p1, *p2, *p3;
        float weight;
    }    rect[CV_HAAR_FEATURE_MAX];
}CvHidHaarFeature;

typedef struct CvHidHaarTreeNode{
    CvHidHaarFeature feature;
    float threshold;
    int left;
    int right;
}CvHidHaarTreeNode;

typedef struct CvHidHaarClassifier{
    int count;
    CvHidHaarTreeNode* node;
    float* alpha;
}CvHidHaarClassifier;

typedef struct CvHidHaarStageClassifier{
```

```
    int   count;
    float threshold;
    CvHidHaarClassifier* classifier;
    int two_rects;
    struct CvHidHaarStageClassifier* next;
    struct CvHidHaarStageClassifier* child;
    struct CvHidHaarStageClassifier* parent;
}CvHidHaarStageClassifier;

struct CvHidHaarClassifierCascade{
    int   count;
    int   is_stump_based;
    int   has_tilted_features;
    int   is_tree;
    double inv_window_area;
    CvMat sum, sqsum, tilted;
    CvHidHaarStageClassifier* stage_classifier;
    sqsumtype *pq0, *pq1, *pq2, *pq3;
    sumtype *p0, *p1, *p2, *p3;
    void** ipp_stages;
};
```

HaarCascade and HidHaarCascade have stage-classifier pointers, which store the address of the stage-classifier arrays respectively. Similarly stage-classifier structures have classifier pointers that store the classifier arrays, and classifier structures have features in them.

When the implementation of Haar Classifier is made parallel on the GPU using OpenCL, the HaarCascade and HidHaarCascade data should be transferred to the GPU. Proper data will not be transferred to the GPU when both the structures are sent to the GPU. Hence both the cascades should be made contiguous as shown in Figure 10.14.

Even when the cascade structures are made contiguous and transferred to GPU, the pointers present in the structures hold the addresses of the CPU pointers. These pointers need to be mapped properly according to the pointers of GPU.

Haar Classifier OpenCL Functionalities

To port the Haar Classifier functionality onto the GPU, all the data required for processing the frame has to be loaded into the GPU.

The Haar Cascade data is loaded into the application using the XML files. This XML file data will be loaded in nested structures of Haar Cascade using

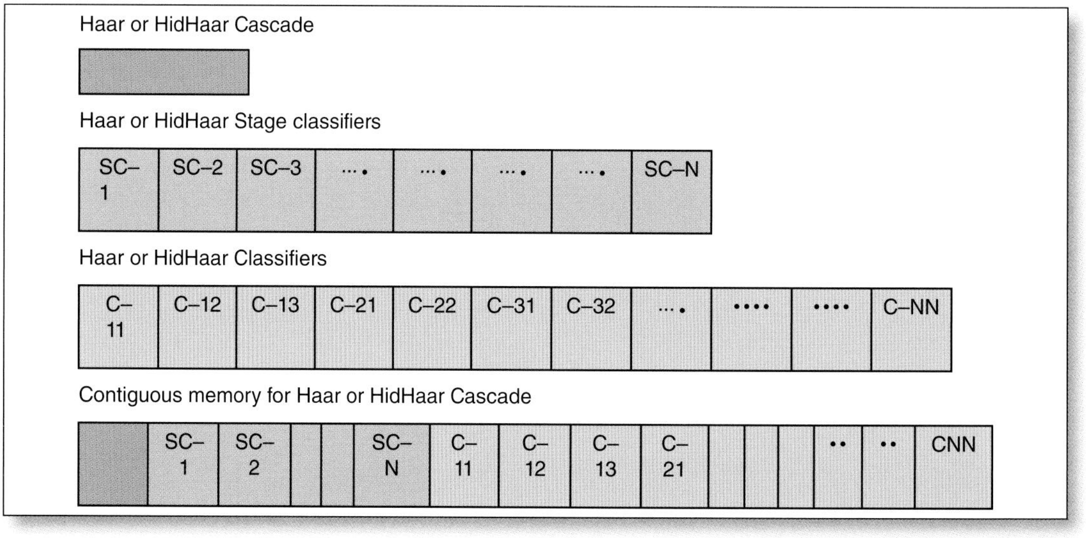

Figure 10.14 Contiguous Cascades

cvLoad function. The data loaded into the cascade would be used in later stages. The loading of data is a single time activity, which is done during the initialization of the application.

The function explanation for icvCreateHidHaarClassifierCascade_OCL describes the steps followed in porting Haar Classifier onto the GPU using OpenCL.

■ The purpose of this function is to create Hid-Haar Cascade from the data in the Haar cascade. Haar and Hid-Haar cascades contain the data required for Haar functionality hence the data has to be taken to GPU.

■ Haar and Hid-Haar cascades are multilayered structures with different number of elements at different levels. For proper implementation both the cascades need to be converted into contiguous memories and transferred to GPU.

■ Even the data in the cascades is transferred to GPU; the pointers in these cascades will not be properly mapped. The pointer would be holding addresses of CPU. A kernel CreateHaarCascade_kernel is created to map all the data properly on to GPU.

High Data Parallelism

The frame is processed for faces, either the whole frame or in the boxes in which the motion has been detected using MotionHistory. Once the region of interest is fixed, it needs to be searched for faces of all sizes. So the selected region has to be searched for all possible scales of face sizes.

Figure 10.15 shows the base code flow of SetImages function. The functionality of the SetImages function is to set the scale factor and assign the addresses to all the feature pointers present in the Hid-Haar cascade.

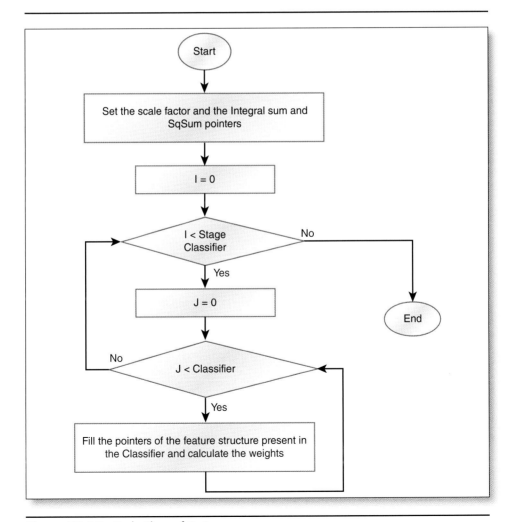

Figure 10.15 Code Flow of SetImage

As the functionality of the Haar classifier is moved to GPU, so the mapping of pointers in Haar Cascade should be done in GPU.

The mapping can be done on a two-dimensional level in the GPU for each classifier using SetImages_kernel, as illustrated in Figure 10.16. This kernel has to be run for each classifier (number of stage classifier × maximum number of classifiers in a stage classifier).

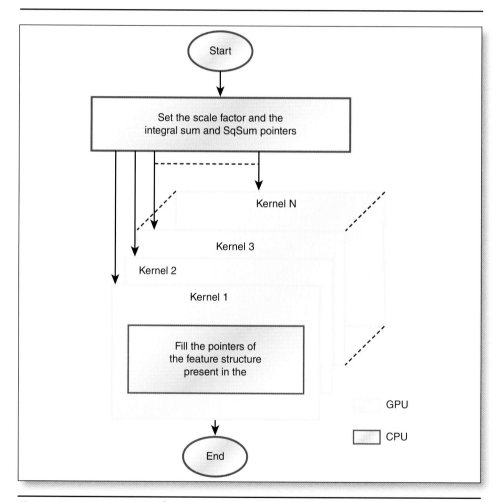

Figure 10.16 Execution of SetImages Kernels on the GPU

DetectFaces_OCL

Figure 10.17 shows the base code flow of DetectFaces function.

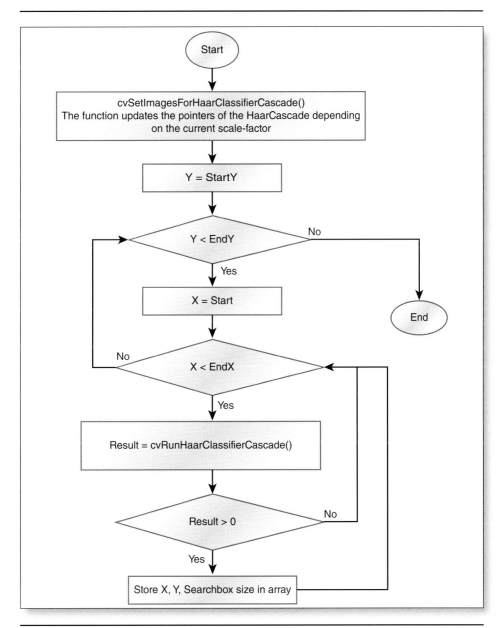

Figure 10.17 Code Flow of DetectFaces in Base Code

The functionality of DetectFaces_OCL is to evaluate and move the selected sub-window in an overlapped manner all over the image. Each of the sub-windows goes through different stages. Each stage consists of different classifiers. Each classifier is evaluated over each sub-window, which will be compared with the existing threshold based on which the classification can be done. This function is computationally very intensive (various MAC operations are required) so this is a proper candidate to port to the GPU.

As the evaluation of each sub-window is independent and not dependent any other input, it can be implemented in parallel.

As the classification of each sub-window can be done in parallel, the rectangle coordinates where the face is detected need to be store in the buffer in global memory space.

It may happen on some occasions where the same face is detected at different sizes; in such a case the rectangle with the bigger dimensions will be stored in the buffer.

Once the whole of the video frame is processed, the data buffer where the coordinates of the detected faces are kept is read back to the CPU stored in an array (see Figure 10.18).

Porting Issues on Ivy Bridge GPUs

The Haar classifier functionality when ported to GPUs was not working as expected on the Ivy Bridge GPU due to the following reasons:

■ The Haar Cascade structure has to be taken over to the GPU, as the structures had pointers; the structures had to be mapped onto the GPU context, which is not happening properly over the Ivy Bridge GPU.

■ The values in the Haar Cascade structure are of double precision and as the Ivy Bridge has only float precision support, the cascade structures had to be modified to float precision and all the calculations were done in float to maintain proper accuracy. The change in the accuracy is minimal.

■ Due to complex nested structures in Haar Classifier, the code cannot be built at the Ivy Bridge GPU.

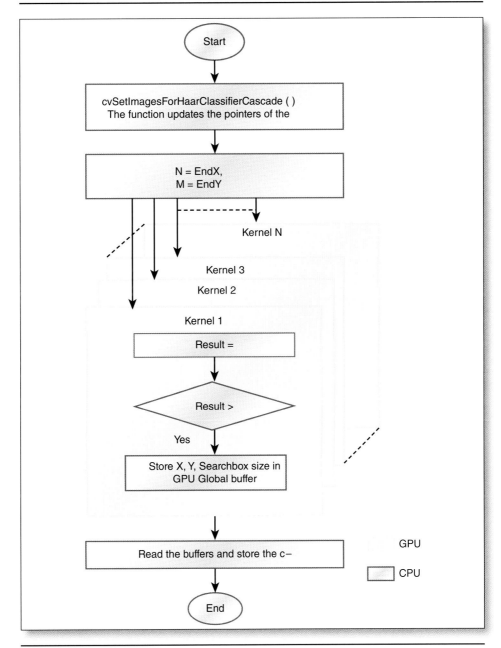

Figure 10.18 Execution of DetectFaces of GPU

Other Hotspot Functions (GPU Candidates) from the Intel® AIM Suite Application

Similarly there are four hotspot functions besides Haar classifier that satisfy the criteria of a suitable GPU candidate. Among them only CvResize and cvIntegral functions take more time. These functions can be made parallel internally on the GPU using OpenCL. Other functions take less time in execution, so the performance achieved using OpenCL would be lost due to data transfer overheads.

The cvResize Function

In porting the cvResize function onto the GPU using OpenCL:

■ We have changed the actual logic of the Resize function. In this new logic we made three kernels. Among these three kernels two are calculating x-offsets and y-offsets. In our code these two kernels are executed once in initialization as the resize factor is common for all frames. The third kernel calculates pixel intensities of the destination buffer and is executed for every frame. The cvResize function down-samples input frame to (80x60) size. As output buffer size is less, time required for data transfer is less.

■ The Intel TBB code in the process frame function is rearranged, so that task parallelism can be achieved.

■ Performance is improved at GPU level.

Figure 10.19 shows the original Resize function, and Figure 10.20 shows the CvResize function after OpenCL optimization.

The cvIntegral Function

When porting the cvIntegral function onto the GPU using OpenCL, a number of approaches were attempted

■ The actual logic of the integral image has been changed to achieve parallelism internally, as shown in Figures 10.21 and 10.22. In the new logic, horizontal summation of all rows is computed in parallel using work items. Vertical summation of all columns is computed in parallel using work items. Performance degraded due to cache misses in vertical addition.

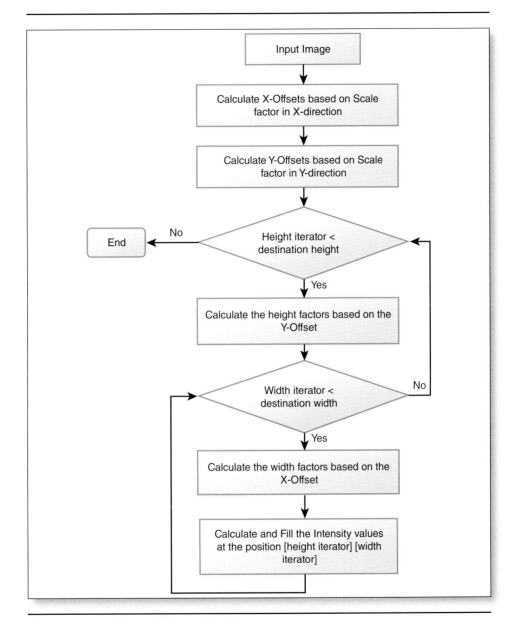

Figure 10.19 Original Resize Function

■ To avoid cache misses one transpose function is used. Using this, vertical additions are made horizontal. Inverse transpose is used to get back the compute buffer in original format. The vectorization concept of OpenCL is used for faster execution. Local workgroup size is used explicitly instead of default. Performance was improved.

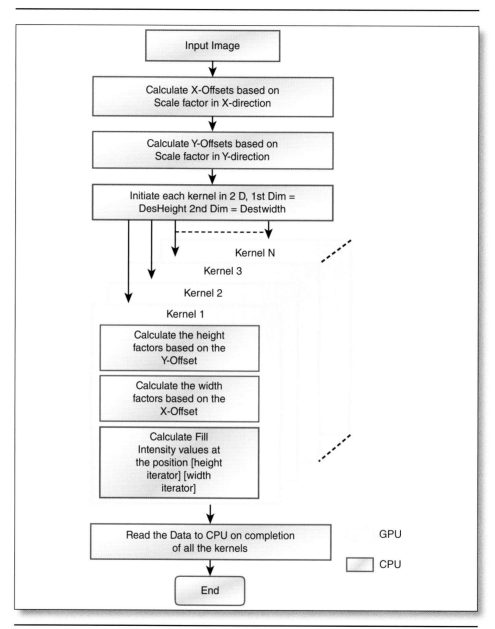

Figure 10.20 Parallel Execution of Kernel on GPU Using OpenCL

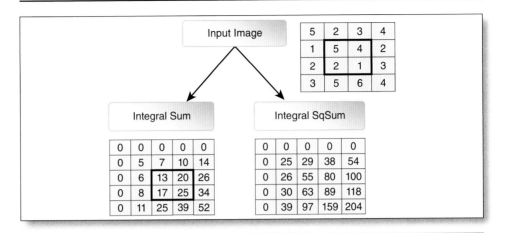

Figure 10.21 Integral Image in Base Code

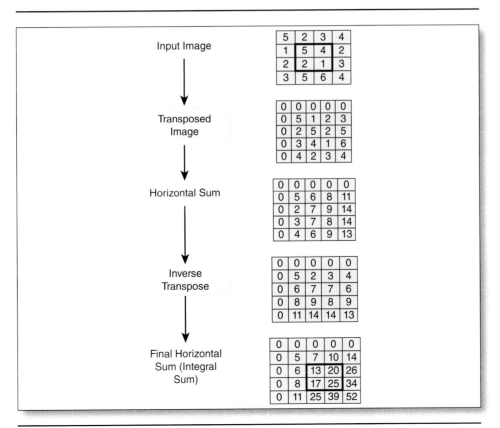

Figure 10.22 Integral Image—a New Approach for Porting to GPU

■ The outputs were needed on the CPU for further processing. The output buffers were of input frame size. The performance was lost due to large data transfer from GPU to CPU.

Code Difference between Nvidia and Ivy Bridge

Here is a summary of code difference between Nvidia and Ivy Bridge:

■ In Ivy Bridge, typecasting is not allowed, whereas in Nvidia it is allowed so we need to modify code accordingly to run it on Ivy Bridge.

■ In Ivy Bridge the maximum number of workgroup size is 512, whereas in Nvidia GeForce GTX 570 and GeForce GTS 450 workgroup size is 1024, so we need to change workgroup size with respect to Ivy Bridge.

■ OpenCL creates a handle and the handle remains live with each call. It is not reused. This way we can run out of memory if we are creating an event and not releasing in a loop. It all happens inside the framework. There is no information for programmers. They may eat up little memory and can cause memory leaks. The Nvidia driver may be smart enough and release the handle so in Nvidia we need not explicitly release the events. In Ivy Bridge the issue is if it is not releasing the handle and program wait for that event again, then code will crash and we need to explicitly release the events, because the event handle for the kernel is not taken care by the Intel OpenCL SDK.

■ In Ivy Bridge the double data type is not supported, so code having double data type will not run on Ivy Bridge.

CPU Optimization with Intel® Threading Building Blocks (Intel® TBB)

For optimizing code on the CPU, Intel Threading Building Blocks (Intel TBB) can be used to fully utilize CPU cores. The advantage of Intel Threading Building Blocks is that it works at a higher level than logical threads, and does not require high level languages or compilers. It can be used with any compiler supporting ISO C++.

Internally the tasks, in Intel TBB, are controlled by task scheduler. The task scheduler is the engine that controls the loop templates. These templates abstract the complexity of the scheduler.

Task-Based Programming (Intel® TBB Threading Model)

When performance is the main concern, programming in terms of logical tasks is better than multithreaded programming in order to get:

■ Balanced parallelism of available resources

■ Faster task startup and end, because starting and terminating a task is much faster than starting and terminating a thread. This is because a thread has its own copy of a lot of resources, such as register state and a stack, and this is not the case with tasks.

■ Proper load balancing

■ Abstraction from lower level details. The main advantage of using tasks instead of threads is that you need not bother about low level of physical threads; instead they allow you to concentrate on the logical dependencies between tasks and leave the efficient scheduling to the scheduler.

The threads that are created with a threading package are logical threads that map onto the physical threads of the hardware. Ideally there must be exactly one running logical thread per physical thread to avoid mismatching among physical and logical threads. *Undersubscription* occurs when the number of logical threads is less than physical threads, so some of the physical threads are not working. *Oversubscription* occurs when there are more running logical threads than physical threads.

In the case of oversubscription, time-sliced execution of logical threads is required.

The scheduler tries to avoid oversubscription by having one logical thread per physical thread and mapping tasks to logical threads in a way that tolerates interference by other threads from the same or other processes.

It is recommended to design programs to create more tasks than that of logical threads and let the task scheduler choose the mapping from tasks to threads.

There are cases when the task scheduler is not appropriate. The task scheduler is intended for high-performance algorithms composed from nonblocking tasks. It still works if the tasks rarely block. However, if threads block frequently, performance is reduced when using the task scheduler because while the thread is blocked, it is not working on any tasks.

The Intel TBB task scheduler was designed in such a way that you can easily mix your own threads with Intel Threading Building Blocks tasks.

Features of the Task Scheduler in Intel® TBB

A task in Intel Threading Building Blocks is typically a small routine and cannot be interrupted at the task level (though its logical thread can be interrupted).

Unfair scheduler. Tasks in Intel Threading Building Blocks are efficient because the scheduler is unfair. Thread schedulers typically distribute time slices in a round-robin fashion. This distribution is called "fair," because each logical thread gets its fair share of time. Thread schedulers are generally fair because it is the safest strategy to undertake without understanding the higher-level organization of a program. In task-based programming, the task scheduler does have some higher-level information, and so can sacrifice fairness for efficiency.

Load balancing. The scheduler does load balancing. In addition to using the right number of threads, it is important to distribute work evenly across those threads. As long as you break your program into enough small tasks, the scheduler usually does a good job of assigning tasks to threads to balance load. Design your programs to try to create many more tasks than there are threads, and let the task scheduler choose the mapping from tasks to threads. With tasks, you can concentrate on the logical dependencies between tasks, and leave the efficient scheduling to the scheduler.

If we use Intel TBB, its task scheduler may be best to hide lower level details behind higher-level interface, as the templates parallel_for, parallel_reduce, and so on.

Explanation of the Intel® TBB Intel® AIM Suite Application

Here is a quick overview of the algorithmic modifications made in the Intel AIM Suite. There are three main algorithmic changes made in the Intel AIM Suite computer vision stack:

1. *Optical flow and integral image calculation.* Using "parallel_invoke" construct, integral image and optical flow calculations are done in parallel (see Figure 10.23).

2. *Face scanning.* Scanning of faces in a frame is done in parallel for multiple scales. In Intel AIM Suite, faces are scanned at predefined scales. Each scale is assigned to an Intel TBB thread and that thread

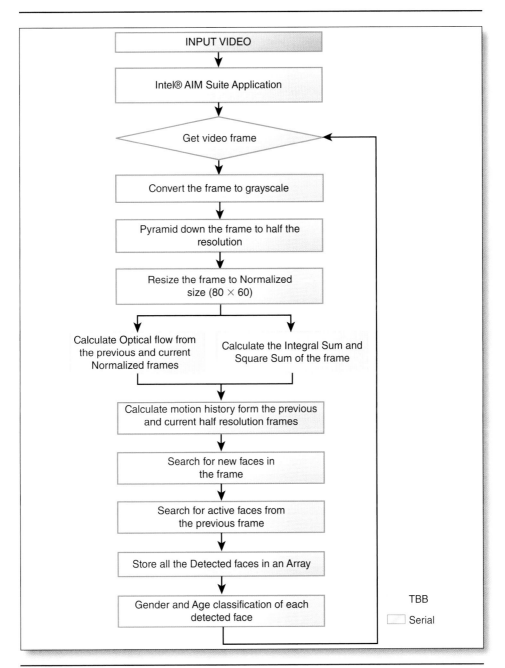

Figure 10.23 Code Flow of Intel® TBB

performs the scanning task (see Figures 10.24 and 10.25). Some modifications in cascade data structure were made to allow for parallel thread-safe access. This is done using "parallel_for" construct.

3. *Face tracking.* Tracking of faces in the neighborhood of a given face is done in parallel. In Intel AIM Suite, apart from detecting new faces, faces from previous frames are tracked. In a neighborhood rectangle around an already found face from the previous frame, face scanning is performed to track the old face in the new frame (see Figure 10.26). Intel TBB parallelizes this tracking across different faces. Each face is assigned to a thread and that thread performs the search for a similar face in the neighborhood (see Figure 10.27). Some data-structure changes were made to allow for a parallel thread-safe access. This is done using a "parallel_for" construct.

Intel® Streaming SIMD Extensions (Intel® SSE)

In the list of hotspots functions in the AIMCore library Haar classifier, cvResize and cvIntegral functions were hotspots and they could be ported onto the GPU using OpenCL. Other functions could not be ported as their execution time was less and involved data transfers from CPU to GPU.

GetOpticalFlowLK and cvCalcopticalFlowLk were the feasible functions for optimization using Intel SSE. The execution time taken by these functions is less and most of the functionality is add and accumulation. By using Intel SSE, performance was achieved.

The CvCalcopticalFlowLk Function

This function computes flow for every pixel, thus output images must have the same size as input. The Lucas-Kanade technique is implemented in this algorithm. The Lucas-Kanade method is a widely used differential method for optical flow estimation. It assumes that the flow is essentially constant in a local neighborhood of the pixel under consideration, and solves the basic optical flow equations for all the pixels in that neighborhood, by the least squares criterion.

By combining information from several nearby pixels, the Lucas-Kanade method can often resolve the inherent ambiguity of the optical flow equation. It is also less sensitive to image noise than pointwise methods. On the other hand, since it is a purely local method, it cannot provide flow information in the interior of uniform regions of the image.

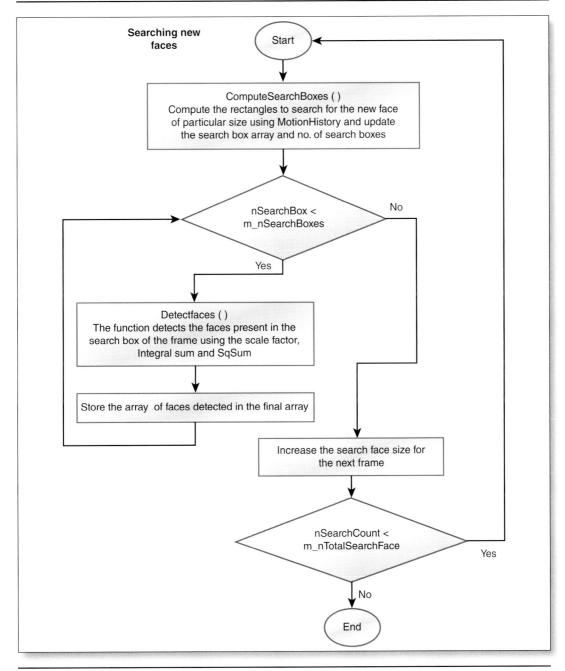

Figure 10.24 Code Flow of Face Scanning in Intel® TBB

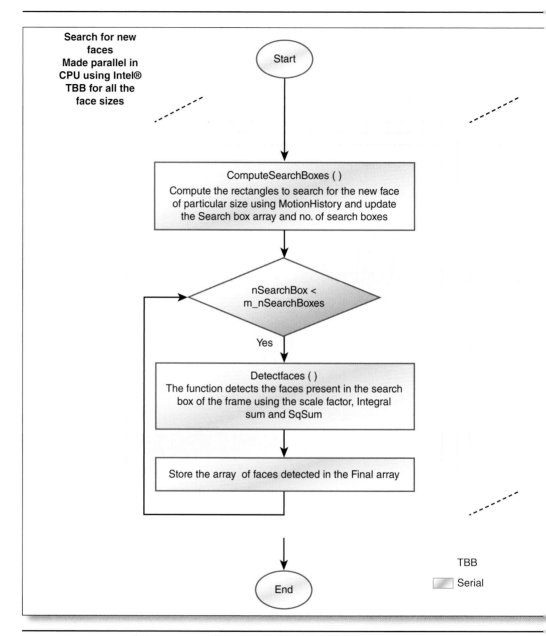

Figure 10.25 Parallel Execution of Searching New Face in Intel® TBB

The GetOpticalFlowLK Function

This function does motion prediction based on optical flow. It will use the output data from the cvCalcopticalFlowLk function for further processing.

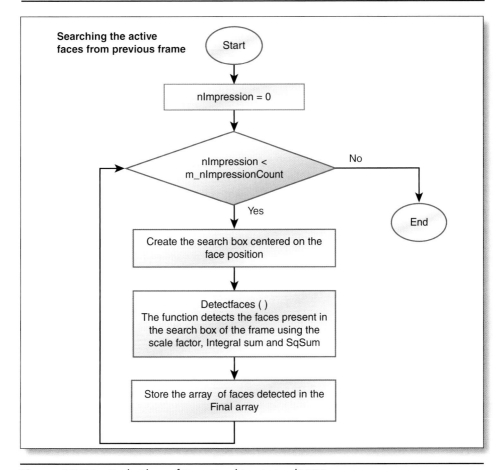

Figure 10.26 Code Flow of Face Tracking in Intel® TBB

The following code snippets gives a brief idea about Intel SSE optimization. The first is unoptimized code using GetOpticalFlowLK:

```
for(int y = nStartY;y < nEndY;y++)   {
float *pXData = (float *)m_pImgVelocityXLK->imageData  +
 (y * m_pImgVelocityXLK->width + nStartX);
  float *pYData = (float *)m_pImgVelocityYLK->imageData +
           (y * m_pImgVelocityYLK->width + nStartX);
 for(int x = nStartX;x < nEndX;x++){
      float fVelX = *pXData;
      float fVelY = *pYData;
      // Accumulate motion vectors
      if(true){ //fVelX > 0.01 || fVelY > 0.01)
      fSumVelX += fVelX;              // Accumalation of data
```

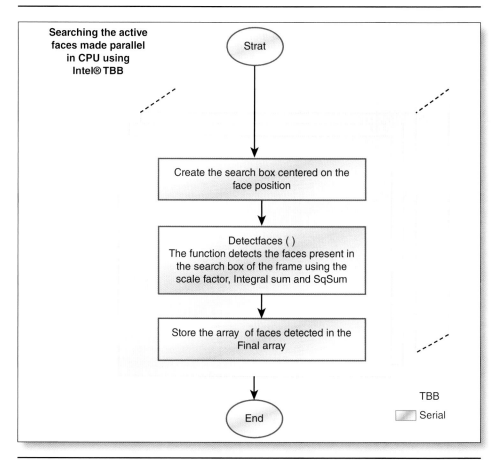

Figure 10.27 Parallel Execution of Face Tracking in Intel® TBB

```
        fSumVelY += fVelY;
        nCount++;
    }      pXData++; pYData++;
    }
}
```

The second code snippet shows optimization using Intel SSE:
```
for(y = nStartY; y < nEndY; y++){
    pXData   = (float *)m_pImgVelocityXLK->imageData +
          (y * m_pImgVelocityXLK->width + nStartX);
    pYData   = (float *)m_pImgVelocityYLK->imageData +
          (y * m_pImgVelocityYLK->width + nStartX);
    for(x = nStartX;x <= (nEndX-OFFSET);x += OFFSET){
        // Accumulate motion vectors
        M128XData    = _mm_loadu_ps(pXData);
```

```
          M128YData    = _mm_loadu_ps(pYData);
      // accumulation process handled parallely by using
SSE this will improve performance by great extent
          M128XSumData = _mm_add_ps(M128XSumData,M128XData);
//add and accumulation into sse variables
          M128YSumData = _mm_add_ps(M128YSumData,M128YData);
          nCount += OFFSET; pXData += OFFSET; pYData +=
OFFSET;
      }//End - for(x = nStartX;x < nEndX-4;x+=4)
      for(; x < nEndX; x++){
          fVelX1 += *pXData;  fVelY1 += *pYData;  pXData++;
pYData++;   nCount++;
      }
}//END - for(y = nStartY;y < nEndY;y++)
// Four values in the register added by  using dot produt
operation
_mm_store_ss(&fSumVelX, _mm_dp_ps(M128XSumData,_mm_set1_
ps(1.0),241));// horizontal sum and store
_mm_store_ss(&fSumVelY, _mm_dp_ps(M128YSumData,_mm_set1_
ps(1.0),241));//horizontal sum and store
```

CPU-GPU Combined Optimization

Figure 10.28 shows CPU-GPU combined optimization.

Data Transfer between CPU-GPU

Memory objects are categorized into two types: buffer objects and image objects. A buffer object stores a one-dimensional collection of elements, whereas an image object is used to store a two- or three- dimensional texture, frame buffer, or image.

The following functions enqueue commands to read from a buffer object to host memory or write to a buffer object from host memory. A buffer object is created using the clCreateBuffer API, in which we will specify the size and type of the buffer that needs to be created.

■ *Data transfer from CPU to GPU:* clEnqueueWriteBuffer – The OpenCL API is used to transfer data required to the GPU memory. The GPU buffer should be created with options CL_MEM_READ_WRITE or CL_MEM_READ_ONLY. The data will be written into the buffer of GPU from the memory location that is specified. The API call can be made blocking by setting the block read flag.

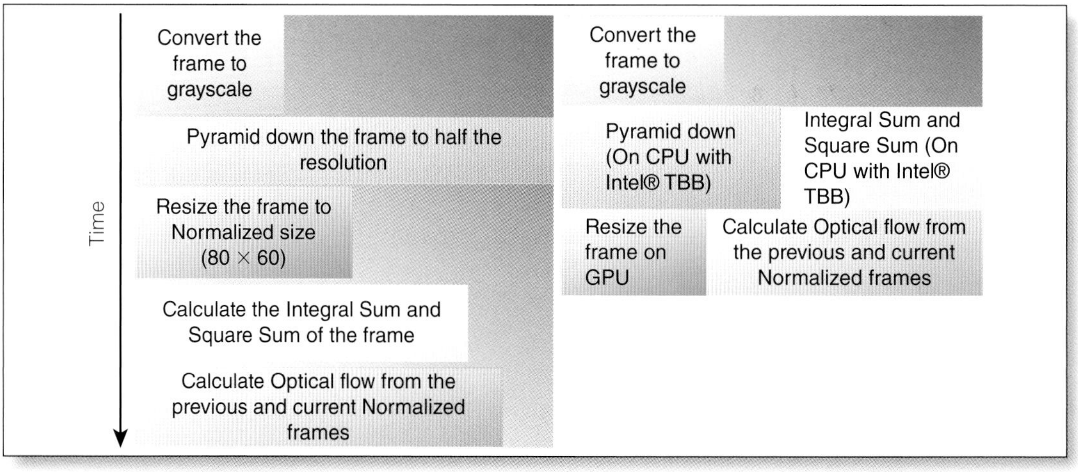

Figure 10.28 Time for Sequential and Parallel Execution (CPU-GPU Combined Optimization) of Intel® AIM Suite Application

■ *Data transfer from GPU to CPU:* clEnqueueReadBuffer – The OpenCL API is used to transfer data required from GPU to the CPU memory. The data will be read from GPU and written into the buffer of the CPU at the memory location that is specified. The API call can be made blocking by setting the block read flag.

Thread Interaction between CPU and GPU

In the case of the Intel AIM Suite application, parallelism is achieved by using Intel TBB at the CPU level and by using OpenCL at the GPU level. Intel TBB has its task scheduler to maintain and OpenCL also has its scheduler (warp scheduler in case of Nvidia CUDA) to manage the number of threads running concurrently. In the case of Intel TBB and OpenCL combined optimization, simultaneous threads are running on the CPU using Intel TBB (the number of threads depends on the number of CPU cores and the Intel TBB scheduler) and at the same time for each Intel TBB thread inside sequential execution is made parallel by using OpenCL-based optimization on the GPU. So here the scenario is, for each Intel TBB thread, one OpenCL command queue is created and the program has to wait until all commands of the command queue finish their execution. Due to this kind of thread divergence, threads have to wait for some time and it will serialize execution to some extent, so full optimization and speedup could not be achieved.

Optimization Using Intel® TBB (Haar Classifier) and OpenCL (Haar Classifier)

Selection of Intel® TBB + OpenCL (Haar Classifier)

Intel TBB is used for executing the application utilizing the multi-core capabilities of the CPU. As Haar classifier functionality when ported onto the GPU was giving performance, integration of OpenCL with Intel TBB was considered for giving improved performance. The Intel TBB code that runs in parallel on the CPU will invoke kernels that will run on the GPU.

Intel TBB + OpenCL Functionalities (Haar Classifier)

In the Intel TBB + OpenCL implementation, the Intel TBB will handle the parallelism at sub-window size level; that is, different window sizes will be processed in parallel. The parallelism at the inner levels will be handled by OpenCL.

To process the video frame for all window sizes in parallel, we need different cascades that will store the data for each window. Hence once the Haar Cascade is loaded from the XML file and a Hid-Haar Cascade is created, multiple copies of both the cascades are made and stored in an array.

As the Haar Classifier implementation is done using OpenCL, the multiple copies of Haar and Hid-Haar Cascades should be copied to the GPU and the pointers in the cascades need to be mapped in the OpenCL context. A class CreateParallelCloneCascade is created with an objective to implement the copying and mapping of memory objects created in the GPU in parallel in the CPU using Intel TBB. This is done only once during the initialization of the application.

The processing of the video frame happens in the processframe function of the CimpressionTracker class. In the processframe function, the detection of faces happens in two functions:

- *ParallelMultiScaleScanFaces_GPU:* The video frame is scanned for faces and stored in the array m_arrLiveImpression. This function helps for searching the faces that are not moving very much from the previous frame. A class "CParallelMultiScaleFaceScanner_GPU" is created with an objective to search the faces of different sizes in parallel using Intel TBB

- *ParallelTrackFaces_GPU:* The video frame is scanned for faces and stored in the array m_arrLiveImpression. This function helps for searching the new faces in the areas where the motion is detected when compared to the previous frame. A class "CParallelFaceTracker_GPU" is created with an objective to search the faces of different sizes in parallel using Intel TBB.

These functions will call the detectFaces_OCL function of the CfaceDetector class internally. In the function the faces are detected in the frame for the selected sub-window size. All the sub-window sizes will execute in parallel in the GPU using OpenCL. For each detection, coordinates would be stored in the global buffer of the GPU memory. As the execution is going in parallel both in the CPU and the GPU, the rectangle coordinates that are stored will be brought from GPU to CPU and stored in the m_arrLiveImpression in the end of these functions.

Issues in Combination of Intel® TBB and OpenCL for Haar classifier

It has been observed after integrating Intel TBB and OpenCL:

■ The performance is slower than the Intel TBB code.

■ The accuracy results of face detection using Intel TBB + OpenCL is poor compared to Intel TBB code.

■ The results of the integrated code were random in nature, as certain scale factors were not dumped properly.

■ As the Haar classifier cannot be ported onto the Ivy Bridge GPU due to its complex nested structure, the combination of Intel TBB and OpenCL for Haar classifier cannot be ported onto the Ivy Bridge GPU.

Optimization Using Intel TBB (Haar Classifier) + OpenCL (Non-Haar Classifier Hotspot Functions)

Optimization of Haar classifier using Intel TBB is explained in an earlier section.

Accuracy Model

The following section discusses the accuracy model.

Method of Calculating Accuracy

The comparator measures accuracy of Intel AIM Suite optimized detection against Intel AIM Suite base code output. The comparator generates accuracy matrices based on the Intel AIM Suite output files. The base code and optimized code output is generated for test videos. The accuracy report file contains parameters like TME, GME, ICE, AME, FPR, and FNR generated by the comparator. The input parameters of operation are explained below.

For performance metrics following parameters are calculated.

■ *TME (Track Match Error):* For the objects, which are present in both Base and Intel AIM Suite optimized code detection, TME is calculated. This is calculated by taking average Euclidean distance error in the track match across all frames.

$$\text{TME} = \frac{\Sigma(\text{Euclidean Distance between matched objects in all frames})}{(\text{Total number of matched objects})}$$

■ *GME (Gender Match Error):* For the objects that are present in both base and Intel AIM Suite optimized code detection, GME is calculated. Calculating incorrect number of gender matches averaged across all frames.

$$\text{GME} = \frac{\Sigma(\text{Gender Match Error between matched objects in all frames})}{(\text{Total number of matched objects})}$$

■ *AME (Age Match Error):* For the objects that are present in both base and Intel AIM Suite optimized code detection, AME is calculated. Incorrect number of age matches averaged across all frames.

$$\text{AME} = \frac{\Sigma(\text{Age Match Error between matched objects in all frames})}{(\text{Total number of matched objects})}$$

■ *FPR (False Positive Rate):* If the object is present in Intel AIM Suite optimized detection and the object is not present in base code detection, then it is called a false positive (FP). Number of false positives (Intel AIM Suite optimized code detected faces unmatched in base code) per frame.

$$\text{FPR} = \frac{(\text{Total number of false Positive Detections})}{(\text{Total number of processed frames in AIMS})}$$

■ *FNR (False Negative Rate):* If the object is not present in Intel AIM Suite optimized code detection and the object is present in base code, then it is called a false negative (FN); that is, number of false negatives (faces missed by Intel AIM Suite optimized code) per frame. This rate can also be defined as "percentage of faces missed by Intel AIM Suite optimized code per frame."

$$FNR = \frac{(\text{Total number of false Negative Detections})}{(\text{Total number of processed frames in AIMS})}$$

■ *ICE (Impression Count Error):* Ratio of difference between Intel AIM Suite optimized code and Intel AIM Suite base code impression count to Intel AIM Suite base code impression count. This will be calculated as follows:

$$ICE = \frac{(\text{AIM Suite Impression Count} - \text{GT Count})}{\text{GT Count}}$$

■ *VTE (View Time Error):* The difference between average Intel AIM Suite optimized code viewing time and average Intel AIM Suite base code viewing time. Average Viewing Time is total length of impressions divided by the number of impressions.

$$VTE = \frac{(\text{Accumulate all IDs Viewing Time for AIMS})}{(\text{Number of Ids in AIMS})}$$
$$- \frac{(\text{Accumulate all IDs Viewing Time for GT})}{(\text{Number of Ids in GT})}$$

Accuracy of OpenCL (Haar Classifier)

The accuracy is being maintained in the OpenCL implementation of Haar Classifier. There might be one pixel change in the size of the detected faces. To gain the performance, data transfer from GPU to CPU should be minimal. Hence, the detections of faces are made parallel and the face coordinates are read back to the CPU from the GPU only once, where as the original Implementation stores in a serial fashion.

Accuracy Results

Figures 29, 30 and 31 are the graphs generated for test videos. The graphs are generated by considering above errors and various parameters.

Accuracy of Intel® TBB (Haar Classifier) + SSE

There is no degradation in the accuracy of the code. Accuracy is maintained for all functions. The result of accuracy checking is same as that of the results given earlier.

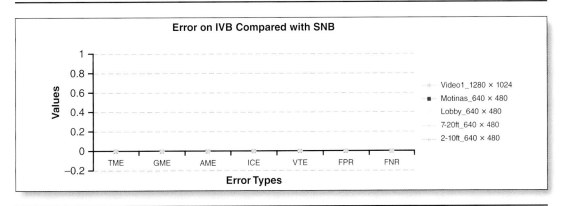

Figure 10.29 Different Errors in Optimized Intel® AIM Suite Code

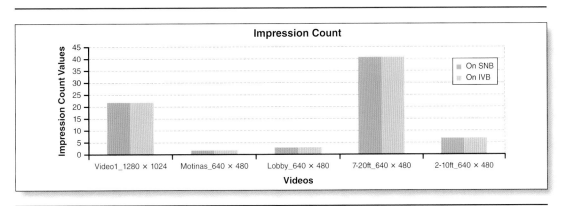

Figure 10.30 Impression Count of Different Videos for Optimized and Base Code for SNB (Sandy Bridge) and IVB (Ivy Bridge)

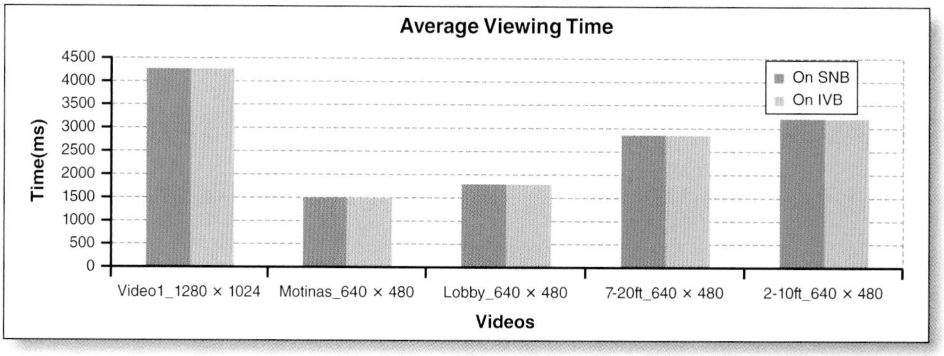

Figure 10.31 Average Viewing Time for Videos for Optimized and Base Code

Accuracy of Intel® TBB + OpenCL (Haar Classifier)

The Haar classifier functionality of the TBB base code delivered was converted into kernels. It was observed that the accuracy of TBB + OpenCL integrated code is poor.

Accuracy of Intel® TBB (Haar Classifier) + OpenCL (Non-Haar Classifier)

The result of accuracy checking is same as that of the results given earlier.

Performance Measurement

The following section discusses performance measurement.

GPU Performance

The following section discusses GPU performance.

Performance of OpenCL (Haar Classifier)

Performance is achieved for videos which have the high resolution and high motion (see Figures 10.32, 10.33, and 10.34).

CPU Performance

The following section discusses CPU performance.

CPU Info : i7 CPU × 990, 3.47GHz 12 GB RAM, 64 bit, Windows7								
Video	Resolution	Number of frames	Motion in Video	Base code executed on CPU		OpenCL code executed on CPU devices		
				Total Time for executing video in ms	Avg Time Per Frame in ms	Total Time for executing video in ms	Avg Time Per Frame in ms	Performance Calculation over Base code (in %)
Video1_1280 × 1024	1280 × 1024	1162	High motion near camera	202306.1905	174.101713	86890.3909	74.77658425	57.05005829
Motinas_640 × 480	640 × 480	99	Medium motion near camera	6976.120227	70.46586088	2580.136077	26.06198058	63.01474182
Lobby_640 × 480	640 × 480	3000	Motion away from camera	85594.07208	28.53135736	42306.61836	14.10220612	50.57295753
7-20ft_640 × 480	640 × 480	8425	Light Motion away from camera	210485.2413	24.98341143	124413.5821	14.76719075	40.89201632
2-10ft_640 × 480	640 × 480	5114	Light Motion away from camera	96228.30581	18.81664173	73118.8552	14.29778162	24.0152317

Figure 10.32 Performance of Haar Classifier OpenCL Code on Intel Sandy Bridge CPU

Performance of Intel® TBB and Intel® TBB + Intel® SSE

Figures 10.35, and 10.36 show and compare the performance of Intel TBB + Intel SSE and Intel TBB.

CPU + GPU Performance

The following section discusses CPU + GPU performance.

Performance of Intel® TBB + OpenCL (Haar Classifier)

Figure 10.37 shows the performance for Intel TBB + OpenCL (Haar Classifier) on an Intel CPU.

Performance of Intel® TBB + OpenCL (Non-Haar Classifier)

Performance is achieved for videos which have the highest resolution. Figure 10.38 shows Intel CPU performance. Figure 10.39 shows Nvidia GPU performance. Figures 10.40 and 10.41 show Ivy Bridge CPU and GPU performance, respectively. Figure 10.42 compares the various platforms.

					Base code executed on CPU		OpenCL code executed on GPU device		
Sr. No	Video	Resolution	Number of frames	Motion in Video	Total Time for executing video in ms	Avg Time Per Frame in ms	Total Time for executing video in ms	Avg Time Per Frame in ms	Performance Calculation over Base
1	Video1_1280 × 1024	1280 × 1024	1162	High motion near camera	202306.1905	174.101713	139526.2085	120.0741898	31.0321606
2	Motinas_640 × 480	640 × 480	99	Medium motion near camera	6976.120227	70.46586088	5964.99955	60.25252071	14.494026
3	Lobby_640 × 480	640 × 480	3000	Motion away from camera	85594.07208	28.53135736	89591.20698	29.86373566	−4.66987351
4	7-20ft_640 × 480	640 × 480	8425	Light Motion away from camera	210485.2413	24.98341143	226698.6292	26.90784916	−7.7028621
5	2-10ft_640 × 480	640 × 480	5114	Light Motion away from camera	96228.30581	18.81664173	116928.2785	22.86434855	−21.5113136

CPU Info : i7 CPU × 990, 3.47GHz 12 GB RAM, 64 bit, Windows7
GPU Info : NVIDIA GE Force GTX570, Shadow cores 480, Memory-1280MB , GDDR5 320 bit, Clk - 1464MHz, Compute Units – 15

					Base code executed on CPU		OpenCL code executed on GPU device		
Sr. No	Video	Resolution	Number of frames	Motion in Video	Total Time for executing video in ms	Avg Time Per Frame in ms	Total Time for executing video in ms	Avg Time Per Frame in ms	Performance Calculation over Base
1	Video1_1280 × 1024	1280 × 1024	1162	High motion near camera	202306.1905	174.101713	201560.2795	173.459793	0.36870401
2	Motinas_640 × 480	640 × 480	99	Medium motion near camera	6976.120227	70.46586088	7938.277859	80.18462484	−13.7921595
3	Lobby_640 × 480	640 × 480	3000	Motion away from camera	85594.07208	28.53135736	111099.5241	37.03317471	−29.7981524
4	7-20ft_640 × 480	640 × 480	8425	Light Motion away from camera	210485.2413	24.98341143	264228.095	31.36238516	−25.5328371
5	2-10ft_640 × 480	640 × 480	5114	Light Motion away from camera	96228.30581	18.81664173	134282.1958	26.25776219	−39.5454224

CPU Info : i7 CPU × 990, 3.47GHz 12 GB RAM, 64 bit, Windows7
GPU Info : NVIDIA G4 GTS450, 1024 Global memory, GDDR5 1764MHz, Compute Units – 4

					Base code executed on CPU		OpenCL code executed on GPU device		
Sr. No	Video	Resolution	Number of frames	Motion in Video	Total Time for executing video in ms	Avg Time Per Frame in ms	Total Time for executing video in ms	Avg Time Per Frame in ms	Performance Calculations over Base
1	Video1_1280 × 1024	1280 × 1024	1162	High motion near camera	202306.1905	174.101713	2847291.969	2450.337322	−1307.41712
2	Motinas_640 × 480	640 × 480	99	Medium motion near camera	6976.120227	70.46586088	149862.9774	1513.767449	−2048.22813
3	Lobby_640 × 480	640 × 480	3000	Motion away from camera	85594.07208	28.53135736	1301882.681	433.9608936	−1420.99631
4	7-20ft_640 × 480	640 × 480	8425	Light Motion away from camera	210485.2413	24.98341143	3641774.165	432.2580611	−1630.18029
5	2-10ft_640 × 480	640 × 480	5114	Light Motion away from camera	96228.30581	18.81664173	1193010.777	233.2832962	−1139.77115

CPU Info : i7 CPU×990, 3.47GHz 12 GB RAM, 64 bit, Windows7
GPU Info : NVIDIA NVS 295, 231 MB Global memory, GDDR5, 64-bit, Compute Units – 1

Figure 10.33 GPU Performance Comparison

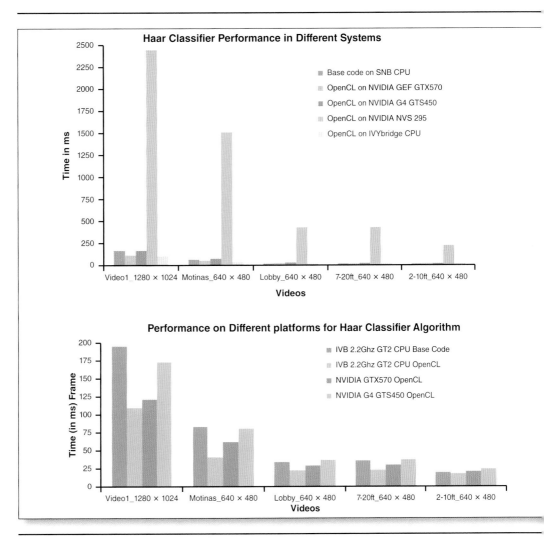

Figure 10.34 Haar Classifier Performance

CPU Info : i7 CPU × 990, 3.47GHz 12 GB RAM, 64 bit, Windows7									
Sr. No.	Video	Resolution	Number of frames	Motion in Video	Base code timings		TBB+SSE code executed on CPU device		
					Total Time for executing video in ms	Avg Time Per Frame in ms	Total Time for executing video in ms	Avg Time Per Frame in ms	Performance Calculations over Base (in %)
1	Video1_1280 × 1024	1280 × 1024	500	High motion near Camera	93210.66637	186.4213327	29100.99286	58.20198572	68.77933182
2	Motinas_640 × 480	640 × 480	99	Medium motion near Camera	7410.742515	74.855985	2327.041543	23.50547013	68.59907711
3	Lobby_640 × 480	640 × 480	2000	Motion away from Camera	61375.20469	30.68760235	24174.87571	12.08743785	60.61133184
4	7-20ft_640 × 480	640 × 480	2000	Light Motion away from Camera	54849.23245	27.42461623	22112.19893	11.05609946	59.68549068
5	2-10ft_640 × 480	640 × 480	2000	Light Motion away from Camera	38640.37907	19.32018953	19841.83784	9.920918922	48.64999174

CPU Info : i7 CPU × 990, 3.47GHz 12 GB RAM, 64 bit, Windows7									
Sr. No.	Video	Resolution	Number of frames	Motion in Video	Base code timings		TBB code executed on CPU device		
					Total Time for executing video in ms	Avg Time Per Frame in ms	Total Time for executing video in ms	Avg Time Per Frame in ms	Performance calculations over Base (in %)
1	Video1_1280 × 1024	1280 × 1024	500	High motion near Camera	93210.66637	186.4213327	37388.29213	74.77658425	59.88839734
2	Motinas_640 × 480	640 × 480	99	Medium motion near Camera	7410.742515	74.855985	2327.452995	23.50962621	68.593525
3	Lobby_640 × 480	640 × 480	2000	Motion away from Camera	61375.20469	30.68760235	23861.07623	11.93053811	61.12261239
4	7-20ft_640 × 480	640 × 480	2000	Light Motion away from Camera	54849.23245	27.42461623	22400.70464	11.20035232	59.15949297
5	2-10ft_640 × 480	640 × 480	2000	Light Motion away from Camera	38640.37907	19.32018953	20287.72918	10.14386459	47.49603998

Figure 10.35 Performance of Intel® TBB + Intel® SSE

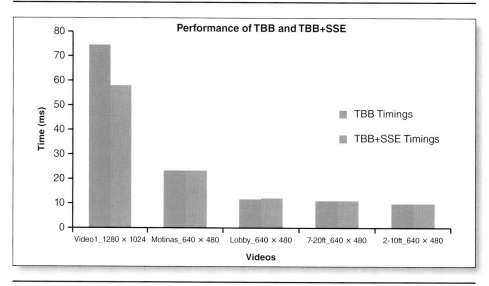

Figure 10.36 Performance of Intel® TBB and Intel® TBB + Intel® SSE

Sr. No	Videos	Resolution	Number of frames	Motion in Video	Base code timings		Base code executed on CPU device		
CPU Info : i7 CPU × 990, 3.47GHz 8 GB RAM, 64 bit, Windows7									
GPU Info : NVIDIA GE Force GTX570, Shadow cores 480, Memory- 1280MB , GDDR5 320 bit, CIK1464MHz, Compute Units – 15									
					Total Time for executing video in ms	Avg Time Per Frame in ms	Total Time for executing video in ms	Avg Time Per Frame in ms	Performance calculations over Base (in %)
1	Video1_1280 × 1024	1280 × 1024	500	High motion near camera	93210.66637	186.4213327	37388.29213	74.77658425	59.88839734
2	Motinas_640 × 480	640 × 480	99	Medium motion near camera	7410.742515	74.855985	2327.452995	23.50962621	68.593525
3	Lobby_640 × 480	640 × 480	2000	Motion away from camera	61375.20469	30.68760235	23861.07623	11.93053811	61.12261239

Sr. No	Videos	Resolution	Number of frames	Motion in Video	Base code timings		Base_OCL code executed on CPU-GPU device		
CPU Info : i7 CPU × 990, 3.47GHz 8 GB RAM, 64 bit, Windows7									
GPU Info : NVIDIA GE Force GTX570, Shadow cores 480, Memory- 1280MB , GDDR5 320 bit, CIK-1464MHz, Compute Units – 15									
					Total Time for executing video in ms	Avg Time Per Frame in ms	Total Time for executing video in ms	Avg Time Per Frame in ms	Performance calculations over Base (in %)
1	Video1_1280 × 1024	1280 × 1024	500	High motion near camera	93210.66637	186.4213327	54290.01372	108.580027	41.75557816
2	Motinas_640 × 480	640 × 480	99	Medium motion near camera	7410.742515	74.855985	5346.324354	54.0032763	27.8571028
3	Lobby_640 × 480	640 × 480	2000	Motion away from camera	61375.20469	30.68760235	34568.48855	17.2842443	43.67678491

Figure 10.37 Performance of Intel® TBB + OpenCL (Haar Classifier) on Intel CPU

Sr. No	Image	Resolution	Number of frames	Motion in Video	TBB code timings on CPU		(OpenCL+TBB) code timings on CPU device		
CPU Info : i7 CPU × 990, 3.47GHz 12 GB RAM, 64 bit, Windows7									
					Total Time for executing video in ms	Avg Time Per Frame in ms	Total Time for executing video in ms	Avg Time Per Frame in ms	Performance calculations over TBB (in %)
1	Video1_1280 × 1024	1280 × 1024	1162	High motion near camera	67172.73389	57.80786049	60959.92133	52.46120596	9.249009544
2	Motinas_640 × 480	640 × 480	99	Medium motion near camera	2285.288486	23.08372208	2323.841567	23.47314714	−1.687011563
3	Lobby_640 × 480	740 × 516	9073	Motion away from camera	78526.59083	8.654975292	70937.63849	7.818542763	9.664181591
4	7-20ft_640 × 480	640 × 480	8425	Light Motion away from camera	97915.01332	11.62196004	100664.8221	11.94834683	−2.808362736
5	2-10ft_640 × 480	640 × 480	5114	Light Motion away from camera	49552.65264	9.689607478	47415.02721	9.271612672	4.313846632

Figure 10.38 Performance of Intel® TBB + OpenCL (Non-Haar Classifier) on Intel CPU

CPU Info : i7 CPU × 990, 3.47 GHz 12 GB RAM, 64 bit, Windows7

GPU Info : NVIDIA GE Force GTX570, Shadow cores 480, Memory-1280MB, GDDR5 320 bit, Clk - 1464 MHz, Compute Units - 15, Driver version 8.17.12.6658

Sr. No	Image	Resolution	Number of frames	Motion in Video	TBB code timings on CPU		(OpenCL+TBB) code timings on (GPU + CPU) devices		
					Total Time for executing video in ms	Avg Time Per Frame in ms	Total Time for executing video in ms	Avg Time Per Frame in ms	Performance calculations over TBB (in %)
1	Video1_1280 × 1024	1280 × 1024	1162	High motion near camera	67172.73389	57.80786049	61645.71548	53.05139025	8.228068291
2	Motinas_640 × 480	640 × 480	99	Medium motion near camera	2285.288486	23.08372208	2452.94784	24.77725091	−7.336463428
3	Lobby_640 × 480	740 × 516	9073	Motion away from camera	78526.59083	8.654975292	76241.29176	8.403096193	2.910223205
4	7-20ft_640 × 480	640 × 480	8425	Light Motion away from camera	97915.01332	11.62196004	103602.9478	12.29708579	−5.809052411
5	2-10ft_640 × 480	640 × 480	5114	Light Motion away from camera	49552.65264	9.689607478	49970.57256	9.771328227	−0.843385548

CPU Info : i7 CPU × 990, 3.47 GHz 12 GB RAM, 64 bit, Windows7

GPU Info : NVIDIA G4 GTS450, 1024 Global memory, GDDR5 1764MHz, Compute Units – 4, Driver version-8-17.12.6759

Sr. No	Image	Resolution	Number of frames	Motion in Video	TBB code timings on CPU		(OpenCL+TBB) code timings on (GPU + CPU) devices		
					Total Time for executing video in ms	Avg Time Per Frame in ms	Total Time for executing video in ms	Avg Time Per Frame in ms	Performance calculations over TBB (in %)
1	Video1_1280 × 1024	1280 × 1024	1162	High motion near camera	67172.73389	57.80786049	61215.37162	52.68104271	8.86872087
2	Motinas_640 × 480	640 × 480	99	Medium motion near camera	2285.288486	23.08372208	2330.874864	23.54419055	−1.994775639
3	Lobby_640 × 480	740 × 516	9073	Motion away from camera	78526.59083	8.654975292	72218.20896	7.959683562	8.033434032
4	7-20ft_640 × 480	640 × 480	8425	Light Motion away from camera	97915.01332	11.62196004	101672.1376	12.06790951	−3.837127903
5	2-10ft_640 × 480	640 × 480	5114	Light Motion away from camera	49552.65264	9.689607478	48066.23216	9.398950363	2.999678943

CPU Info : i7 CPU × 990, 3.47GHz 12 GB RAM, 64 bit, Windows7

GPU Info : NVIDIA NVS 295, 231MB Global memory, GDDR3, 64-bit. Compute Units – 1, Driver version-8.17.12.7628

Sr. No	Image	Resolution	Number of frames	Motion in Video	TBB code timings on CPU		(OpenCL+TBB) code timings on (GPU + CPU) devices		
					Total Time for executing video in ms	Avg Time Per Frame in ms	Total Time for executing video in ms	Avg Time Per Frame in ms	Performance calculations over TBB (in %)
1	Video1_1280 × 1024	1280 × 1024	1162	High motion near camera	67172.73389	57.80786049	61773.29758	53.16118553	8.038136903
2	Motinas_640 × 480	640 × 480	99	Medium motion near camera	2285.288486	23.08372208	2332.970026	23.5653538	−2.086456055
3	Lobby_640 × 480	740 × 516	9073	Motion away from camera	78526.59083	8.654975292	77880.14619	8.583726021	0.823217505
4	7-20ft_640 × 480	640 × 480	8425	Light Motion away from camera	97915.01332	11.62196004	105270.2765	12.49498831	−7.511884998
5	2-10ft_640 × 480	640 × 480	5114	Light Motion away from camera	49552.65264	9.689607478	49999.90962	9.777064845	−0.902589363

Figure 10.39 Performance of Intel® TBB + OpenCL (Non-Haar Classifier) with Nvidia GPU

CPU Info : IVYbridge, 2.2GHz 8 GB RAM, 64 bit, Windows7								
Sr. No.	Video	Resolution	Number of frames	Motion in Video	TBB code timings on CPU		(OpenCL+TBB) code timings on devices		
					Total Time for executing video in ms	Avg Time Per Frame in ms	Total Time for executing video in ms	Avg Time Per Frame in ms	Performance calculations over TBB (in %)
1	Video1_1280 × 1024	1280 × 1024	1162	High motion near camera	99675.45409	85.77922039	97437.43609	83.85321522	2.245305045
2	Motinas_640 × 480	640 × 480	99	Medium motion near	3924.588735	39.64231045	3565.675918	36.01692846	9.145233838
3	Lobby_640 × 480	740 × 516	9073	Motion away from camera	148923.0502	16.41387085	136477.87	15.04219883	8.35678574
4	7-20ft_640 × 480	640 × 480	8425	Light Motion away from	148851.1148	17.66778811	152320.2896	18.07955959	−2.330634038
5	2-10ft_640 × 480	640 × 480	5114	Light Motion away from	68336.03669	13.36254139	67326.83082	13.16519961	1.476828217

Figure 10.40 Performance of Intel® TBB + OpenCL (Non-Haar Classifier) with Ivy Bridge CPU

CPU Info : IVYbridge, 2.2 GHz 8 GB RAM, 64 bit, Windows7								
GPU Info : IVYBridge, Memory- 1790MB, CIK - 400MHz, Compute Units - 16, Driver version 8.15.10.2531								
Sr. No.	Video	Resolution	Number of frames	Motion in Video	TBB code timings on CPU		(OpenCL+TBB) code timings on (GPU + CPU) devices		
					Total Time for executing video in ms	Avg Time Per Frame in ms	Total Time for executing video in ms	Avg Time Per Frame in ms	Performance calculations over TBB (in %)
1	Video1_1280 × 1024	1280 × 1024	1162	High motion near camera	99675.45409	85.77922039	96566.71481	83.10388538	3.118861417
2	Motinas_640 × 480	640 × 480	99	Medium motion near	3924.588735	39.64231045	3775.309848	38.13444291	3.803682298
3	Lobby_640 × 480	740 × 516	9073	Motion away from camera	148923.0502	16.41387085	140169.85	15.44911826	5.877666494
4	7-20ft_640 × 480	640 × 480	8425	Light Motion away from	148851.1148	17.66778811	154191.1032	18.30161463	−3.587469532
5	2-10ft_640 × 480	640 × 480	5114	Light Motion away from	68336.03669	13.36254139	69168.84895	13.52539088	−1.21870143

Figure 10.41 Performance of Intel® TBB + OpenCL (Non-Haar Classifier) with Ivy Bridge GPU

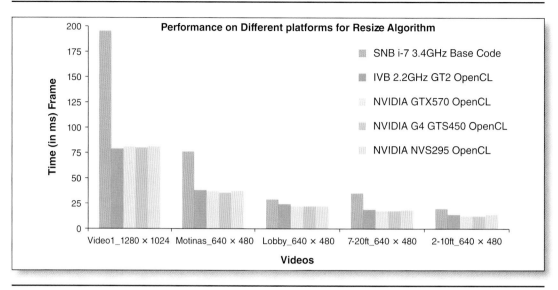

Figure 10.42 Performance of Intel® TBB + OpenCL (Non-Haar Classifier) on Different Platforms

Appendix

Synthetic Video Generation

This appendix discusses the creation of synthetic videos as a measure for ground truth. A computer vision algorithm application needs vast training data set. The synthetic video generation tool is used to generate videos with individuals of different demographics in different scenarios. These videos make up the training set and are used to train the algorithms. Taking a video of a group of people can be considered as violation of privacy, so this tool provides a solution to all the factors. There are different steps in the creation of the synthetic video generation tool.

Camera Field of View Conditions

The location of the camera is an important aspect in the synthetic video generation. The camera is placed at height h, so the camera coordinates in space are 0, h, 0. As seen in Figure A.1, the x, y, and z coordinate's sign conventions are from the point of view of camera. The positive value of x means the individual is on the right side of camera. Negative value of x means that the individual is on the left side of camera. The positive value of y means the individual is above the ground. Negative value of y means that the individual is below the ground level. Similarly, the positive value of z means the individual is away from the camera and negative value of z means that the individual is either towards or behind the camera.

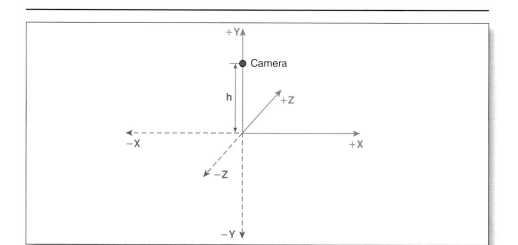

Figure A.1   Different Planes with Respect to the Position of the Camera

Field of View (FOV) is the total area that is covered by the camera. As seen in Figure A.2, in FOV, we are introducing two vertical planes, Z-near frame and Z-far frame. Any face outside these limits of z-axis will not be considered as a face, and hence should be neglected.

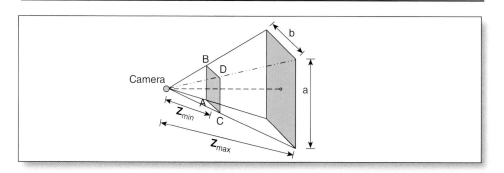

Figure A.2   Face Should Lie between Zmin and Zmax

In order to decide if the individual's face is within the FOV of the camera, we have to form the equations for the minimum and maximum limits of the following parameters of a face such as X, Y and Z parameters and also Pan (α) and Tilt (β). We also have to consider the two angles Θ and Φ. These are the angles generated by the FOV of the camera. Thus $2 \times \Theta$ is the horizontal FOV of camera and $2\times \Phi$ is the vertical FOV of camera. The angle Θhas positive values towards right side of camera and negative values towards left; Φ has positive values in upward direction of camera and negative values downwards.

Conditions for GT Data Marking

The ground truth data is used as the baseline for finding the performance of the computer vision algorithm output. The synthetic video generation tool is used to generate the GT data. This makes it easier instead of generating GT data by manually marking the images. We can pass parameters to the tool such as gender, X, Y, Z coordinates for the face. GT data gets generated for either a Pan or Tilt scenario. To get marked, the face should satisfy the following conditions: It must be present within the FOV of camera. It should make valid Pan and Tilt angle with camera and it should not be occluded by other face. To achieve this, we have to form the equations of (Xmax, Xmin), (Ymax, Ymin) and (Zmax,Zmin) for the face at any point in the FOV. Then we have to set the Pan and Tilt angle limits of the face with camera. We also have to set the occlusion limits. Since the distances are set of the Z-near and Z-far planes, Zmin = distance of Z-near. Zmax = distance of Z-far. The value of Z should lie between Zmin and Zmax. Figure A.3 shows the side view of the ideal scenario.

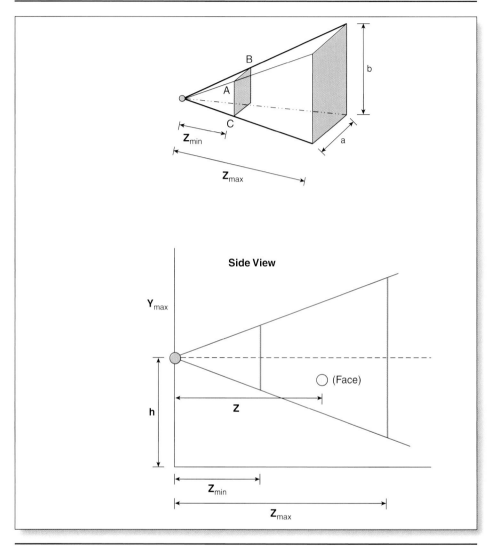

Figure A.3   Side View of the Ideal Scenario

The horizontal FOV of the camera is $2 \times \Theta$. For any face, at any instance, since the Z coordinate is known it is used to calculate the X coordinate value. Thus,

$$\text{Xmax} = Z \times \tan(\Theta),$$
$$\text{Xmin} = Z \times \tan(-\Theta) = -Z \times \tan(\Theta).$$

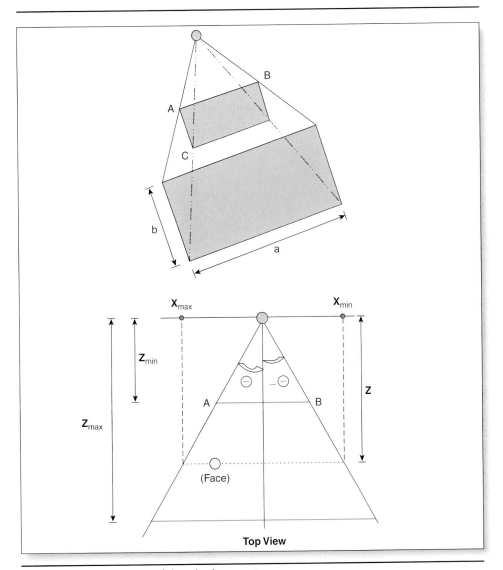

Figure A.4 Top View of the ideal scenario

The value of the X coordinate should be greater than Xmin and less than Xmax. Figure A.4 shows the top view of the ideal scenario.

Now we need to calculate Φ (see Figure A.5), for further equations. We also need to consider the aspect ratio of frame in camera FOV, which is (a:b). At this time Θ is also known. Using this information we can calculate the value of Φ

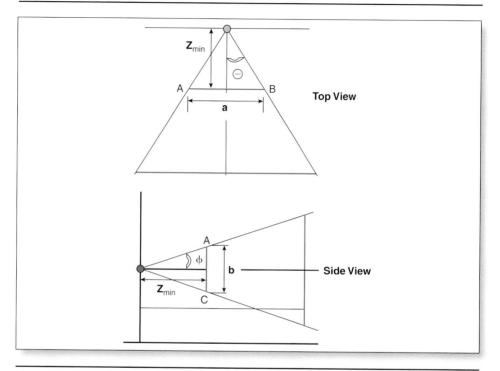

Figure A.5   Calculating Φ

$$\text{len(AB)} = \text{Zmin} \times \tan(\Theta) \times 2$$

$$\text{len(AC)} = \text{len(AB)} \times (b / a)$$

$$\tan(\Phi) = (\text{len(AC)} / 2) / \text{Zmin}$$

The values of Ymin and Ymax are variable. They depend on Z. Z is known at any point. Thus,

$$y1 = Z * \tan(\Phi)$$

$$\text{Ymin} = h - y1$$

$$\text{Ymax} = h + y1$$

The value of Y lies between Ymin and Ymax (see Figure A.6).

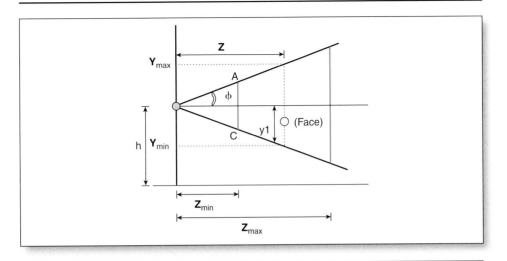

Figure A.6   Face between Ymin and Ymax

Now we have the values for X, Y, and Z coordinates; now we calculate the Pan and Tilt. The Pan angle is with respect to camera and not with respect to the 2D-plane of camera. Hence, if a person is exactly looking at the camera, its Pan is 0°, irrespective of X, Y, Z coordinates. For better results, as observed in Direct-3D, the maximum and minimum Pan values can be set as 30° and -30°. Within these limits of Pan, a face will be detected by the camera (see Figure A.7).

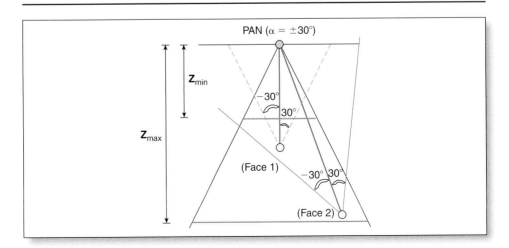

Figure A.7   Setting Maximum and Mininum Pan Values as 30° and −30°

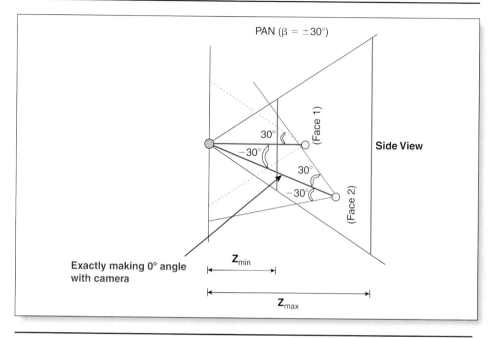

Figure A.8 Setting Maximum and Minimum Tilt Values as 30° and −30°

Similarly the Tilt angle is also calculated with respect to camera, and not with respect to the 2D-plane of camera. Hence, if a person is exactly looking at the camera, its Tilt is 0°, irrespective of X, Y, Z coordinates. For better results, as observed in Direct-3D, the maximum and minimum Tilt values can be set as 30° and -30°. Within these limits of Tilt, a face will be detected by the camera (see Figure A.8).

Thus we have all the five values we were looking for marking the GT data.

Face Movements

This section deals with the issue of the same face as perceived by the camera when the face moves away. With the help of the radius of the face, the camera can predict the new position of the face. Since using this tool we are simulating the movement of the face, we have to use current information to predict the future location of the face. In the following paragraph we explain how the new position is calculated for different scenarios. From the input scenario, we are getting the radius (R) of a face, which is measured exactly at the Zmin plane, with the center coordinates 0, h, Zmin (see Figure A.9).

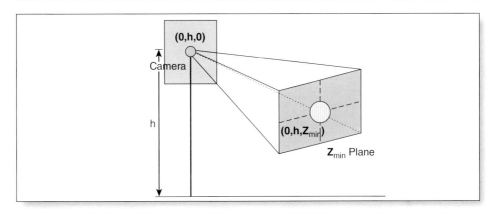

Figure A.9   Finding the Current Position of the Face

The side view of this Zmin center position is shown in Figure A.10.

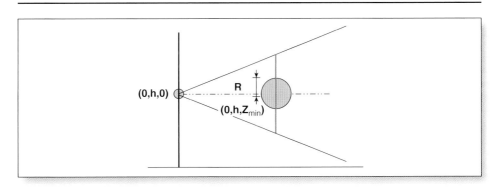

Figure A.10 Side View of the Current Position of the Face in Z Direction

With the help of this radius (R), we can calculate the new radius of the same face as perceived by the camera when the face moves away. Let's first consider that the face is moving only in the Z-direction, without changing X and Y coordinates. The new position coordinates of the face is 0, *h*, Zreal. Projections are drawn from the camera to the face at new position. In the Zmin plane, where the projecting lines intersect, it gives us the new size (radius) of the face. Now, we can easily calculate the new radius *Rnew*. From symmetry, (Rnew / Zmin) = (R / Zreal) where Zmin, R, and Zreal are known, hence, we get Rnew (see Figure A.11).

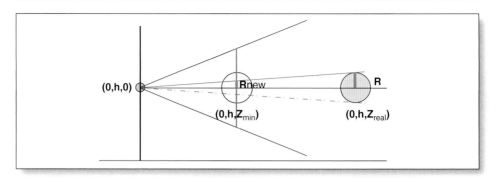

Figure A.11 Side View of the Perceived New and Real Positions of the Face in Z Direction

Now let's consider the case when a face with radius R moves in X direction. Even though the Z coordinate is constant, the perceived size of the face to the camera reduces (see Figure A.12).

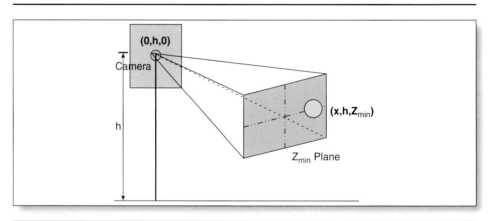

Figure A.12 Movement of the Face in X Direction

In this case, the face is moved in X direction, with Y being constant. Here the perceived size of the face is smaller than at its previous position. Zreal can be calculated using distance formula.

$$\mathbf{Z}real = \sqrt{(\sqrt{(X2 - X1)} + \sqrt{(Y2 - Y1)} + \sqrt{(Z2 - Z1)})}$$

$$\mathbf{Z}real = \sqrt{(\sqrt{(X - 0)} + \sqrt{(h - h)} + \sqrt{(Z - 0)})}$$

$$\mathbf{Z}real = \sqrt{(\sqrt{X} + \sqrt{Z})}$$

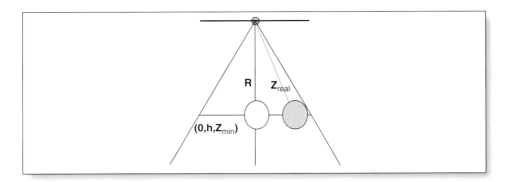

Figure A.13 Top View of the Movement of the Face in X Direction

Now, bring this face radially on the z-axis, at $Z = Zreal$ (see Figure A.13).

The new position coordinates of the face are 0, h, Zreal. We are drawing the projections from the camera to the face at new position. At the Zmin plane, where the projecting lines intersect, gives us the new size (radius) of the face. Now, we can easily calculate the new radius Rnew. From symmetry, (Rnew / Zmin) = (R / Zreal)

Zmin, R and Zreal are known, hence, we get Rnew (see Figure A.14).

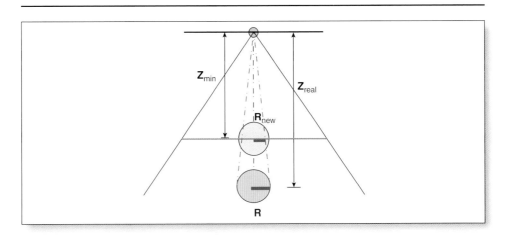

Figure A.14 Top View Showing the Radius of the New Position of the Face

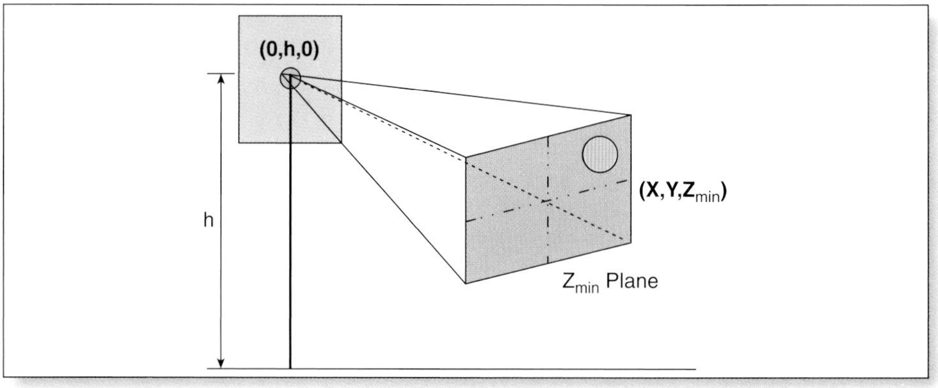

Figure A.15 Movement of theFace in X,Y Direction

Consider the scenario where the face moves in X as well as Y direction. The perceived size gets reduced as seen in Figure A.15.

The aim is to calculate the actual distance of the face from camera (Zreal) and the perceived size (radius) of the face at 0, h, Zreal. The situation can be represented as shown in Figure A.16. Camera is at 0, h, 0 and Face is at X, Y, Z

The distance between camera and face is Zreal. It can be calculated by using distance formula as follows:

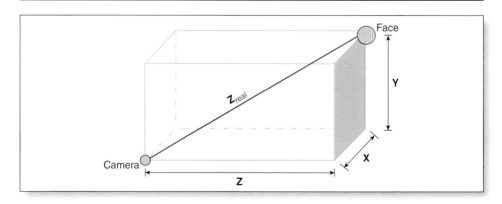

Figure A.16 Calculating the Actual Distance of the Face

$$\mathbf{Z}\text{real} = \sqrt{(\sqrt{(x2 - x1)} + \sqrt{(y2 - y1)} + \sqrt{(z2 - z1)})}$$

$$\mathbf{Z}\text{real} = \sqrt{(\sqrt{(\mathbf{X} - 0)} + \sqrt{(\mathbf{Y} - \mathbf{h})} + \sqrt{(\mathbf{Z} - 0)})}$$

$$\mathbf{Z}\text{real} = \sqrt{(\sqrt{(\mathbf{X})} + \sqrt{(\mathbf{Y} - \mathbf{h})} + \sqrt{(\mathbf{Z})})}$$

Now we have the Zreal value. Bring the face radially to the coordinates 0, *h*, Zreal. At this Z-coordinate, the perceived size of the face will be, Rnew = (R/Zreal) × Zmin

Zmin, R, and Zreal are known, hence, we get Rnew (see Figure A.17).

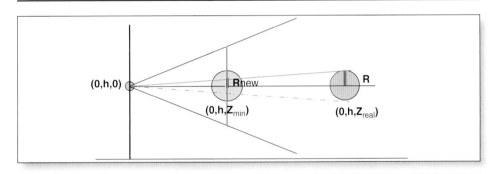

Figure A.17 Side View of the New Position of the Face

Calculation of the Bounding Box for Pan, Tilt, and Roll

The illustrations in Figure A.18 represent the side view and top view of a face looking directly at the camera. Note: blue circles represent eyes. This is the condition without Pan, Tilt, or Roll.

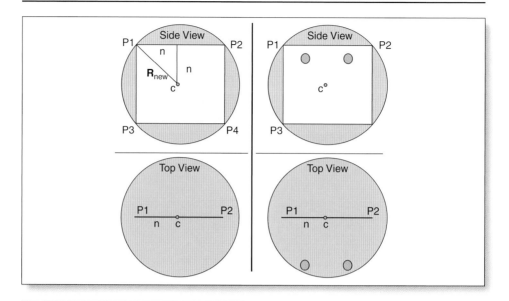

Figure A.18 Side and Top View of a Face Looking Directly at the Camera

Calculation of the Bounding Box for Pan

When the face pans, the chin is lifted upwards. We will see how the coordinates change when the face pans (see Figure A.19).

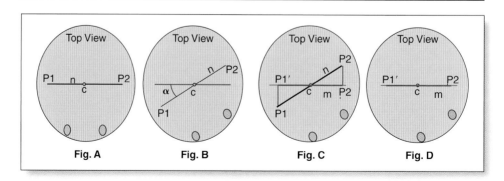

Figure A.19 Top View of the Face in Pan Position

The face is rotated along the y-axis and makes Pan angle α. The projected width of the frame is changed from $(2 \times n)$ to $(2 \times m)$; m can be calculated by the formula

$$m = n \times \cos(\boldsymbol{\alpha})$$

Displacement of the Bounding Box for Pan

To bind the eyes, we have to displace the bounding box. The displacement of the bounding box is $(c1 - c)$, as shown in Figure A.20.

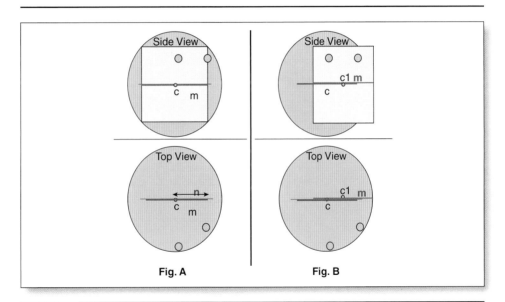

Figure A.20 Side and Top View of the Pan Scenario

This can be calculated by the formula

$$\Delta \mathbf{C}x = (c1 - c) = n \times \sin(\alpha)$$

since the displacement is only in X direction. This formula can be illustrated as follows. During the calculation of the intersection points Figure A.20b shows the face rotated at 88º along the y-axis. (We are not considering exact 90º, because the projection of line at 90º gives just a point.) To bind the eyes in the box, we have to move the box approximately by n. In Figure A20a, where rotation is 0°, we are not displacing the box. It means for the rotation range 0° to 90°, the displacement range is 0 to n. Hence the generic equation for displacement is:

$$\text{displacement} = n \times \sin(\alpha)$$

(See Figure A.21.)

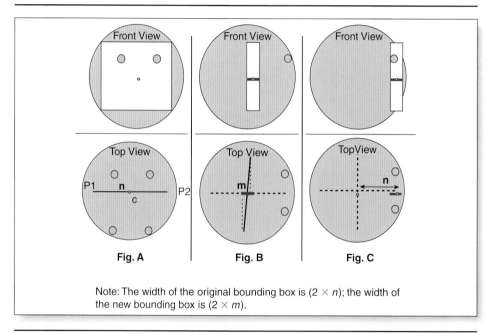

Note: The width of the original bounding box is $(2 \times n)$; the width of the new bounding box is $(2 \times m)$.

Figure A.21 Front and Top View of Face Rotation in the Pan Scenario

Calculation of the Bounding Box for Tilt

The face is rotated along the x-axis and makes Tilt angle β. The projected height of the frame is reduced from $(2 \times n)$ to $(2 \times t)$ where t can be calculated by the formula

$$t = n \times \cos(\beta)$$

To bind the eyes, we have to displace the bounding box. The displacement of the bounding box is $|c2 - c|$. This can be calculated by the formula

$$\Delta Cy = (c2 - c) = n \times \sin(\beta)$$

since the displacement is only in Y direction (see Figure A.22).

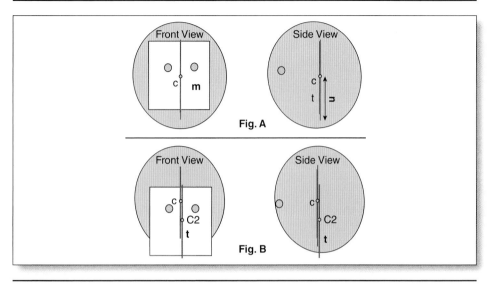

Figure A.22 Front and Side View for the Tilt Scenario

Combining the Effects of Pan and Tilt

For a face making Pan or Tilt or both (see Figure A.23), the new center of the bounding box can be calculated by the formula

$$\mathbf{C}\text{new-X} = \mathbf{C}x + \Delta\mathbf{C}x$$

$$\mathbf{C}\text{new-Y} = \mathbf{C}y + \Delta\mathbf{C}y$$

The sign conventions are already taken into consideration while deriving the formula for displacement.

The Effect of Roll on the Bounding Box

A face makes Roll angle, when it rotates along the z-axis. The boundary limit for Roll is ±15°, so that it should not lose the face features. While making Roll, the bounding box is equivalent to original bounding box; that is, when the face is looking directly at the camera. If a face makes Pan and Tilt and then

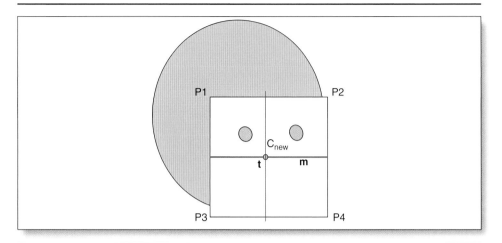

Figure A.23 The Pan and Tilt Scenarios in Combination

if it makes Roll, the bounding box gets affected only because of Pan and Tilt, whereas Roll does not affect the bounding box, but it checks the limit of Roll angle made by the face.

Roll Angle Limits

Roll angle limits are shown in Figure A.24.

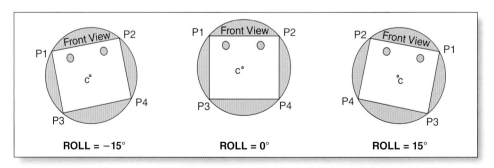

Figure A.24 Front View of the Roll Scenario

Occlusion Scenario

We will have to consider occlusion during the synthetic video generation. The occlusion can be caused by the face being blocked by another face or by an object. The detection of occlusion consists of various steps. We first have to find the intersection point of the face, then using the intersection point we find the center point.

Introduction to Intersection Points

If we consider a face at coordinates X, Y, Z in the FOV of camera, the projections of the face on the camera intersect the Zmin plane. This intersection gives the perceived size of the face as seen in Figure A.25. We can then calculate the new center point (C) coordinates of the perceived face. P1, P2, P3, and P4 are the four vertices of the rectangle that is encapsulated by the face. Refer to Figure A.26.

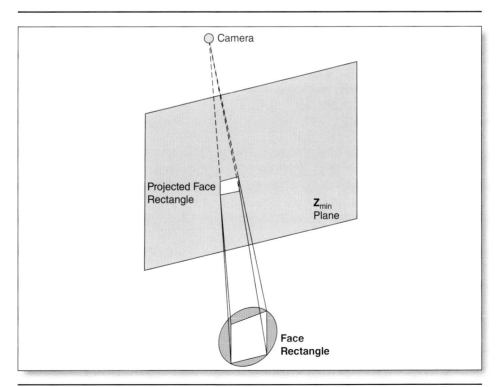

Figure A.25 Projections of the Face on the Camera in the Z Plane

Figure A.26 Rectangle Encapsulating the Face

Calculation of Center Point and Intersection Points

After the intersection points are calculated, we can calculate the center point. Refer the top view for X coordinate calculation. Let Cx be the X-coordinate of the perceived face at Zmin. By the symmetry, $Cx / Zmin = X / Z$, thus we get the Cx value (see Figure A.27).

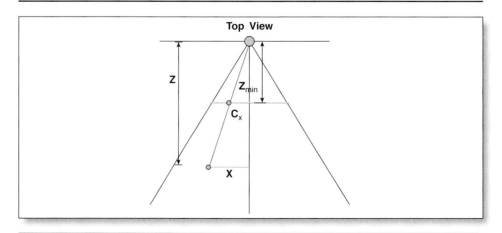

Figure A.27 Top View for X Coordinate Calculation

Refer to the side view for Y coordinate calculation (Figure A.28). Let Cy be the X coordinate of the perceived face at Zmin. By the symmetry, Cy / Zmin = Y / Z. We get the Cy value.

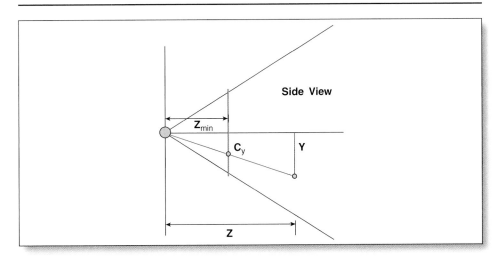

Figure A.28 Side View for Y Coordinate Calculation

Now we have the center (Cnew) coordinates (Cnew-x, Cnew-y). We know the values m and t. We can calculate the coordinates of P1, P2, P3, and P4 as follows:

$$P1x = \text{Cnew-}x + m$$

$$P1y = \text{Cnew-}y + t$$

(See Figure A.29.) Similar calculation can be done for remaining points.

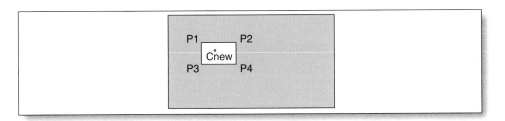

Figure A.29 Projection of Bounding Box at Zmin

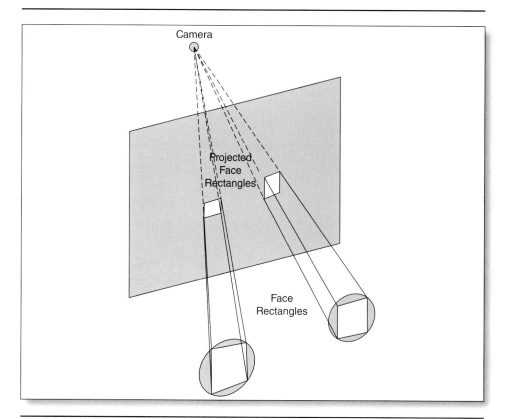

Figure A.30 Two Separate Faces, About to Show Occlusion

Occlusion Condition and Its Cases

In the scenario with two or more faces, draw the projections and calculate the four vertices of each of the rectangles on the Zmin plane as explained in the previous sections (see Figure A.30).

For occlusion to happen there should be intersection of these two rectangles. In Figure A.31, the two rectangles are not intersecting, so no occlusion.

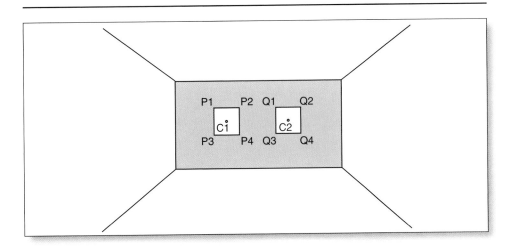

Figure A.31 Faces Getting Closer, About to Occlude

If there is intersection of the two rectangles, occlusion occurs, as shown in Figure A.32.

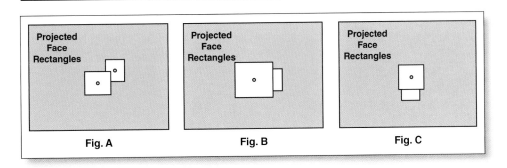

Figure A.32 Occlusion Occurs

For occlusion to happen, following condition (as shown in Figure A.33) should be true:

$$((P1x > Q1x > P2x) \;||\; (P1x > Q2x > P2x)) \;\&\&$$
$$((P1y > Q1y > P3y) \;||\; (P1y > Q3y > P3y))$$

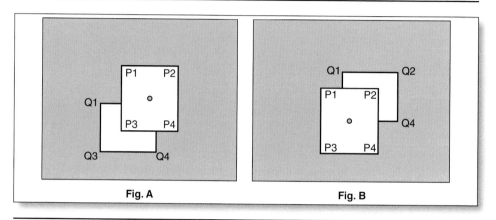

Figure A.33 Occlusion Condition

If the occlusion occurs, then the face having the greater value for the Z coordinate (far from the camera) will not be marked and lesser valued face (near to camera) will be marked.

References

Abdel-Hakim, Alaa E., Aly A. Farag. 2006. "CSIFT: A SIFT Descriptor with Color Invariant Characteristics." CVPR (2), pp. 1978–1983.

Achanta, Radhakrishna, Appu Shaji, Kevin Smith, Aurelien Lucchi, Pascal Fua, and Sabine Strunk. 2010. "SLIC Superpixels." EPFL Technical Report 149300 (June).

Ade, F. 1983. "Characterization of textures by 'Eigenfilters'" *Signal Processing*, 5:451–57.

Adelson, E. H., C. H. Anderson, J. R. Bergen, P. J. Burt, J. M. Ogden. 1984. "Pyramid methods in image processing." *RCA Engineer*, pp. 29–60 (Nov/Dec) (http://persci.mit.edu/pub_pdfs/RCA84.pdf).

Agrawal, R. and R. Srikant. 1994. "Fast algorithms for mining association rules." *Proc. Int. Conf. Very Large DataBase*, pp. 487–499, Santiago, Chile.

Agrawal, R. and R. Srikant. 1995. "Mining sequential patterns." 11th Int. Conf. Data Engineering, pp. 3–14, Taipei, Taiwan.

Agrawal, R., T. Imielinski, and A. Swami. 1993. "Mining Associations between Sets of Items in Massive Databases." *Proc. of the ACM-SIGMOD 1993 Int'l Conference on Management of Data*, Washington D.C. (May).

Aioanei, Stelu, Arati Kurani, and Dong-Hui Xu. 2002. "Texture Analysis for Computed Tomography Studies." DePaul University.

Akhter, S. and J. Roberts. 2006. *Multi-core Programming: Increasing Performance Through Software Multi-threading*. Hillsboro, OR: Intel Press.

Aldavert, David, Ramisan Arnau, Ramon Lopez de Mantara, and Ricardo Toledo. 2010. "Real-Time Object Segmentation Using a Bag of Features Approach." Computer Vision Center, Dept. Ciencies de la Computació, Universitat Autonòma de Barcelona, Catalunya, Spain.

Anand Lal Shimpi. 2011. "Intel's Ivy Bridge Architecture Exposed." Anandtech. http://www.anandtech.com/show/4830/intels-ivy-bridge-architecture-exposed/5.

Bajcsy, R.K. 1973. "Computer identification of visual surfaces." *Computer Graphics and Image Processing* (October).

Baker, Simon and Iain Matthews. 2003. "Lucas-Kanade 20 Years On: A Unifying Framework?" The Robotics Institute, Carnegie Mellon University.

Bay, Herbert, Andreas Ess, Tinne Tuytelaars, and Luc Van Gool. 2008. "Speeded-Up Robust Features (SURF)." *Computer Vision and Image Understanding* CVIU, vol. 110, pp. 346–359.

Belongie, S., J. Malik, and J. Puzicha. 2002. "Shape Matching and Object Recognition Using Shape Contexts." PAMI (April).

Bellotti, Victoria, and Abigail Sellen. 1993. "Design for privacy in ubiquitous computing environments." ECSCW'93.

Berns, Roy S., 2000. *Billmeyer and Saltzman's Principles of Color Technology*, 3rd Edition, John Wiley & Sons: New York.

Bradski, Gary and Adrian Kaeler. *Learning OpenCV: Computer Vision with the OpenCV Library.* 2008. O'Reilly Media: Sebastopol, CA.

Bram van Ginneken and Jan J. Koenderink. 1999. "Texture Histograms as a Function of Irradiation and Viewing Direction." International Journal of Computer Vision, vol. 31, no. 2–3, pp. 169–184.

Breiman, L. 1996. "Bagging Predictors." *Machine Learning*. 24. pp. 123–140.

Breiman, L., J. Frieman, .R. Olshen, and C. Stone. 1984. *Classification and Regression Trees*. Stamford, CT: Wadsworth International Group.

Canny, John. 1986. "A Computational Approach to Edge Detection." *IEEE Transactions on Pattern Analysis and Machine Intelligence*, vol. 8, no. 6 (November).

Cavoukian, Ann. 2010. "Privacy by Design: The 7 Foundational Principles." Stanford Law School.

Chandrasekhar, Vijay, Gabriel Takacs, David Chen, Sam Tsai, Radek Grzeszczuk, and Bernd Girod. 2009. CHoG: Compressed Histogram of Gradients A Low Bit-Rate Feature Descriptor" 2009 IEEE Conference on Computer Vision and Pattern Recognition.

Chow, C. K. and C. N. Liu. 1968. "Approximating Discrete Probability Distributions with Dependence Trees." *IEEE Trans. on Info. Theory* 14:462–467.

Chun-Rong Huang, Chu-Song Chen, and Pau-Choo Chung. 2008. "Contrast context histogram—An efficient discriminating local descriptor for object recognition and image matching." *Pattern Recognition,* vol. 41, no. 10 (October), pp. 3071–77.

Cohen, W. 1995. "Fast Efficient Rule Induction." ICML95.

Collett, Stacy. 2010. "5 indispensable IT skills of the future." *Computerworld* (August 23). http://www.computerworld.com/s/article/350908/5_Indispensable_IT_Skills_of_the_Future.

Comaniciu, D. and P. Meer. 2002. "Mean shift: a robust approach toward feature space analysis." PAMI, pp. 603–19.

Cossairt, O. 2011. "Tradeoffs and Limits in Computational Imaging." PhD thesis, Columbia University. Technical Report, Department of Computer Science, Columbia University CUCS-042-11 (September).

Cossairt, Oliver S., Daniel Miau, and Shree K. Nayar. 2011. "Gigapixel Computational Imaging" 2011 IEEE International Conference on Computational Photography (ICCP).

Cristianini N. and J. Shawe-Taylor. 2000. *An Introduction to Support Vector Machines and other kernel-based learning methods.* Cambridge: Cambridge University Press.

Dalal, Navneet. 2006. "Finding people in images and videos." PhD thesis, Institut National Polytechnique de Grenoble/INRIA Grenoble, (July).

Davis, L. S. 1979. "Computing the spatial structures of cellular texture." *Computer Graphics and Image Processing,* 11(2):111–22 (October).

Dorian, P. 1999. *Data Preparation for Data Mining.* San Francisco: Morgan Kaufmann Publishers.

Dougherty, J., R. Kohavi, and M. Sahami. 1995. "Supervised and unsupervised discretization of continuous features." A. Preiditis A. and S. Russel (eds). *Proceedings of 12th ICML,* Morgan Kaufmann publishers.

Duda, R. and P. Hart. 1973. *Pattern Classification and Scene Analysis.* New York: John Wiley & Sons.

Eichmann, G. and T. Kasparis. 1988. "Topologically invariant texture descriptors." *Computer Vision Graphics and Image Processing*, 41(3):267–81 (March).

Fairchild, M. D. 2005. *Color Appearance Models*, Second Edition, Wiley-IS&T Series in Imaging Science and Technology: Chichester, UK.

Fairchild, M. D. and G. M. Johnson. 2004. "The iCAM framework for image appearance, image differences, and image quality." *Journal of Electronic Imaging.*

Faraday, Michael. 1936. "Thoughts on Ray Vibrations." Experimental researches in chemistry and physics, Harvard library 1936 reprinted from the Philosophical Transactions and The Journal of the Royal Institution of 1821–1857.

Fayyad, U., G. Piatetsky-Shapiro, and P. Smyth. 1996. "Knowledge Discovery and Data Mining: Towards a Unifying Framework." Proc. of KDD-96. Menlo Park, CA: AAAI Press, pp. 82–88.

Felzenszwalb, Pedro F. and Daniel P. Huttenlocher. 2004. "Efficient Graph-Based Image Segmentation." IJCV.

Felzenszwalb, Pedro F., Ross B. Girshick, David McAllester, and Deva Ramanan. 2010. "Object Detection with Discriminatively Trained Part Based Models." *IEEE Transactions on Pattern Analysis and Machine Intelligence,* vol. 32, no. 9, pp. 1627–45.

Fife, Keith, Abbas El Gamal, H.-S. Philip Wong. 2006. "A 3D multi-aperture image sensor architecture." Custom Integrated Circuits Conference; IEEE.

Fleuret, F. 2004. "Fast Binary Feature Selection with Conditional Mutual Information." *Journal of Machine Learning Research.*

Friedman, N., D. Geiger, and M. Goldszmidt. 1997. "Bayesian Network Classifiers." *Machine Learning*, 29, pp. 131–163.

GeForce. n.d. http://uk.geforce.com/hardware/desktop-gpus/geforce-gtx-570/architecture.

Geiger, D. and D. Heckerman. 1996. "Knowledge representation and inference in similarity networks and Bayesian multinets." *Artificial Intelligence,* 82, pp. 45–74.

Gellman, Robert. 1997. "Does Privacy Law Work?" in Technology and Privacy: *The New Landscape*. Cambridge, MA: MIT Press.

Georgeiv, Todor, Ke Colin Zheng, Brian Curless, David Salesin, Shree Nayar, and Chintan Intwala. 2006. "Spatio-Angular Resolution Tradeoff in Integral Photography." Eurographics Symposium on Rendering.

Giles, Mike. n.d. (Lecture notes from Oxford University Mathematical Institute, Oxford e-Research Centre). http://p eople.maths.ox.ac. uk/gilesm/cuda/lecs/lec2-2x2.pdf.

Girshick, Ross. 2009. "Object Detection with Heuristic Coarse-to-Fine Search." Master's thesis, University of Chicago (May 29).

Gollan, B., B. Wally, and A. Ferscha. 2011. "Automatic Attention Estimation in an Interactive System based on Behaviour Analysis." *Proceedings of the 15th Portuguese Conference on Artificial Intelligence* (EPIA2011).

Gonzalez, Rafael C. and Richard Eugene Woods. 2007. *Digital Image Processing*, Third Edition. Prentice Hall: Upper Saddle River, NJ.

Grauman, Kristen and Trevor Darrell. 2005. "The Pyramid Match Kernel: Discriminative Classification with Sets of Image Features." *Tenth IEEE International Conference on Computer Vision*, vol. 2, pp. 1458–65.

Hadjidemetriou, E., M. D. Grossberg, and S. K. Nayar. 2004. "Multiresolution Histograms and their use for Recognition." *IEEE Transactions on Pattern Analysis and Machine Intelligence*, vol. 26, no. 7, pp. 831–847 (July).

Haja, Andreas, Bernd Jahne, and Steffen Abraham. 2008. "Localization Accuracy of Region Detectors." *IEEE Conference on Computer Vision and Pattern Recognition*, pp. 1–8.

Han J., J. Pei, and Y. Yin. 2000. "Mining Frequent Patterns without Candidate Generation." SIGMOD.

Han-Pang Chiu and Tomas Lozano-Perez. 2006. "Matching Interest Points Using Affine Invariant Concentric Circles" *18th International Conference on Pattern Recognition*, vol. 2, pp. 167–170.

Haralick, R. M., K Shanmugam, and Its'Hak Dinstein. 1973. "Textural Features for image Classification." *IEEE Transactions on Systems, Man and Cybernetics,* vol. SMC-3, no. 6 (November 1973), pp. 610–621.

Haralick, R., K. Shanmugam, and I. Dinstein. 1973. "Textural features for Image Classification." *IEEE Transactions on Systems, Man and Cybernetics* (November).

Haralick, Robert M. 1979. "Statistical and Structural Approaches to Texture." *Proceedings of the IEEE*, vol. 67, no. 5 (May).

Harris, C. and M. J. Stephens. 1988. "A combined corner and edge detector." *Alvey Vision Conference,* pp. 147–52.

Haykin, S. 2001. *Neural Networks—A Comprehensive Foundation* (Second Edition). Beijing: Tsinghua University Press.

Horn, B. K. P. and B. G. Schunck. 1980. "Determining optical flow." AI Memo 572. Massachusetts Institute of Technology.

Huang Chun-Rong, Chen Chu-Song, and Chung Pau-Choo. 2008. "Contrast context histogram—An efficient discriminating local descriptor for object recognition and image matching." Pattern Recognition, vol. 41, no. 10 (October), pp. 3071–77.

Jianbo Shi and Carlo Tomasi. 1994. *"Good Features to Track." IEEE Conference on Computer Vision and Pattern Recognition,* pp. 593–600.

Jiarong Hong. 1997. *Induction learning—algorithm, theory and application* (in Chinese). Science Press.

Jiawei Han and Micheline Kamber. 2006. *Data Mining: Concepts and Techniques,* 2d ed. San Francisco: Morgan Kaufmann Publishers.

Johnson, Norman L., Samuel Kotz, and N. Balakrishnan. 1995. *Continuous Univariate Distributions, Volume* 2 (2d ed., Section 27). Wiley Series in Probability and Statistics. New York: John Wiley & Sons.

Kadir, Timor and Michael Brady. 2001. "Scale, Saliency and Image Description." *International Journal of Computer Vision.* 45 (2):83–105 (November).

Kadir, Timor, Andrew Zisserman, and Michael Brady. 2004. "An Affine invariant salient region detector." *Lecture Notes in Computer Science*, Volume 3021/2004, 228–241. doi: 10.1007/978-3-540-24670-1_18.

Kaizer, H. 1955. "A Quantification of Textures on Aerial Photographs." Master's thesis, Boston University.

Kellokumpu, Vili, Guoying Zhao, and Matti Pietikänien. 2008. "Human Activity Recognition Using a Dynamic Texture Based Method." BMVC08.

Keyun Hu, Fengzhan Tian, and Houkuan Huang. 2008. *Data mining: theory and application* (in Chinese). Tsinghua University Press and Beijing Jiaotong University Press (April).

Kirk, D. and W. Hwu. 2010. *Programming Massively Parallel Processors: A Hands-On Approach*. Burlington, MA: Morgan Kauffman.

Klein, Georg and David Murray. 2007. "Parallel Tracking and Mapping for Small AR Workspaces." 6th IEEE and ACM International Symposium on Mixed and Augmented Reality.

Kohavi, R. and G. H. John. 1997. "Wrappers for feature subset selection." *Artificial Intelligence,* 97(1–2):273–324.

Kourosh Khoshelham * and Sander Oude Elberink, "Accuracy and Resolution of Kinect Depth Data for Indoor Mapping Applications", Sensors Journal 2012.

Koutsojannis, Constantinos, Eman Nabil, Maria Tsimara, and Ioannis Hatzilygeroudis. 2009. "Using Machine Learning Techniques to Improve the Behaviour of a Medical Decision Support System for Prostate Diseases." ISDA.

Kodratoff. "The comprehensibility Manifesto." 1994. *AI Communications*, Vol. 7, No. 2, pp. 83–85. doi: 10.3233/AIC-1994-7201 Vo1 7.

Kreinin, Yossi. 2011. "SIMD < SIMT < SMT: parallelism in NVIDIA GPUs." (Blog post on November 10) http://www.yosefk.com/blog/simd-simt-smt-parallelism-in-nvidia-gpus.html.

Krig, Scott A. 1993. "Object-Oriented Imaging." *Advanced Imaging Magazine* (November).

Krig, Scott A. 1994. "Image Texture Analysis using Spatial Dependency Matrices." Krig Research White Paper Series (October).

Krig, Scott A. 1995. "Volume Rendering in the Picture Center environment." (January) Technical White Paper Series.

Kuthirummal, S. a..5nd S. K. Nayar. 2006. "Multiview Radial Catadioptric Imaging for Scene Capture." *ACM Trans. on Graphics* (also Proc. of ACM SIGGRAPH) (July).

Kuthirummal, S. and S. K. Nayar. July 2006. "Multiview Radial Catadioptric Imaging for Scene Capture." ACM Trans. on Graphics (also Proc. of ACM SIGGRAPH).

Lam, S. W. C. and H. H. S. Ip. 1994. "Structural texture segmentation using irregular pyramid." *Pattern Recognition Letters,* 15(7):691–98 (July).

Lam, Stephen W. C. and Horace Ho-Shing Ip. 1993. "Adaptive Pyramid Approach to Texture Segmentation." CAIP '93 Proceedings of the 5th International Conference on Computer Analysis of Images and Patterns, pp. 267–274.

Laws, K. I. 1979. "Texture energy measures." In Proc. Image Understanding Workshop (November), pp. 47–51.

Laws, K. I. 1980b. Textured Image Segmentation. PhD thesis, University of Southern California.

Laws, K. I. Rapid texture identification. 1980a. SPIE, 238:376–80.

Lee, K. L. and L. H. Chen. 2002. "A New Method for Coarse Classification of Textures and Class Weight Estimation for Texture Retrieval." *Pattern Recognition and Image Analysis,* vol. 12, no. 4, pp. 400–10.

V. Lepetit and P. Fua, Keypoint Recognition using Randomized Trees. IEEE Transactions on Pattern Analysis and Machine Intelligence, Vol. 28, Nr. 9 2006

Lepetit, Vincent and Pascal Fua. 2004. "Towards Recognizing Feature Points using Classification Trees." Swiss Federal Institute of Technology (EPFL) Technical Report IC/2004/74.

Levinshtein, A., A. Stere, K. Kutulakos, D. Fleet, S. Dickinson, and K. Siddiqi. 2009. "Turbopixels: Fast superpixels using geometric flows." PAMI.

Levy, Marc 1992. "Volume Rendering using the Foutier Projection Slice Theorum." Technical Report: CSL-TR-92-521 (April), Computer Systems Laboratory, Stanford University.

Liu, H. and R. Setiono. 1995. "Chi2: Feature selection and discretization of numeric attributes." *Proceedings of 7th IEEE Int. Conf. on Tools with Artificial Intelligence.*

Lowe, David G. 2004. "Distinctive Image Features from Scale Invariant Features." *International Journal of Computer Vision,* vol. 60, no. 2, pp. 91–110.

Lowe, David G. 1999. "Object Recognition from Local Scale-Invariant Features." *The Proceedings of the Seventh IEEE International Conference on Computer Vision,* vol. 2, pp. 1150–57.

Lucas, Bruce D. and Takeo Kanade. 1981. "An Iterative Image Registration Technique with an Application to Stereo Vision." International Joint Conference on Artificial Intelligence, pp. 674–79.

Matas, J., O. Chum, M. Urba, and T. Pajdla. 2002. "Robust wide baseline stereo from maximally stable extremal regions." *Proc. of British Machine Vision Conference, pp. 384–396.*

McCallister, Erika, Tim Grance, and Karen Scarfone. 2010. "Guide to Protecting the Confidentiality of Personally Identifiable Information (PII)." National Institute of Standards and Technology (April).

Mehta, M., R. Agrawal, and J. Rissanen. 1996. "SLIQ: A fast scalable classifier for data mining." Proc. 1996 intl. Conf. on Extending Database Technology (EDBT'96). Avignon, France.

Mikolajczyk, K., T. Tuytelaars, C. Schmid, A. Zisserman, J. Matas, F. Schaffalitzky, and T. Kadir, L. Van Gool. 2006. "A Comparison of Affine Region Detectors" IJCV.

Mikolajczyk, Krystian and Cordelia Schmid. 2004. "Scale & Affine Invariant Interest Point Detectors." *International Journal of Computer Vision,* vol. 60, no. 1, 63–86, doi: 10.1023/B:VISI.0000027790.02288.f2.

Mikolajczyk, Krystian and Cordelia Schmid. 2005. "A performance evaluation of local descriptors." PAMI.

Mitchell, Tom M. 1997. "Machine Learning." *McGraw-Hill Science/ Engineering/Math* (March), pp. 112–140.

Muja, Marius, and David G. Lowe. 2009. "Fast Approximate Nearest Neighbors with Automatic Algorithm Configuration." *International Conference on Computer Vision Theory and Application (VISSAPP'09)*, pp. 331–340.

Murthy, S. K. 1998. "Automatic Construction of Decision Trees from Data: A Multi-Disciplinary Survey." *Data Mining and Knowledge Discovery*, vol. 2, no. 4.

Nayar, Shree K. 2011. "Computational Cameras: Approaches, Benefits and Limits." Columbia University, Technical Report No. CUCS-001-11 (January 15).

Newcombe, Richard A., Shahram Izadi, Otmar Hilliges, David Molyneaux, David Kim, Andrew J. Davison, Pushmeet Kohli, Jamie Shotton, Steve Hodges, and Andrew Fitzgibbon. 2011. "KinectFusion: Real-Time Dense Surface Mapping and Tracking." IEEE International Symposium on Mixed and Augmented Reality.

Newcombe, Richard A., Steven J. Lovegrove, and Andrew J. Davison. 2011. "DTAM: Dense Tracking and Mapping in Real-Time." 2011 IEEE International Conference on Computer Vision (ICCV), pp. 2320–7.

Nister, David and Henrik Stewenius. 2006. "Scalable Recognition with a Vocabulary Tree." *CVPR '06 Proceedings of the 2006 IEEE Computer Society Conference on Computer Vision and Pattern Recognition*, 2:2161–2168. doi: 10.1109/CVPR.2006.264.

NIST. 2010. "Guide to protecting the Confidentiality of Personally Identifiable Information (PII)". Special Publication 800-122.

Ojala, T., M. Pietikäinen, and D. Hardwood D. 1994. "Performance evaluation of texture measures with classification based on Kullback discrimination of distributions." *Proc. International conference on Pattern Recognition.*

Ojala, T., M. Pietikäinen, and D. Hardwood D. 1996. "A comparative study of texture measures with classification based on feature distributions," *Pattern Recognition*, vol. 29.

Oliva, Aude. 2001. "Modeling the Shape of the Scene: A Holistic Representation of the Spatial Envelope." IJCV.

Özuysal, Mustafa, Michael Calonder, Vincent Lepetit, and Pascal Fua. 2010. "Fast Keypoint Recognition using Random Ferns." IEEE Transactions on Pattern Analysis and Machine Intelligence, vol. 32, no. 3, pp. 448–461.

Özuysal, Mustafa, Pascal Fua, and Vincent Lepetit. 2007. "Fast Keypoint Recognition in Ten Lines of Code." IEEE Conference on Computer Vision and Pattern Recognition.

Pagès, J. and J. Salvi. 2005. "Coded light projection techniques for 3D reconstruction." Institute of Informatics and Applications, University of Girona, Spain. *J3eA, Journal sur l'enseignement des sciences et technologies de l'information et des systèmes,* vol. 4, Hors-Série 3, 1. doi: 10.1051/2005801.

Pawlak, Z. 1991. *Rough sets: Theoretical Aspects of Reasoning about Data.* Dordrecht: Kluwer Academic Publishers.

Perronnin, F., Yan Liu, J. Sánchez, and H. Poirier. 2010. "Large-Scale Image Retrieval with Compressed Fisher Vectors." 2010 IEEE Conference on Computer Vision and Pattern Recognition (CVPR).

Pietikäinen Matti and Janne Heikkilä. 2011. "Image and Video Description with Local Binary Pattern Variants." Tutorial CVPR (June 24). Machine Vision Group, University of Oulu, Finland.

Pietikäinen, M., A. Hadid, G. Zhao, T. Ahonen. 2011. *Computer Vision Using Binary Patterns. Series: Computational Imaging and Vision*, vol. 40. New York: Springer

Pietikäinen, M., A. Hadid, G. Zhao, T. Ahonen. 2011. *Computer Vision Using Binary Patterns. Series: Computational Imaging and Vision*, vol. 40. New York: Springer.

Poh, M. Z., D. J. McDuff, and R. W. Picard. 2011. "A Medical Mirror for Noncontact Health Monitoring." ACM SIGGRAPH Emerging Technologies (August).

Pratt, William K. 2007. *Digital Image Processing: PIKS Scientific Inside*, Fourth Edition. John Wiley & Sons: New York.

Proesmans, M., L. Van Gool, E. Pauwels, and A. Oosterlinck. 1984. "Determination of optical flow and its Discontinuities using non-linear diffusion." In 3rd European Conference on Computer Vision, ECCV'94, vol. 2, pp. 295–304.

Pun, C. M. and M.C. Lee. 2003. "Log-polar wavelet energy signatures for rotation and scale invariant texture classification." *IEEE Trans. Pattern Analysis and Machine Intelligence,* 25(5):590–03 (May).

Quinlan, J. R. 1993. *C4.5: Programs for Machine Learning*. San Francisco: Morgan Kaufmann Publishers.

Raja, Yogesh and Shaogang Gong. 2006. "Sparse Multiscale Local Binary Patterns." BMVC 2006.

Roth, Gerhard. 2008. "Homography." (Course notes: http://people.scs.carleton.ca/~c_shu/Courses/comp4900d/notes/homography.pdf).

Rublee, Ethan, Vincent Rabaud, Kurt Konolige, and Gary Bradski. 2011. "ORB: An efficient alternative to SIFT or SURF." 2011 International Conference on Computer Vision. doi: 10.1109/ICCV.2011.6126544.

Russ, John C. 2011. *The Image Processing Handbook*, Sixth Edition. CRC Press: Boca Raton, FL.

Salsman, Kenneth. October 4, 2010. "3D vision for computer based applications." Director New Technology, Aptina, Inc.

Samarjiva, Rohan. 1991. *Interactivity as Though Privacy Mattered*. Cambridge, MA: MIT Press.

Schapire, R. E. and Y. Singer. 1998. "Improved boosting algorithms using confidence-rated predictions." *Proceedings of the Eleventh Annual Conference on Computational Learning Theory.*

Shankar, M, R. Willett, N. Pitsianis, T. Schulz, R. Gibbons, R. Te Kolste, J. Carriere, C. Chen, D. Prather, and D. Brady. 2008. "Thin infrared imaging systems through multichannel sampling." Applied Optics (April 1).

Shearer, Colin. 2000. "The CRISP-DM model: the new blueprint for data mining." *Journal of Data Warehousing*, vol. 5, no. 4, pp. 13–22.

Shi, J. and C. Tomasi. 2004. "Good Features to Track." *9th IEEE Conference on Computer Vision and Pattern Recognition*. Springer.

Shi, J. and J. Malik. 2000. "Normalized cuts and image segmentation." PAMI.

Shu Liao and Albert C. S. Chung. 2008 "Texture Classification by Using Advanced Local Binary Patterns and Spatial Distribution of Dominant Patterns." Hong Kong University of Science and Technology.

Siagian, Christian and Laurent Itti. 2007. "Rapid Biologically-Inspired Scene Classification Using Features Shared with Visual Attention." PAMI.

Smith, Joshua Reynolds. 1999. "Electric Field Imaging." PhD thesis, Massachusetts Institute of Technology (February).

Spence, A., M. Robb, M. Timmins, and M. Chantler. 2003. "Real-time per-pixel rendering of textiles for virtual textile catalogues." In Proc. INTEDEC, Edinburgh, 22–4 (September).

Szeliski, R. 2011. *Computer Vision: Algorithms and Applications.* New York: Springer.

Takacs Gabriel, Chandrasekhar Vijay, Tsai Sam, Chen David, Grzeszczu Radek and Girod Bernd. 2010. " Unified Real-Time Tracking and Recognition with Rotation-Invariant Fast Features. CVPR.

Tola, Engin, Vincent Lepetit, and Pascal Fua. 2010. "An Efficient Dense Descriptor Applied to Wide-Baseline Stereo." PAMI.

Tomasi, Carlo and Takeo Kanade. 1991. "Detection and Tracking of Point Features." Carnegie Mellon University Technical Report CMU-CS-91-132 (April).

Vedaldi, A. and S. Soatto. 2008. "Quick shift and kernel methods for mode seeking." ECCV.

Vincent, Luc and Pierre Soille. 1991. "Watersheds in digital spaces: An efficient algorithm based on immersion simulations." PAMI, vol. 13, no. 6, (June) pp. 583–98.

Viola, Paul and Michael J. Jones. 2004. "Robust Real-Time Face Detection." *International Journal of Computer Vision,* 57(2), pp. 137–154.

Viola, Paul and Michael Jones. 2001. "Robust Real-time Object Detection." Second International Workshop On Statistical and Computational Theories of Vision—Modeling, Learning, Computing, and Sampling (Vancouver, Canada, July 13).

Wang, Albert, Patrick Gill, and Alyosha Molnar. 2009. "Light field image sensors based on the Talbot effect." *Applied Optics*, vol. 48, no. 31, pp. 5897–905.

Wernick, M. N., Y. Yang, J. G. Brankov, G. Yourganov, and S. C. Strother. 2010. "Machine Learning in Medical Imaging." Invited Review Paper: *IEEE Sig. Proc.*

Wikipedia. 2012. http://en.wikipedia.org/wiki/Optical_flow.

Wilburn, B., N. Joshi, V. Vaish, et al. 2005. "High Performance Imaging Using Large Camera Arrays." Proc. SIGGRAPH.

Zhao, Guoying and Matti Pietikäinen. 2007. "Dynamic Texture Recognition Using Local Binary Patterns with an Application to Facial Expressions." *IEEE Transactions on Pattern Analysis and Machine Intelligence.*

Index

Note: Page numbers followed by *f* and *t* indicate figures and tables respectively.

A

AAAI. *see* American Association for Artificial Intelligence (AAAI)
accuracy, real-world intelligent systems and, 10
accuracy model, 392–396
    method of calculating accuracy, 393–394
AdaBoost training algorithm, 21, 104, 107–110, 117, 205–206
adaptive local thresholding, 53, 53*t*, 53*f*
adaptive morphology methods, 49, 50*f*
additive perturbation, in randomization method, 227
Adobe RGB color space, 26, 26*f*
advertiser input scheduler, CMS, 260, 261*f*
advertising
    agency, 246
    aggregator, 245
    category model, IAF, 249
    digital signage in, 3–4, 4*f*
    list generator, CMS, 259–260, 260*f*, 262
    model learning, 275–276
    models creation, 290–303
        advertising rule deployment and selection, 300–303, 300*f*, 301*t*–303*t*
        algorithm selection and orchestration, 290–292, 291*t*–292*t*
        sample advertising models, 297–299, 298*t*–299*t*, 297*f*
        training and retraining process, 292–297
    new attribute derivation and, 233
    refresh, CMS, 262
    selection based on models, 282–283, 282*t*, 283*t*
        for context-based targeting, 283
        for prediction-based targeting, 283, 283*t*
        for seeing-based targeting, 282–283, 282*t*
advertising rules
    deployment and selection, 300–303, 300*f*, 301*t*–303*t*
    example, 280–282
        context-based targeting rules, 282
        prediction-based targeting rules, 281
        seeing-based targeting rules, 280
agglomerative hierarchical clustering method, 215–217, 215*f*. *see also* clustering methods
Agrawal, R., 222
algorithm quasi-optimal (AQ) rule induction method, 186–188, 187*t*
algorithm selection and orchestration, 290–292, 291*t*–292*t*
ALU. *see* arithmetic logic unit (ALU)
American Association for Artificial Intelligence (AAAI), 176
analysis of variance (ANOVA)
    healthcare studies and, 331
analytic server, 245
ANN. *see* artificial neural network (ANN)
anonymization, for privacy-preserving data mining, 225–226, 226*f*

anonymous video analytics (AVA), 241, 274
  targeted advertising process, 274, 275
ANOVA. *see* analysis of variance (ANOVA)
Apriori algorithm, 222–223
AQ. *see* algorithm quasi-optimal (AQ) rule
    induction method
AR. *see* augmented reality (AR)
architecture, IAF, 242–247, 242*f*, 247*f*, 244*f*
  content management system (CMS), 243
  data mining module (DMM), 242
  data ownership, 243–246, 244*f*
  digital player (DP), 243
  digital signage, 242
  real time triggering, 246, 247*f*
  targeted advertising, 246
area operations, image preprocessing and, 39
arithmetic logic unit (ALU), 344
artificial intelligence (AI), 1
  devices, industries and, 2–6
    digital signage, 3–4, 4*f*
    home energy management, 6
    intelligent medical devices, 6
    retail intelligence, 5–6, 5*f*
  real-world deployments (*see* real-world
      intelligent systems)
  technologies for enabling, 2, 2*t*
artificial neural network (ANN), 182–186, 183*f*
  BP, 184, 185
  FNN, 182, 184–185
  usage of trained, 183–184
aspect ratio, of positive bounding boxes, 139
association rules, 218–225
  basic concepts, 219–222, 219*t*–222*t*
  learning, 248
  mining, 222–224
    Apriori algorithm, 222–223
    FP-growth algorithm, 223–224
attribute reduction, rough set generation for,
    197–199, 198*t*, 199*t*
audience targeting methods, 278–279
  context-based targeting, 279
  prediction-based targeting, 278
  seeing-based targeting, 278
augmented reality (AR), 62
autocorrelation, 60

auto-thresholding methods, 51, 51*t*–52*t*, 52*f*
AVA. *see* anonymous video analytics (AVA)

B

back propagation (BP) algorithm, 184, 185
  learning rate, 186
  number of nodes in hidden layer, 185–186
backward regression, 210
bagging, ensemble classifier and, 204–206
balanced iterative reducing and clustering using
    hierarchies (BIRCH) algorithm, 216
BAN. *see* Bayesian network augmented Naïve Bayes
    (BAN) classifier
base classifier, 204
Bayesian classifiers, 193–197, 194*f*
  BAN, 196, 194*f*
  BMN, 196, 196*f*
  GBN, 196*f*, 197
  NB, 194–195, 194*f*
  TAN, 195–196, 194*f*
Bayesian models, 332
Bayesian multi-net (BMN) classifier, 196, 196*f*
Bayesian network augmented Naïve Bayes (BAN)
    classifier, 196, 194*f*
benchmarking, 10
BHIM. *see* binary histogram intersection
    minimization (BHIM)
big data, 328
binary class training data, 186–187, 187*t*
binary histogram intersection minimization
    (BHIM), 21
binary morphology, 47
  adaptive auto-threshold for, 49, 50*f*
  operations, 47–49
  overview, 47, 48*f*
binary region mask, 47
binocular imaging, 31
BIRCH. *see* balanced iterative reducing and
    clustering using hierarchies (BIRCH)
    algorithm
block of cells, overlapping
  normalize contrast in, 132–133, 132*f*
BMN. *see* Bayesian multi-net (BMN) classifier
boosting, ensemble classifier and, 204–206
border, rough set and, 197

bounding boxes
  calculation, synthetic video generation,
      421–432, 422*f*
    center point, 428–429
    combining effects of pan and tilt, 425, 426*f*
    effect of roll on, 425–426
    intersection points, 427–429, 427*f*, 428*f*
    occlusion and, 427, 430*f*–432*f*, 430–432
    for pan, 422–424, 422*f*–424*f*
    roll angle limits, 426, 426*f*
    for tilt, 424–425, 425*f*
  positive, aspect ratio of, 143
BP. *see* back propagation (BP) algorithm
BRIEF, 92, 93*f*, 97*t*
BRISK, 92, 97*t*
BrowseModelContent, DMM, 257

C

cache architecture, 344–345, 344*f*
CAdRefreshInterface, CMS, 265
CAdvertiserInputInterface
  CMS, 265
  DP, 273
CAIMSuiteInterface, DP, 273
calibration method, 24
Calpella platform, 145, 146, 147
Canny detector, 70
cascade, 366, 366*f*
CCD. *see* charge-coupled device (CCD) cells
CCH. *see* contrast context histogram (CCH)
CCMSAdListGenerator, CMS, 263
CCMSAdvertiserInputScheduler, CMS, 263
CCMSInterface, DP, 273
CCMSModelExtractor, CMS, 263
CCMSPlayerSpecificModelExtractor, CMS, 263
CCMSTentativePlayListGenerator, CMS, 263
CCMSTimer, CMS, 263
CDisplay, DP, 273
CDMMModuleInterface, CMS, 263
CDPInterface, CMS, 265
CDPModelAnalyzer, DP, 271, 273
CDPOffline, DP, 273
CDPOnline, DP, 273
CDPScheduler, DP, 273
CDPTentativePlayListGenerator, DP, 273

CDPTimer, DP, 270–271
CDPVADataAnalyzer, DP, 271
cells
  defined, 131
  orientation bins and, 131, 131*f*, 132*f*
center point, calculation, 428–429
central processing unit (CPU), 338
  CPU-GPU combined optimization, 389–392
  data transfer between GPU and, 363–364
  optimization with Intel® TBB, 380–389, 383*f*,
      385*f*–388*f*
  performance, 396–397, 400*f*
  thread interaction between GPU and, 390
chain code histograms, 96*t*
chameleon algorithm, 216
charge-coupled device (CCD) cells, 23
CI. *see* conditional independence (CI) assumption
classification, DMM, 248
cloud-based data mining, 245
  services, 238–240
    compute cloud, 240
    create new model service, 240
    DaaS, 239
    data management cloud, 240
    IaaS, 239, 240
    overview, 238–239
    PaaS, 239
    query model content service, 240
    retrain existing model service, 240
    SaaS, 238–239
    storage cloud, 240
    Systems management as a Service, 239
clustering methods, 211–218, 333
  density-based (*see* density-based clustering
      methods)
  DMM, 248
  hierarchical (*see* hierarchical clustering methods)
  outlier analysis, 218–219
  partitioning method, 212–214
clustering using representatives (CURE) algorithm,
    216
cluster ordering, 217
CMI. *see* conditional mutual information (CMI)
CMIM. *see* conditional mutual information
    maximization (CMIM)

CMOS cells, 23
CMS. *see* content management system (CMS)
Collett, Stacy, 175
color
    de-mosaicing, 27–29, 27*f*, 28*f*, 29*f*
    morphology, 49
    segmentation, 56
comma-separated values (CSV), 118
compiler, data ownership and, 243
computational imaging, 29–39
compute cloud, 240
computer vision, 2, 9, 10
    advertising, 3
    fundamental visual metrics for (*see* visual metrics, for computer vision)
    home energy management, 6
    medical devices and, 6
    in retail industry, 5
condensation, in privacy-preserving data mining, 227
conditional independence (CI) assumption, 194, 195, 196, 197
conditional mutual information (CMI), 195
conditional mutual information maximization (CMIM), 21
confusion matrix, 173, 173*f*
constant memory, 353
Consultant, 335
consumer, data ownership and, 243
content management system (CMS), 245, 246, 257–265, 258*f*–262*f*, 264*f*
    class, 263–265, 264*f*
    data flow, 261–262, 262*f*
    functionality of
        advertising list generator, 259–260, 260*f*
        model extractor, 259, 259*f*
        player-specific model extractor, 258, 258*f*
        tentative playlist generator and advertiser input scheduler, 260, 261*f*
context-based targeting, 279
    advertising selection for, 283
    rules, 282
contingency table, 173, 173*f*
contrast context histogram (CCH), 98*t*

co-occurrence matrices, as texture metrics, 63–65, 63*f*, 64*f*, 65*f*
correlation, digital, 77
CPoPInterface, CMS, 263
CPreference, DP, 273
CPU. *see* central processing unit (CPU)
CPU-GPU combined optimization, 389–392
The Creative Destruction of Medicine: How the Digital Revolution Will Create Better Health Care, 328–329
creator, data ownership and, 243
CRISP-DM. *see* cross-industry standard process for data mining (CRISP-DM) process model
cross-correlation, 60
cross-industry standard process for data mining (CRISP-DM) process model, 228–229, 230*f*
cross-selling and bundle sales, KDD application, 179
cross-validation, 236
C45rules, rule induction method, 188
cryptographic techniques, in privacy-preserving data mining, 227–228
CSQLServerDBInterface, CMS, 263
CSV. *see* comma-separated values (CSV)
CURE. *see* clustering using representatives (CURE) algorithm
CureTogether, 329
customer, KDD application
    churn prediction, 178
    segmentation, 178
    value analysis, 179
cut set, defined, 197
CvCalcopticalFlowLk function, 384
cvIntegral function, 376–380, 379*f*
cvResize function, 376, 377*f*, 378*f*

D

DaaS. *see* Desktop as a Service (DaaS)
Daisy descriptor, 93, 93*f*, 96*t*
data
    analysis module, 313*f*, 311–312
    anonymizing, 313, 314*f*, 315*f*
    capture module, 309–311, 309*f*
    collection and preparation, training (*see* training)
    connector

advertising model learning, 275–276
DMM, 250, 252
management cloud, 240
ownership, IAF architecture, 243–246, 244f
claiming data, 243–245
preparation, 231–233
data scope determination, 233
discretization, 233
feature selection, 232–233
new attribute derivation, 233
preprocessor
advertising model learning, 275–276
DMM, 250, 252
transfer, 363–364
between CPUs and GPUs, 363–364,
389–390
unsecured sensor, 311
understanding, 231–232, 230t
basic, 231
data quality analysis, 232
relevant attributes, 231
data mining, 2, 10, 175–240, 330
algorithms, 179–225, 234–235, 234t
ANN (see artificial neural network (ANN))
association rules (see association rules)
Bayesian classifiers (see Bayesian classifiers)
characteristics of, 234t
classification and prediction, 180–207
clustering (see clustering methods)
decision tree in (see decision tree)
ensemble classifier (see ensemble classifier)
KNN classifier, 201–203, 202f
regression for (see regression, for data mining)
rough set theory (see rough set theory)
rule induction method (see rule induction
method)
sequential rules, 224–225, 224t
SVM (see support vector machine (SVM))
technical evaluation, 236–237
tool selection, 234–235
approaches, privacy-preserving (see privacy-
preserving data mining)
cloud-based, services infrastructure (see cloud-
based data mining, services)
hard negative examples, 143–145, 144f

KDD (see knowledge discovery and data mining
(KDD))
overview, 175–179, 176t
process, 228–238, 235–236
business objective and requirement, 229
business understanding, 229–231
CRISP-DM process model, 228, 230f
data understanding and preparation,
231–233, 232t
deployment and integration, 237
inputs filtering, 235
modeling and evaluation, 233–237, 234t
model update and maintenance, 240
parameter calibration, 235, 236t
problem definition, 229–230
research method, 231
for targeted advertising, 277–283
audience targeting methods (see audience
targeting methods)
dominant passer prediction model, 280, 280t
multiple advertising model training, 277–278
passer distribution prediction model, 280
rules, example, 280–282
selection based on models, 282–283, 282t, 283t
weighted audience counting, 279–280, 280t
Data Mining eXtension (DMX), 237
DataMiningModule, DMM, 255
data mining module (DMM), 242, 245
class, 248, 255–257, 256f
association rule learning, 248
classification, 248
clustering, 248 (see also clustering methods)
regression analysis, 248
data flow, 253, 255f
functionality of, 250–253, 251f, 253f–254f
create new model process, 250–252, 251f
query model content process, 252
retrain existing model process, 252, 254f
daughter wavelets, 80
DBSCAN. see density-based spatial clustering of
applications with noise (DBSCAN) algorithm
decision tree, in data mining algorithm, 180–182
cost matrix, 182
extension of, 181–182
learning from training dataset, 181

mass dataset, 182
with multivariable partition, 181–182
use, 180, 180f
decoder, data ownership and, 244
DefineDMModels, DMM, 257
demographics recognition, 275
de-mosaicing, color, 27–29, 27f, 28f, 29f
dense tracking and mapping (DTAM)
method, 62
density-based clustering methods, 216–218. *see also*
clustering methods
cluster ordering, 217
DBSCAN algorithm, 217, 218f
OPTICS algorithm, 217
density-based spatial clustering of applications with
noise (DBSCAN) algorithm, 217, 218f
deployment
in data mining, 237
stage, privacy safe systems, 315–316
depth sensing, 3D
sensor and optics for (*see* 3D depth sensing)
design stage, privacy safe systems, 312–313
Desktop as a Service (DaaS), 239
DetectFaces_OCL, 373–374, 373f, 375f
devices, intelligent
industries and, 2–6
digital signage, 3–4, 4f
home energy management, 6
intelligent medical devices, 6
retail intelligence, 5–6, 5f
DFA. *see* discriminate function analysis (DFA)
difference of Gaussians (DoG), 73, 88–89, 90f
diffraction gratings, 31–32, 32f
digital correlation, 77, 77f
digital player (DP), 243
class, 269–273, 272f
data flow, 269, 271f
functionality
model analyzer, 265–266, 267f
tentative playlist generator, 266, 268f
VA data analyzer, 265, 266f
operating modes
DP offline mode, 268–269, 270f
DP online mode, 267–268, 269f
digital sign, 245
digital signage, 3–4, 4f, 242

dilation, in binary morphology, 47, 48, 48f
discernibility matrix, for training cases, 198–201,
199t, 200t
discretization, data preparation and, 233
discriminate function analysis (DFA)
healthcare studies and, 331
distributed accumulator, 358–359, 358f
divisive hierarchical clustering method, 215, 215f
DMMAdCategory, DMM, 255, 257
DMMPasserPrediction, DMM, 257
DMX. *see* Data Mining eXtension (DMX)
DoG. *see* difference of Gaussians (DoG)
DoH. *see* Hessian matrix interest point
detector (DoH)
dominant passer prediction model, 280, 280t
dominant passer prediction rule, 281
downgrading application effectiveness
in privacy-preserving data mining, 227
DP. *see* digital player (DP)
DT. *see* dynamic textures (DT)
DTAM. *see* dense tracking and mapping (DTAM)
method
dynamic pattern recognition. *see* predictive
modeling
dynamic programming, 138
dynamic textures (DT), 62–63

E

early warnings, KDD application, 179
EBR. *see* edge-based region methods (EBR)
edge-based region methods (EBR), 69
eigenfilters, 60
Einstein, Albert, 1
electronic medical records (EMR), 320, 328, 334
EMR. *see* electronic medical records (EMR)
ensemble classifier, 203–207, 204f
AdaBoost algorithm, 207–208
bagging and boosting, 204–206
base classifier, 204
random forest algorithm, 204, 206–207
enterprise, data ownership and, 244
Erdos, Paul, 175
erosion, in binary morphology, 47, 48
extraneous data, inadvertent capture of, 310
eye light sensitivity, 27–29, 27f, 28f, 29f

F

face classifier, training
   Viola-Jones algorithm, 104–118
      example face images, 105–106, 106*f*
      Haar features, 106–110, 107*f,* 109*f*
      online resources, 105*t*
      unaligned face images and, 105–106, 106*f*
face detection, 103–124, 274
   frontal, Viola Jones and (*see* frontal face
      detection)
   human, 274
   measuring accuracy of, 118–123
      accuracy metrics, 120–123
      false negative error, 121
      false positive error, 120
      ground truth data (*see* ground truth (GT) data)
      metrics for additional metadata, 123
      track match error, 121–123, 122*f*
   overview, 103–104
face scanning, 382, 384, 385*f,* 386*f*
face sizes, adjusting minimum and maximum, 115
face tracking, 384, 387*f,* 388*f*
false negative error (FNE), in face detection, 121
false negative (FN), 171, 172
false positive error (FPE), in face detection, 120
false positive (FP), 171, 172, 174, 393
false positive rate (FPR), 174, 393
fast Fourier transform (FFT), 34–35, 35*f*
Fayyad, Usama M., 177
feature descriptors/feature signatures/region
     signatures, 14, 16, 41, 44, 74–76, 75*f,* 76*f,* 76*t*
   common and uncommon features, 78–93
      dynamic texture metric using 3D LBPs,
        86–88, 87*f*
      Haar-like features, 78, 79–80, 79*f,* 81*f,* 97*t*
      LBP (*see* local binary patterns (LBP))
      LBP-TOP, 87*f,* 88
      RILBP, 86, 86*f*
      SIFT, 88–91, 89*f,* 90*f,* 91*f*
      VLBP, 87, 87*f*
   methods, variations on, 93, 94*t*–101*t*
feature extraction, local interest points for, 68
feature selection, in data preparation, 232–233
feature signatures. *see* feature descriptors/feature
     signatures/region signatures

feature tracking, 154–155, 155*f*
feature vector, 133, 133*f*
feed-forward neural network (FNN), 182
     BP algorithm, 184, 185
     training, 184–185
Feret Face Database, 105, 106*f*
Fermi cache architecture, 344, 344*f*
ferns, defined, 167
ferns algorithm, 159–174
     checking algorithm accuracy, 171–174, 172*f,*
       173*f*
     creating training model, 160–161, 160*f*
     formation of classes under training, 167–169,
       168*f*
     frame preprocessing, 162, 163*f*
     key point generation, 163–166, 164*f,* 165*f*–167*f*
     object recognition, 161, 162*f*
     recognition phase, 169–171, 170*f*
FFT. *see* fast Fourier transform (FFT)
filter convolution, 147
     base code of, 149–152
Fisher projection (FP)
     healthcare studies and, 331
floating point unit (FPU), 344
FN. *see* false negative (FN)
FNE. *see* false negative error (FNE)
FNN. *see* feed-forward neural network (FNN)
forward regression, 210
Fourier descriptors, 95*t*
Fourier Projection Slice theorem, 34
FP. *see* false positive (FP); Fisher projection (FP)
FPE. *see* false positive error (FPE)
FP-growth algorithm. *see* frequent pattern growth
     (FP-growth) algorithm
FPR. *see* false positive rate (FPR)
FPU. *see* floating point unit (FPU)
fractal methods, 61
frame preprocessing, ferns algorithm, 162, 163*f*
frequent pattern growth (FP-growth) algorithm,
     223–224
Friedman, Nir, 195
FromMediaStart, 233
frontal face detection, Viola Jones algorithm,
     104–118
     algorithm optimizations, 114–117

adjusting minimum and maximum face sizes, 115
delaying scans to subsequent frames, 115–116
global motion detection, 116–117
local object tracking, 116
skipping pixels, 115
detecting faces, 110–114, 111*f*, 112*f*, 113*f*, 114*f*
training face classifier (*see* face classifier, training)
training more advanced classifiers, 117–118
funder, data ownership and, 244

G

Gabor functions, 80
gamma compression, normalization and, 127, 128*f*
gamma curves, 26, 27
Gamutvision software, 26
Gantz, John, 176
Gaussian smoothing, 60, 73, 129
GBN. *see* general Bayesian network (GBN) classifier
GeForce GTX 400/500 Fermi architecture, 342–344, 343*f*
gender match error (GME), 123, 393
general Bayesian network (GBN) classifier, 196*f*, 197
GetOpticalFlowLK function, 386–389
GIST, 96*t*
global image normalization, 127, 128*f*
global memory, 353
global motion detection, face detection algorithm and, 116–117
global thresholding methods, 51–52, 51*t*–52*t*, 52*f*
global uniform texture metrics, 60
GLOH. *see* gradient location and orientation histogram (GLOH)
GME. *see* gender match error (GME)
GPU. *see* graphics processing units (GPU)
gradient-ascent-based superpixel method survey, 55–56
gradient location and orientation histogram (GLOH), 88, 91, 91*f*, 95*t*
graph-based superpixel methods survey, 54–55
graphics processing units (GPU), 9
accuracy model, 392–396
architecture, 338, 339*f*

CPU-GPU combined optimization, 389–392
data transfer between CPU and, 389–390
Intel Ivy Bridge architecture, 339–342
CPU features, 339
GPU features, 340–342, 340*f*, 341*f*
Nvidia GPU architecture, 342–345 (*see also* Nvidia GPU architecture)
optimization
OpenCL, 349
OpenCL Memory Model, 352–354, 352*f*
OpenCL Threading Model, 349–352, 350*f*
techniques, 358–364
using HMPP, 348–349
workgroups, 354–356, 355*f*
work items, 354–356, 355*f*
performance measurement, 396–404, 397*f*–404*f*
porting VA algorithms, 364–365
required algorithm features on, 346
thread interaction between CPU and, 390
grayscale morphology, 47, 49
ground truth (GT) data, 118–119, 171, 411
in face detection algorithm, 118–119
generating, 119–120
synthetic video generation, 411–416, 412*f*–416*f*
GS-FH method, 55
GT. *see* ground truth (GT) data

H

Haar cascade classifier, 80
Haar classifier
optimization using OpenCL, 365–375, 366*f*, 370*f*–373*f*, 375*f*
Haar features, 79–81, 79*f*, 81*f*
face classifier training and, 106–110, 107*f*, 109*f*
Haar wavelet detectors, 74–75
Haralick metrics, 63, 64*f*
Harris corner detector, 71
healthcare
analytics in, 329–335, 332*f*
consumerization of data, 328–329
growing demand, 317–319, 318*f*
machine learning, 334–335 (*see also* machine learning)
predictive modeling, 331–332, 332*f*

real-time analytics
 display processing, 325–326, 325f, 326f
 distribution of performance, 326–328,
  326t–327t, 327f
 envelop detector, 324, 324f
 receive beamformer, 322f, 323–324
 ultrasound basics, 320–322, 321f, 322f
 ultrasound software prototype, 322–323,
  322f, 323t
 standards, 319–320
health information exchange (HIE), 328, 329, 334
Hessian matrix interest point detector (DoH),
 72–73
HIE. see health information exchange (HIE)
hierarchical clustering methods, 215–216. see also
 clustering methods
 agglomerative, 215–216, 215f
 BIRCH algorithm, 216
 chameleon algorithm, 216
 CURE algorithm, 216
 divisive, 215, 215f
 ROCK algorithm, 216
high dynamic range (HDR) images, 17, 28
histogram of gradients (HoG), 89, 91, 91f, 95t
 object detection algorithm, 125–133
  block diagram, 126f
  feature vector, 133, 133f
  filter calculation steps, 136–137, 137f
  flow diagram of, 127f
  image gradients, computation, 127–130,
   128f, 129t–130t
  normalization of gamma and color, 127, 128f
  normalize contrast in overlapping block of
   cells, 132–133, 132f, 133f
  orientation binning, 131, 131f
  training, latent SVM and (see latent SVM)
  weighted votes for gradients orientation over
   spatial cells, 130–131, 130f, 131f
histograms, 66–68. see also histogram of gradients
 (HoG)
 chain code, 96t
 multiresolution, 66, 67f
 multiscale, 66–67, 68f
 orientation, 131
 processing, 51

of textural features, 67
HM. see homography matrix (HM)
HMPP tool, GPU optimization and, 348–349
HoG. see histogram of gradients (HoG)
home energy management, 6, 23
homography matrix (HM), 161
Hotspot function
 extraction, 348
 Intel AIM Suite application, 376–380,
  377f–379f
Hough transforms, 61
human face detection, 274. see also face detection
Huxley, Thomas Henry, 125

I

IaaS. see Infrastructure as a Service (IaaS)
IAF. see intelligent advertising framework (IAF)
IBM, 177
IBR. see intensity-based region methods (IBR)
IDEAL, 235
illumination pattern synthesis, multiple, 37–38, 39f
image gradients, computation, 127–130, 128f,
 129t–130t
image preparation, visual metrics and, 18
image preprocessing
 for visual metrics, 39–41
  area operations, 39
  Intel® IPP, 41, 42f
  Kernel operations, 39
  OpenCV Library (Open Computer Vision),
   41, 43f
  point operations, 39
implementation stage, privacy safe systems,
 313–315, 314f, 315f
industries, intelligent devices in, 2–6
 digital signage, 3–4, 4f
 home energy management, 6
 medical devices, 6
 retail intelligence, 5–6, 5f
Infrastructure as a Service (IaaS), 239
input interfaces, ineffective design of, 310
input scheduler, CMS, 262
integral image, 111–113, 112f, 113f, 365
 defined, 73
integration, in data mining, 237

Intel® advanced vector extensions (Intel® AVX), optimizations using, 146
Intel Audience Impression Metrics Suite (Intel AIM Suite), 338–346, 347f
  application, 382, 384, 383f, 385f–388f
  hotspot functions (GPU candidates), 376–380, 377f–379f
Intel® AVX. *see* Intel® advanced vector extensions (Intel® AVX)
Intel® Integrated Performance Primitives (Intel® IPP), 41, 42f, 145–146
Intel® IPP. *see* Intel® Integrated Performance Primitives (Intel® IPP)
Intel Ivy Bridge architecture, 339–342
  CPU features, 339
  GPU features, 340–342, 340f, 341f
  optimizing VA algorithms for, 346
  porting issues on, 374
  vs. Nvidia GPU architecture, 345, 345t
    code difference, 380
intelligent advertising framework (IAF)
  advertising
    category model, 249
    models creation (*see* advertising, models creation)
  architecture, 242–247, 242f, 247f, 264f
  CMS, 243, 257–265, 258f–262f, 264f
  components in, 248–273
  data collection (*see* training, data collection and preparation)
  data mining for targeted advertising (*see* data mining, for targeted advertising)
  data ownership, 243–246, 244f
  digital signage, 242
  DMM, 242, 248–257 (*see also* data mining module (DMM))
  DP (*see* digital player (DP))
  passer pattern model, 250
  real time triggering, 246, 247f
  targeted advertising (*see* targeted advertising, IAF architecture)
  working modes, 276–277
intelligent systems. *see also* artificial intelligence (AI)
  introduction, 1–11
  real-world, building (*see* real-world intelligent systems)

intelligent systems, privacy in
  concerns, 307–312, 308f, 309f
    data analysis module, 311–312
    data capture module, 309–311
    output module privacy, 312
  information privacy, 306–307
    PII, 306–307
  privacy safe systems, development of
    deployment stage, 315–316
    design stage, 312–313
    implementation stage, 313–314, 314f, 315f
Intel Performance Tuning Utility (Intel PTU), 338
Intel® SSE. *see* Intel® streaming SIMD extensions (Intel® SSE)
Intel® streaming SIMD extensions (Intel® SSE), 384–389
  optimizations using, 146
Intel® TBB Threading Model, 381–382
Intel Threading Building Blocks (Intel TBB), 338
  CPU optimization with, 380–389, 383f, 385f–388f
intensity-based region methods (IBR), 69
intensity proxy, 28
intensity thresholding refinements, for improved morphology, 49
interest points, 19, 68–74, 69f
  Canny detector, 70
  DoG, 73
  DoH, 72–73
  feature descriptors and, 88–91
  Harris corner detector, 71
  local, for feature extraction, 68
  LoG, 71
  Moravic corner detection, 74
  salient regions, 73–74
  Shi-Tomasi corner detector, 71
  Sobel operator, 70
intersection points, bounding box calculation
  synthetic video generation, 427–429, 427f, 428f
intimate space deployment, 315
intra-class variation, 136, 136f

J

JMP, 235

K

k-anonymity, 225–226
KDD. *see* knowledge discovery and data mining (KDD)
kernel architecture, single *vs.* multiple kernel, 360–363
kernel execution time, 357–358
kernel function, optimal hyperplane and, 193
kernel operations, image preprocessing and, 39
key points. *see* interest points
Kinect approach, 38
k-means algorithm, 212–214, 214*f*
k-medoids algorithm, 212, 214
k nearest neighbors (KNN) classifier, 201–203, 202*f*
KNN. *see k* nearest neighbors (KNN) classifier
knowledge discovery and data mining (KDD), 176–178, 319. *see also* data mining algorithms
    machine learning in, 178
    statistics in, 177–178
  applications, 178–179
  characteristics, 177
  defined, 177
  OLAP and, 178

L

Laplacian of Gaussian (LoG), 71
Laplacian operator, 71
latent SVM, training HoG model using, 133–145, 134*f*, 135*f*
  data mining hard negative examples, 143–145, 144*f*
  HoG feature, 136–137, 137*f*
  mixture model and intra-class variation, 136, 136*f*, 141*f*
  multiscale pyramid approach, 137–138, 138*f*, 139*f*
  star-structured deformable part model, 134, 135*f*
  training procedure, 139–143
    negative training examples, selection, 142–143, 143*f*
LBP. *see* local binary patterns (LBP)
"learning inquiries," 335

leave-one-out, 236
light field cameras. *see* plenoptic cameras
linear regression model, 207–210, 208*f*, 209*t*
  attribute selection, 210
  backward regression, 210
  forward regression, 210
  input and output attributes in, 207
  SSE in, 208, 209
  SSR in, 208, 209
  stepwise regression, 210
linear SVM, 192. *see also* support vector machine (SVM)
local binary patterns (LBP), 61, 81–85, 99*t*
  binary coded, 83
  calculation, 84–85, 84*f*
  feature flow for feature detection, 83*f*
  histogram of local texture descriptors, 85*f*
  as image processing operator, 82, 82*f*
  LBP-TOP, 88, 87*f*
  3D, dynamic texture metric using, 86–88, 87*f*
  value assignment details, 85*f*
  variants, 99*t*–101*t*
  VLBP, 87, 87*f*
  weighting values, 84, 84*f*
local feature descriptor methods, 20
  interest points for feature extraction, 68
local memory, 353
local object tracking, face detection algorithm and, 116
local thresholding methods, 52–53, 53*t*, 53*f*
LoG. *see* Laplacian of Gaussian (LoG)
logistic regression model, 210–211
  binary output attribute, 210
Lucas Kanade algorithm, 154–159, 155*f*, 157*f*, 158*f*, 159*f*, 384
  accuracy checker, 158–159, 159*f*

M

MAC. *see* multiply and accumulation (MAC) operation
machine learning, 2, 10
  algorithms on GPU (*see* graphics processing units (GPU))
  clustering in (*see* clustering methods)
  in healthcare, 6, 334

in KDD algorithms, 178

Machine Learning Toolbox (MLT) P2154, 335

MANOVA. *see* multivariate analysis of variance (MANOVA)

Markov random field methods, 61

maximally stable extrema regions (MSER), 98*t*
    interest region detection, 46–47

maxima points, 69

MDDS. *see* Medical Device Data Systems (MDDS)

mean shift, 55

Medical Device Data Systems (MDDS), 329

medical devices, intelligent, 6. *see also* devices, intelligent

medical imaging methods, Fourier Projection Slice theorem in, 34

metrics set, 45

Microsoft, 177

Microsoft Color Management System, 25

Microsoft Kinect, 38

Microsoft SSAS, 235

minima points, 69

minimum description length (MDL) principle, 188

mining association rules, 222–224
    Apriori algorithm, 222–223
    FP-growth algorithm, 223–224

mixture model, 136, 136*f*, 141*f*

model analyzer, DP, 265–266, 267*f*

model-based approaches, for texture classification, 60–61

model constructor
    advertising model learning, 276
    DMM, 252

ModelContent, DMM, 257

model extractor, CMS, 259, 259*f*, 261

model images, 160

model learner, advertising model learning, 276

model trainer, DMM, 252

Moravic corner detection, 74

morphology, mathematical, 47

mother wavelets, 80

MotionHistory, 371

MSER. *see* maximally stable extrema regions (MSER)

MSLBP. *see* multi-scale local binary patterns (MSLBP)

multiple advertisers, 246

multiple advertising model training, 277–278

multiple processing cores, 9

multiplicative perturbation, in randomization method, 227

multiply and accumulation (MAC) operation, 358

multiresolution histograms, 66–68

multiscale histograms, 66–67, 68*f*

multi-scale local binary patterns (MSLBP), 21

multiscale pyramid approach, 137–138, 138*f*, 139*f*

multivariable partition, decision tree with, 181–182

multivariate analysis of variance (MANOVA)
    healthcare studies and, 331

multivariate descriptor, 81

multiview radial cameras, 32, 33*f*

Munsell Color Science Laboratory, 25

N

Naïve Bayes (NB) classifier, 194–195, 194*f*

National Institute of Standard and Technology (NIST), 306

National Institutes of Health (NIH), 48

NB. *see* Naïve Bayes (NB) classifier

negative instances, in binary class training data, 186–187, 187*t*

negative region, rough set theory and, 197, 198*f*

new attribute derivation, data preparation and, 233

NIST. *see* National Institute of Standard and Technology (NIST)

normalization, block used for, 132–133, 132*f*, 133*f*

normalized cuts, 55

Nvidia GPU architecture, 342–345
    GeForce GTX 400/500 Fermi architecture, 342–344, 343*f*
    vs. Intel Ivy Bridge architecture, 345, 345*t*
        code difference, 380

Nyquist Frequency, 24

O

object descriptors, 45–46

object detection, 125–152
    algorithms, 125–145
        HoG (*see* histogram of gradients (HoG), object detection algorithm)
    ferns algorithm, 161, 162*f*
    optimization, 145–152

coding methodology, 147–152
coding techniques, 147
evaluating code for SIMD possibility, 146
filter convolution (*see* filter convolution)
Intel® IPP and, 145–146
Intel® IPP/Intel® SSE/Intel® AVX and, 146
overview, 125
object segmentation, 5
object shape, visual metrics and, 20
occlusion, bounding box calculation
synthetic video generation, 427, 427*f*–432*f*, 430–432
octant shifting, 34–35
OLAP. *see* on-line analytical processing (OLAP)
on-line analytical processing (OLAP), 178
OpenCL. *see* Open Computing Language (OpenCL)
OpenCL Memory Model, GPU optimization and, 352–354, 352*f*
OpenCL Threading Model, GPU optimization and, 349–352, 350*f*
Open Computer Vision (OpenCV) Library, 40, 41, 43*f*
Open Computing Language (OpenCL), 9, 349
function
overhead time, 358
profiling of, 356–358, 356*t*–357*t*
GPU optimization and, 349
Haar classifier optimization using, 365–375, 366*f*, 370*f*–375*f*
OpenCV. *see* Open Computer Vision (OpenCV) Library
optical flow algorithms, 153–154
Lucas Kanade, 154–159, 155*f*, 157*f*, 158*f*, 159*f*
Optical Flow Pyramid LK algorithm, 155
OPTICS. *see* ordering points to identify clustering structure (OPTICS) algorithm
optics, for 3D depth sensing. *see* 3D depth sensing
optimal classifier. *see* Bayesian classifiers
optimal separating hyperplane, 190–192, 190*f*
optimizations
GPU
OpenCL, 349
OpenCL Memory Model, 352–354, 352*f*
OpenCL Threading Model, 349–352, 350*f*

techniques, 358–364
using HMPP, 348–349
workgroups and work items, 354–356, 355*f*
object detection, 145–152
coding methodology, 147–152
coding techniques, 147
evaluating code for SIMD possibility, 146
filter convolution (*see* filter convolution)
Intel® AVX, 146
Intel® IPP and, 145–146
Intel® SSE and, 146
to texture metrics, 61
Oracle, 177
ORB descriptor, 92–93, 97*t*
ordering points to identify clustering structure (OPTICS) algorithm, 217
orientation binning, in object detection algorithm, 131, 130*f*, 131*f*
orientation histogram, 131
outdoor surveillance system, 23
outlier analysis, 218
KDD application, 179
output module privacy, 309*f*, 312
overlapping block of cells, normalize contrast in, 132–133, 132*f*, 133*f*
oversubscription, 381

P

PaaS. *see* Platform as a Service (PaaS)
packager, data ownership and, 244
PACS. *see* picture archiving and communication system (PACS)
pan, bounding box calculation
synthetic video generation, 422–424, 422*f*–424*f*
parallel tracking and mapping (PTAM) method, 62
partitioning method, clustering algorithms, 212–214
k-means algorithm, 212–214, 214*f*
k-medoids algorithm, 212, 214
passer distribution prediction model, 280
passer distribution prediction rule, 281
passer pattern models, IAF, 250
passer prediction models, 250, 280
dominant passer prediction, 280, 280*t*
passer distribution prediction, 280

patch recognition, 159
  ferns algorithm (*see* ferns algorithm)
PatientsLikeMe, 329
Pawlak, Zdzislaw I., 197
PCA. *see* principal component analysis (PCA)
personalized services, KDD application, 179
personally identifiable information (PII), 306–307
  defined, 306
  incomplete processing of, 312
  unsecured
    storage, 311–312
    transmission, 311
personal space deployment, 315
perturbation, in randomization method, 226–227
PHoG. *see* pyramidal histogram of gradients (PHoG)
photo-diode sensor cells, 24
picture archiving and communication system (PACS), 319
PII. *see* personally identifiable information (PII)
pixels
  remapping, 51
  skipping, 115
Platform as a Service (PaaS), 239
player event collection, 285–286, 285*f*, 285*t*, 286*t*
player-specific model extractor, CMS, 258, 258*f*, 261
playlist finalization, 276
plenoptic cameras, 32–35, 34*f*, 35*f*
PMK. *see* pyramid match kernel (PMK)
PMML. *see* predictive model markup language (PMML)
point-of-sale (POS), 241
point operations, image preprocessing and, 39
PoP analyzer, CMS, 262
POS. *see* point-of-sale (POS)
positive bounding boxes, aspect ratio of, 139–140
positive instances, in binary class training data, 186–187, 187*t*
positive region, rough set and, 197, 198*f*
prediction-based targeting, 278
  advertising selection for, 283, 283*t*
  rules, 281
predictive data, 245
predictive modeling, 331–333, 332*f*
  healthcare, 331–333, 332*f*

predictive model markup language (PMML), 237
primary playlist creation, 276
principal component analysis (PCA), 98*t*
  healthcare studies and, 331
privacy
  in intelligent systems (*see* intelligent systems, privacy in)
  real-world intelligent systems and, 10
Privacy by Design, 10
privacy-preserving data mining, 225–228
  anonymization, 225–226, 226*f*
  condensation, 227
  cryptographic techniques, 227–228
  downgrading application effectiveness, 227
  randomization method for, 226–227
private memory, 354
processing speed, real-world intelligent systems building and, 7–9
  GPUs, 9
  multiple processing cores, 9
  SIMD instructions, 7–9, 8*f*
process optimization, KDD application, 179
PTAM. *see* parallel tracking and mapping (PTAM) method
public space deployment, 316
purchaser/licenser as owner, 245
pyramidal histogram of gradients (PHoG), 17
  descriptors, 95*t*
pyramid match kernel (PMK), 94*t*
pyramid wide convolution, 147, 148*f*

Q

query engine, advertising model learning, 276
query model content process, DMM, 252
quick shift method, 55

R

random forest algorithm, 204, 206–207
randomization method, for privacy-preserving data mining, 226–227
reader as owner, 245
real time triggering, IAF architecture, 246, 247*f*
real-world intelligent systems, 7–10
  accuracy and robustness, 10

privacy, 10
processing speed, 7–9
  GPUs, 9
  multiple processing cores, 9
  SIMD instructions, 8–9, 8*f*
recognition phase, ferns algorithm,
  169–171, 170*f*
reducts, 198
refinements, to texture metrics, 61
region segmentation, 45–46, 46*t*
  color as method of, 56
region shape metrics, 56–58, 57*t*–58*t*
region signatures. *see* feature descriptors/feature
  signatures/region signatures
regression
  analysis, DMM, 248
  for data mining, 207–211
    linear regression (*see* linear regression model)
    logistic regression (*see* logistic regression
      model)
retail intelligence, 5–6, 5*f*
RetrainDMModel, DMM, 257
retrain existing model process, DMM, 252, 254*f*
RIFF. *see* rotation-invariant, fast feature (RIFF)
  descriptor
RILBP. *see* rotation invariant LBP (RILBP)
Ripper, rule induction method, 189
robust clustering using links (ROCK)
  algorithm, 216
robustness, real-world intelligent systems and, 10
ROCK. *see* robust clustering using links (ROCK)
  algorithm
roll angle, bounding box calculation, 425–426
  limits, 426, 426*f*
rotation-invariant, fast feature (RIFF) descriptor, 98*t*
rotation invariant LBP (RILBP), 86, 86*f*
rough set theory, 197–201
  border, 197
  classification rules, generation, 199–201, 200*t*
  generation, for attribute reduction, 197–199,
    198*t*, 199*t*
  negative region, 197, 198*f*
  positive region, 197, 198*f*
rule induction method, 186–189
  AQ algorithm, 186–188

C45rules, 188
Ripper, 189

S

SaaS. *see* Software as a Service (SaaS)
salient regions, 73–74
sampling theory, effects of, 24
Sandy Bridge, 145, 146, 147, 339, 342
scale-invariant feature transform (SIFT), 88–91,
  89*f*, 90*f*, 91*f*, 94*t*
scene mapping metrics, 62
scientific discovery, KDD application, 179
SDM. *see* spatial dependency matrices (SDM)
secured data. *see also* data
  storage, 314
  transmission, 314
seeing-based targeting, 278
  advertising selection for, 282–283, 282*t*
  rules, 280
segmentation, visual metrics and, 18–19
  color (*see* color, segmentation)
  object, 5
  region (*see* region segmentation)
  superpixel, 54–56, 54*f*
  texture, 58–62
sensors, image
  color patterns, 27–29, 27*f*, 28*f*, 29*f*
  processing, for visual metrics, 17–18, 22–27
    Adobe RGB color space, 26, 26*f*
    cell size, 24
    characteristics, 23–27, 23*f*, 25*f*, 26*f*
    color response, 24–25, 25*f*
    configuration, 23–27, 23*f*, 25*f*, 26*f*
    resolution, 23–27, 23*f*, 25*f*, 26*f*
  technology, 17–18
  for 3D depth sensing (*see* 3D depth sensing)
sequential floating forward search (SFFS)
  healthcare studies and, 331
sequential rules, data mining algorithms,
  224–225, 224*t*
SetImages function, 371, 372, 371*f*, 372*f*
SFFS. *see* sequential floating forward search (SFFS)
shape descriptors, 45–46
Shi-Tomasi corner detector, 71
SIFT. *see* scale-invariant feature transform (SIFT)

silicon spectral response, 25
SIMD. *see* single instruction multiple data (SIMD)
simple binary thresholding, 51
simple linear iterative clustering (SLIC), 54–55
SIMT. *see* single instruction multiple thread (SIMT)
single instruction multiple data (SIMD), 350, 351
    instructions, 7–9, 8*f*
    possibility, evaluating code for, 146
single instruction multiple thread (SIMT), 351–352
single-precision floating point (SP FP), 340
skipping pixels, 115
SL. *see* superpixel lattice (SL) method
SLIC. *see* simple linear iterative clustering (SLIC)
SM. *see* streaming multiprocessor (SM)
Sobel operator, 70
social space deployment, 315
Software as a Service (SaaS), 238–239
spatial dependency matrices (SDM), 63–65, 63*f,* 64*f,* 65*f*
SP FP. *see* single-precision floating point (SP FP)
SQL ServerDB Interface, DMM, 255
Srikant, R., 222
SSE. *see* streaming SIMD extensions (SSE) instructions; sum of squares of errors (SSE)
SSR. *see* sum of squares of regression (SSR)
star-structured deformable part model, 134, 135*f*
stepwise regression, 210
stereo imaging, 31
storage cloud, 240
streaming multiprocessor (SM), 342–344
streaming SIMD extensions (SSE) instructions, 7–9, 8*f*
structural approaches, for texture classification, 60
structured and coded light, 35–36, 35*f,* 36*f*
subject as owner, 245
sum of squares of errors (SSE)
    in linear regression model, 208, 209
sum of squares of regression (SSR)
    in linear regression model, 208, 209
superpixel lattice (SL) method, 55
superpixel segmentation method, via graph-based and gradient-ascent, 54–56, 54*f*
supervised learning, 211–212

support vector machine (SVM), 189–193
    complexity of, 193
    Kernel function, 193
    latent, training HoG model using (*see* latent SVM, training HoG model using)
    linear, 192
    optimal separating hyperplane, 190–192, 190*f*
support vectors, defined, 191
SUSAN, 98*t*
SVM. *see* support vector machine (SVM)
synthetic video generation
    bounding box, calculation of, 421–432 (*see also* bounding boxes)
    camera field of view conditions, 409–411, 410*f*
    face movements, 416–421, 417*f*–421*f*
    GT data marking, 411–416, 412*f*–416*f*
system evaluation, 333
Systems management as a Service, 239

T

TAN. *see* tree augmented Naïve Bayes (TAN) classifier
targeted advertising, IAF architecture, 246
    data mining for, 277–283 (*see also* data mining, for targeted advertising)
    IAF working modes, 276–277
    process, 274–276
        advertising model learning, 275–276
        demographics recognition, 275
        human face detection, 274
        playlist finalization, 276
        primary playlist creation, 276
        training data integration, 275
        viewing event creation, 274–275
TargetPotential, 233, 235
task parallelism, 359, 359*f*
template feature matching, 77, 77*f*
tentative playlist generator
    CMS, 260, 261*f,* 262
    DP, 266, 268*f*
Teradata, 177
TestModel, DMM, 257
texture analysis, history of key ideas in, 58–62
texture classification, structural and model-based approaches for, 60–61
texture metrics, 58–62

co-occurrence matrix as, 63–65, 63f, 64f, 65f
3D features and robust invariant, 61–62
Haralick, 63, 64f
optimizations and refinements to, 61
texture segmentation, 58–62
texture signatures, 58
texture synthesis, 61
3rd Generation Intel Core, 337, 339
3D depth sensing
    sensor and optics for, 29–38, 30t–31t, 39f, 40f
        diffraction gratings, 31–32, 32f
        Microsoft Kinect, 38
        multiple illumination pattern synthesis, 37–38, 39f
        multiview radial cameras, 32, 33f
        plenoptic cameras, 32–35, 34f, 35f
        stereo, binocular, trinocular imaging, 31
        structured and coded light, 35–36, 36f, 37f
        TOF sensors, 36, 38f
TillMediaEnd, 233, 287
tilt, bounding box calculation, 424–425, 425f
time of flight (TOF) sensors, 36, 38f
TME. *see* track matching error (TME)
TN. *see* true negative (TN)
Topal, Eric, Dr., 328–329
TP. *see* true positive (TP)
TPR. *see* true positive rate (TPR)
tracking algorithms, 5
track matching error (TME), 158–159
    in face detection, 121–123, 122f
training
    AdaBoost algorithm, 21, 104, 107, 108–109, 110, 117, 205–206
    data collection and preparation
        player event collection, 285–286, 285f, 285t, 286t
        training data correlation, 287–290, 288t, 289t, 290t
        viewer event collection, 284–285, 284f, 284t
        weather data collection, 287, 287t
    data correlation, 287–290, 288t, 289t, 290t
    data integration, 275
    face classifier (*see* face classifier, training)
    HoG model using latent SVM (*see* latent SVM, training HoG model using)

retraining process and, 292–297
TrainModel, DMM, 257
tree augmented Naïve Bayes (TAN) classifier, 195–196
trinocular imaging, 31
true negative (TN), 171, 172, 174
true positive rate (TPR), 174
true positive (TP), 171, 172, 174
turbopixel method, 56

U

undersubscription, 381

V

VA. *see* video analytics (VA) algorithms
VA data analyzer, DP, 265, 266f
value difference metric (VDM), 202–203
VDM. *see* value difference metric (VDM)
vectorization, 147
video analytics (VA) algorithms, 337, 338
    Intel Ivy Bridge architecture, optimizing for, 346
    porting to GPU, 364–365
viewer event collection, 284–285, 284f, 284t
Viola-Jones algorithm
    frontal face detection and (*see also* frontal face detection)
        algorithm optimizations, 114–117
    object detection framework, 21, 123, 125
visual metrics, for computer vision
    augmented reality (AR), 62
    binary morphology (*see* binary morphology)
    color de-mosaicing, 27–29, 27f, 28f, 29f
    color morphology, 49
    computational imaging, 29–38, 39f, 40f
    computing topics in vision pipeline, 17–22
        algorithms, classifiers, training, 20–22
        global textural and statistical features, 20
        image preparation, 18
        local feature descriptors, 20
        local features and interest points, 19
        object shape, 20
        segmentation, 18–19
        sensor technology and sensor processing, 17–18

supervised matching, mapping, tracking, 20–22

digital correlation, 77, 77*f*

dynamic textures (DT), 62–63

eye light sensitivity, 27–29, 27*f*, 28*f*, 29*f*

feature descriptors/feature signatures/ region signatures (*see* feature descriptors/feature signatures/ region signatures)

global thresholding methods, 51–52, 51*t*–52*t*, 52*f*

good feature, 41, 44–45, 44*t*

grayscale morphology, 47, 49

histograms, 66–68

history of key ideas in, 15–17

   classified invariant local feature approaches, 16

   finer grain feature and metric composition approaches, 16

   local feature approaches, 16

   multi-modal visual metrics fusion, 16–17

   partial-object approaches, 16

   scene and object modeling approaches, 16

   whole-object approaches, 15–16

image preprocessing (*see* image preprocessing)

intensity thresholding refinements for improved morphology, 49

interest points (*see* interest points)

local interest points for feature extraction, 68

local thresholding methods, 52–53, 53*t*, 53*f*

mathematical morphology, 47

MSER interest region detection, 46–47

multiresolution histograms, 66–68, 67*f*, 68*f*

object descriptors, 45–46

overview, 13–14, 14*f*

region segmentation (*see* region segmentation)

region shape metrics, 56–58, 57*t*–58*t*

scene mapping metrics, 62

sensor color patterns, 27–29, 27*f*, 28*f*, 29*f*

sensor processing for, 22–27

shape descriptors, 45–46

superpixel segmentation via graph-based and gradient-ascent, 54–56, 54*f*

template feature matching, 77, 77*f*

texture metrics (*see* texture metrics)

texture segmentation, 58–62

3D depth sensing, sensor and optics for (*see* 3D depth sensing)

TOF (*see* time of flight (TOF) sensors)

VLBP. *see* volume linear binary pattern (VLBP)

volume linear binary pattern (VLBP), 17, 87

Voronoi polygon tessellation, 61

Vtune™ analyzer, 338

W

Wal-Mart, 219

warps, 344

watershed method, 55

wavelets, Haar features and, 80, 82, 97*t*

weather data collection, 287, 287*t*

weighted audience counting, 279–280, 280*t*

workgroups, GPU optimization and, 354–356, 355*f*

work items, GPU optimization and, 354–356, 355*f*

workspace creation, 348–349

Continuing Education is Essential

It's a challenge we all face—keeping pace with constant change in information technology. Whether our formal training was recent or long ago, we must all find time to keep ourselves educated and up to date in spite of the daily time pressures of our profession.

Intel produces technical books to help the industry learn about the latest technologies. The focus of these publications spans the basic motivation and origin for a technology through its practical application.

Right books, right time, from the experts

These technical books are planned to synchronize with roadmaps for technology and platforms, in order to give the industry a head-start. They provide new insights, in an engineer-to-engineer voice, from named experts. Sharing proven insights and design methods is intended to make it more practical for you to embrace the latest technology with greater design freedom and reduced risks.

I encourage you to take full advantage of Intel Press books as a way to dive deeper into the latest technologies, as you plan and develop your next generation products. They are an essential tool for every practicing engineer or programmer. I hope you will make them a part of your continuing education tool box.

Sincerely,

Senior Fellow and Chief Technology Officer Intel Corporation

Turn the page to learn about titles from Intel Press for system developers

Creating the Infrastructure for Cloud Computing

An Essential Handbook for IT Professionals
By Enrique Castro-Leon, Bernard Golden, Miguel Gomez, Raghu Yeluri, and Charles G. Sheridan

Cloud computing is a logical extension of the technology of virtualization, integrated with application group self-provisioning, enormous scalability, and agile responsiveness borne of a no need to make long-term commitments for compute resources. It promises to make the efficient data center agile enough to meet today's chaotic business environment. However, despite its obvious benefits, cloud computing imposes challenges as well—translating manual processes to automated one is often difficult and always expensive. It remains to be seen which "flavor" of cloud computing—internal, external, public, private—becomes the widest used; there is no doubt at all that the conditions dictating cloud computing will engender its success.

Written for the professional IT engineer "*Creating the Infrastructure for Enterprise Cloud Computing*" is a hands on must-have guide to the theory, practice and implementation of Virtual Service Grids. The book is organized into separate sections that focus on: Virtualization & Cloud technology, General Architecture, Solution Architecture and Reference Implementations. This structure allows the reader to quickly access the information needed to plan and implement a cloud computing project.

"The authors appear to have leveraged Intel's latest nanoscale fabrication technology to achieve unprecedented density of ideas, information, and insight into the theory and practice of cloud computing. In a balanced treatment richly detailed with case studies, process charts, screen captures, and quantitative engineering data, they bring the cloud—which is still hazy to some—to life."

—Joe Weinman,
Vice President,
Strategic and Business
Development, AT&T

Break Away with Intel® Atom™ Processors

A Guide to Architecture Migration
By Lori Matassa and Max Domeika

ISBN 978-1-934053-37-9

Break Away with Intel® Atom™ Processors: A Guide to Architecture Migration provides insight into architecture migration discussing real world software migration issues and highlighting them with case studies. The book covers pertinent topics that are at the heart of the software migration, such as techniques to port code originally written for other processor architectures, as well as capturing the benefits of Intel® Atom™ platform technologies. The reality is that architecture migration is not a one-size-fits-all activity and developers must understand all of the decisions that comprise a successful migration. The authors deliver this information as a handbook to your software migration plan and project activities.

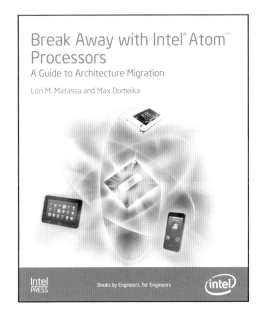

"This is an essential guide to working with the Intel® Atom™ processors that should be read by anyone who wants to understand how to use the platform effectively. The book covers key concepts including power management, parallel applications, and machine virtualization, while providing a clear explanation of the system architecture and how to use it to its fullest advantage."

—Paul Krzyzanowski, CTO, OpenPeak Inc.

"This isn't just a book about Intel extending its reach into the embedded market. In a way that is fresh and exciting, the authors have really understood that it is a powerful software methodology and tools eco-system that is needed for developers to make best use of the multicore and multithreaded world we now live in. The style of this Atom book will be the standard against which all processor architecture books are measured from now on."

—David Stewart, CEO, CriticalBlue

Break Away with Intel® Atom™ Processors

Architecture Migration Activities
By Lori Matassa and Max Domeika

ISBN 978-1-934053-44-7

Learning involves the acquisition of knowledge through the experiences of research, instruction, and practice. Each opportunity for experience increases the depth of understanding and mastering of the subject matter. This study guide can be the companion to the book "*Break Away with Intel® Atom™ Processors: A Guide to Architecture Migration*" or can be used in independent study or supplemental material for professional development. It provides exercises and hands-on labs using practical applications to supplement the knowledge learned in the core technology book.

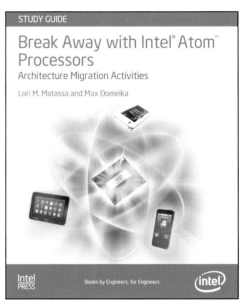

"This study guide of the book is a valued resource for readers to comprehend the key issues discussed in the book. It is intended to give readers familiarity with the rigorous approaches of developing embedded software based on the rich features of Intel's Atom processors.

Dr. Yann-Hang Lee

Professor

School of Computing and Informatics

Ira A. Fulton School of Engineering

Arizona State University

"The Intel Atom hardware is a powerhouse that has enabled us to develop far more involved embedded designs with on-board sensor fusion and optimization & control algorithms that would normally have to be run on an external PC ... the Intel Atom is the brain in the central nervous system of our robotics and it is critical to provide students with references like this book to enable them to explore the capabilities of a powerful tool like the Atom."

Dr. David R. Schneider

Systems Engineering

Cornell University

A Vision for Platform Autonomy

Robust Frameworks for Systems
By Rahul Khanna and Mohan J. Kumari

A Vision for Platform Autonomy provides the holistic overview and the solution to the platform autonomics related to power, thermal, RAS, locality, and resource monitoring.

In addition to providing the theoretical basis of autonomics features, this book introduces the current state of the art in Intel platforms. It also covers the software based models and industry standards relevant to each autonomics feature. Additionally, the emerging concept of low speed wireless interconnects to achieve better platform autonomics is introduced.

The bottom line is that the system is able to maintain the stable equilibrium while hiding the complexity of the autonomics system from the users. It is similar to what its biological inspiration—the autonomic nervous system—does in our bodies.

A Vision for Platform Autonomy
Robust Frameworks for Systems

Rahul Khanna and Mohan J. Kumar

Intel
PRESS

"Driven by nearly a billion people online and a trillion connected objects, the scale of computing technology has exploded over the last decade, mandating the need for autonomic capabilities in IT systems and systems components. *A Vision for Platform Autonomy: Robust Frameworks for Systems* reveals the concepts, architectures, and core methodologies enabling the underlying elements essential to achieve autonomic computing."

—Alan G. Ganek, Chief Technology Officer & Vice President, Strategy and Technology,
   IBM Software Group

"I would highly recommend *A Vision for Platform Autonomy* for data center managers, enterprise management professionals, and platform architects. The authors have made significant contributions to the field of autonomics by providing an implementation framework and real life examples of how various feature and capabilities of modern compute platforms can contribute to a robust solution for autonomics."

—Professor Mariette Awad, Assistant Professor, Electrical and Computer Engineering Department,
   American University of Beirut

Special Deals, Special Prices!

To ensure you have all the latest books
and enjoy aggressively priced discounts,
please go to this Web site:

www.intel.com/intelpress/bookbundles.htm

Bundles of our books are available,
selected especially to address the needs
of the developer. The bundles place
important complementary topics at
your fingertips, and the price for a
bundle is substantially less than
buying all the books individually.

About Intel Press

Intel Press is the authoritative source of timely, technical books to help software and hardware developers speed up their development process. We collaborate only with leading industry experts to deliver reliable, first-to-market information about the latest technologies, processes, and strategies.

Our products are planned with the help of many people in the developer community and we encourage you to consider becoming a customer advisor. If you would like to help us and gain additional advance insight to the latest technologies, we encourage you to consider the Intel Press Customer Advisor Program. You can **register** here:

www.intel.com/intelpress/register.htm

For information about bulk orders or corporate sales, please send email to bulkbooksales@intel.com

Other Developer Resources from Intel

At these Web sites you can also find valuable technical information and resources for developers:

www.intel.com/technology/rr	Recommended Reading list for books of interest to developers
www.intel.com/technology/itj	Intel Technology Journal
developer.intel.com	General information for developers
www.intel.com/software	Content, tools, training, and the Intel Early Access Program for software developers
www.intel.com/software/products	Programming tools to help you develop high-performance applications
www.intel.com/embedded	Solutions and resources for embedded and communications

6191-0153-3660-9269

If serial number is missing, please send an e-mail to Intel Press at **intelpress@intel.com**

IMPORTANT

You can access the companion Web site for this book on the Internet at:

noggin.intel.com/registermybook

Use the serial number located in the upper-right hand corner of this page to register your book and access additional material, including the *Digital Edition* of this book.